ART GALLERY of ONTARIO
the Canadian Collection

ART GALLERY of ONTARIO
the Canadian Collection

McGRAW-HILL COMPANY OF CANADA LIMITED

Toronto Montreal New York London Sydney
Johannesburg Mexico Panama Dusseldorf

ART GALLERY OF ONTARIO
THE CANADIAN COLLECTION

ISBN 0-07-092504-6

Library of Congress Catalog
Card Number: 69-14868

Colour photography by Eberhard Otto
and TDF Artists Limited, Toronto.

Printed and bound by Joh. Enschedé en Zonen, Haarlem, Holland.

TO THE MEMORY OF MARTIN BALDWIN

Curator, Director, Director Emeritus
of
The Art Gallery of Toronto
1932-1968

Si monumentus requiris, circumspice

"Published on the occasion of the Centennial of Canadian Confederation and subsidized by the Centennial Commission".

"Ouvrage publié à l'occasion du Centenaire de la Confédération Canadienne, grâce à une subvention de la Commission du Centenaire".

1867 1967

foreword

The Art Museum of Toronto was incorporated in 1900. From 1906 until June 1913, when Grange House was opened officially as a museum, its activity was limited to a few exhibitions held in the galleries of the Ontario Society of Artists and in the Public and Reference Library. In 1919 the museum's name was changed to The Art Gallery of Toronto by which title it has been widely known. On July 8, 1966, it was reconstituted as the Art Gallery of Ontario by an act passed by the Legislature of the Province of Ontario.

This publication is the first complete record of the Canadian works of art in the Gallery's collection, and represents some sixty years of collecting.* It is hoped

* The handbook, *Art Gallery of Toronto: Painting and sculpture* (1959) was a general guide to a selected number of works in the Canadian and European collections.

that a similar volume of the European collection will be published eventually.

The documentation was begun as a Centennial project because it seemed appropriate that this part of the collection should be published in 1967. Apart from the recognition that such a publication was long overdue for the Gallery, it was undertaken in response to the growing need for reliable information about Canadian art and artists. The only other publication of comparable scope in the Canadian field was published in 1960 by the National Gallery of Canada. While Dr. R. H. Hubbard's publications and, most recently, J. Russell Harper's *Painting in Canada* have made an enormous contribution to our knowledge, there is still a great need for those basic tools of the art historian — the complete and accurate inventories of the major public collections of Canadian art.

This volume includes the entire collection of Canadian painting, water colours, drawings, prints and sculpture acquired before June 30, 1967. Four hundred and four artists are represented by 1553 works, which comprise 909 paintings and water colours, 297 drawings and pastels, 279 prints and 68 pieces of sculpture. It is interesting to note that, among the artists represented, 2 worked in the 18th century, 25 worked in the 19th century, 52 were born prior to Confederation in 1867 but worked into the 20th century, and 325 were or are active in the 20th century.

This publication is intended to serve primarily as a reference book for other galleries and those studying Canadian art. It is hoped that, through its numerous illustrations, it will serve to introduce the general public to a collection of which, owing to the present demands of space, only a small proportion is usually on view. Moreover, a complete listing inevitably reveals the limitations and gaps in the collection as a whole. We hope that the realization of these omissions will provide an added incentive to future acquisitions.

The most significant part of the collection falls into the 20th century and is strongest in works by Ontario artists. There are few works from the 19th century before 1850, though one can point in particular to an 18th century wood carving of the *Virgin and Child* by an Unknown French-Canadian sculptor, and the *Portrait of Lady Robinson with her Daughter Mary* (1847) by G. T. Berthon, Toronto's leading portrait painter of the period. There are also a series of portraits, as yet unattributed, of the Boultons, the original owners of the Grange. Antoine Plamondon's *La Chasse aux Tourtes* (1853), the only example of French-Canadian art of this period, can be considered as one of the most important works of that master.

In the later 19th century there are a number of water colour landscapes of merit, although one would like to see more oils by such artists as Fraser and O'Brien. Otto Jacobi's *Falls of Ste. Anne* (1865) is particularly important as an early example of landscape painting of this period. Robert Harris, one of Canada's finest portraitists, is unfortunately represented only by *The News-boy* (1879). Among the works executed towards the end of the century, one can single out the vigorous naturalism of Homer Watson's *The Old Mill* (1886) and Horatio Walker's more reflective pastoral *Evening, Ile d'Orléans* (1909). Illustrating the influence of French academic art on Canadian painting there are a number of works by Paul Peel, among which perhaps the best known is *The Tired Model* (1889). Lastly, such works as Maurice Cullen's *Moret, Winter* (1895) and James Wilson Morrice's *Return from School* (1900-03) reflect the influence of the avant-garde aspects of French painting.

The Group of Seven first exhibited at the Gallery in 1920 and examples of their work in the collection are more numerous and perhaps more consistently chosen than those of the 19th and early 20th century artists. Tom Thomson's *The West Wind* (1917) and Lawren Harris' *Beaver Swamp, Algoma* (1920) stand almost as archetypes of the movement, though Thomson died before the formation of the Group became a reality. J. E. H. MacDonald's *Mist Fantasy* (1922) shows the degree of formalism which the Group could attain, while Harris' *Above Lake Superior* (c. 1922) shows the increasing tendency towards abstraction in his work. Emily Carr's *Kispiax Village* (1929) and L. L.

Fitzgerald's *Pritchard's Fence* (c.1928) are excellent examples of tendencies which developed essentially outside the Group of Seven.

Since the mid 1930s, when regular purchase funds became available, the main purchasing activity has been in the contemporary field though there have been significant 19th and earlier 20th century acquisitions. In general, the Gallery has tried to acquire what it considers to be the most exciting and significant contemporary work, usually at the time it was executed. Again, its strength in this area lies mainly in its representation of painting in Toronto in the late 1950s and early 1960s, but in the last few years there has been an attempt to broaden the collection to include painters from Montreal, Vancouver and other important Canadian centres.

The way in which a gallery's collection is formed is influenced by a number of factors — the knowledge and individual tastes of its directors and curators, the experience of its purchasing committees, the exhibitions it holds, the private collections it succeeds in attracting and, above all, the funds it has available for purchase.

The Canadian collection like the European has relied heavily on gifts of paintings as well as on a series of special funds, set up between 1930 and 1957, largely for the purchase of Canadian art. There were the Reuben and Kate Leonard Canadian Fund (1926); the Reuben Wells Leonard Estate (1930); the Friends of Canadian Art Fund (1930); the Albert H. Robson Memorial Fund (1939); the Fund of the T. Eaton Co. Ltd. for Canadian Works of Art (1948); the John Paris Bickell Bequest Fund (1951); and the J. S. McLean Fund (1953) and Foundation (1957). It was on these generous gifts that the Gallery depended almost entirely for purchase funds until its Foundation, with a regular income, was set up in the late 1950s. In 1965, a gift of more than fifty paintings, acquired since 1911, was made by the Canadian National Exhibition Association.

It is not possible to list all our benefactors in this brief introduction, but this volume is for the most part a list of their gifts and is their monument. Their names are recorded in connection with the individual works or art. A great debt of gratitude is owed not only to them but to the past presidents and to the members of the various committees whose knowledge and enthusiasm has contributed so much to building up the Canadian collection. Particular tribute should be paid to the late Martin Baldwin to whose memory we dedicate this volume, for it was under his directorship (1932-1961) that the major part of the Canadian collection was formed. It was Dr. Baldwin who initiated and organized the first comprehensive exhibition of Canadian painting in 1945. *The Development of Painting in Canada 1665-1945* was shown also in Ottawa, Montreal and Quebec, and he followed this exhibition with *Fifty Years of Painting in Canada, 1900-1950*, which ushered in the Gallery's jubilee year. Between 1947 and 1960, Dr. Baldwin also organized several important one-man exhibitions of Canadian painters — Harris, Lismer, Jackson and Varley among them.

Helen Pepall Bradfield is responsible for the preparation of this catalogue; the research and compilation of the entries are the result of her work during three years. On her behalf, we would like to acknowledge most gratefully the help and cooperation she has received from colleagues in other museums and galleries both in Canada and abroad, from artists, dealers, and private collectors, and from the staff and libraries of the National Gallery of Canada, the Montreal Museum of Fine Arts, and the Toronto Public Library. Many members of the staff of the Art Gallery of Ontario, both past and present, have offered invaluable suggestions and assistance. The unfailing cooperation and direction of the Registrar, Charles McFaddin, have been sincerely appreciated, while the rich resources of the Gallery's reference library and the encouragement and enthusiasm of the Librarian, Sybille Pantazzi, have been of the greatest help to the compiler.

Finally, we would like to express our gratitude to the J. P. Bickell Foundation in Toronto, through whose generosity we were able to undertake the research on which this publication is based. We would also like to thank the Centennial Commission which, through a grant under provision of their Publications Programme, contributed to the cost of photography and the general expenses of the volume.

William J. Withrow, *Director*
David S. Brooke, former *Curator*.
June, 1970

explanations

The publication comprises the complete collection of Canadian paintings, drawings, prints and sculpture in the Art Gallery of Ontario, to the end of June, 1967; that is 1,553 works by 404 artists.

The arrangement of the documentation is alphabetical according to artist. Unattributed works are classified as "Unknown" pending further information that will enable positive attribution, and are arranged in chronological order, according to factual or stylistic evidence.

A brief biography of the artist precedes entries for all works by that artist. Undated works, or those for which no date has been established, are entered first, followed by dated works in chronological sequence.

The medium in which the work was executed is followed by the dimensions in inches, height preceding width. "Sight" measurements are given for works which could not be removed from the mat, and indicate the size of the opening. For many prints both the size of the impression and that of the paper are given.
Inscriptions are not necessarily in the artist's own hand.

The use of an obligue (/) in signatures and inscriptions indicates a new line.

The names of dealers who have held the work prior to its acquisition by the Gallery are enclosed in square brackets.

The abbreviation and date enclosed in square brackets at the end of provenance refers to the exhibition or sale from which the work was acquired.

Notes regarding preparatory drawings and sketches are included when available, and notes of historical significance are added when deemed relevant.

Most exhibitions in which the work has been shown are listed. In each case, unless otherwise indicated, a catalogue accompanied the exhibition. A question mark (?) indicates a strong possibility that this is indeed the work exhibited but no verification is available.

References cover all published material in which the work in question is mentioned and/or reproduced.

About one-third of the collection is illustrated in half-tone reproduction. No prints are reproduced.

The bibliography at the end of the publication includes, in chronological order, the books referred to in the text and a separate list of the exhibition catalogues cited in the entries. It is followed by a list of annual and biennial exhibitions held in Canada and abroad from 1860, and a list of periodicals referred to in the text. It is not intended as a complete bibliography on Canadian art.

key to abbreviations

A.A.M.	Art Association of Montreal (changed in 1945 to Montreal Museum of Fine Arts).
acc. no.	accession number.
A.G.O.	Art Gallery of Ontario (formerly The Art Gallery of Toronto).
A.G.T.	The Art Gallery of Toronto (called The Art Museum of Toronto, until 1919).
A.R.C.A.	Associate of the Royal Canadian Academy of Arts.
C.G.P.	Canadian Group of Painters.
C.N.E.	Canadian National Exhibition, Toronto.
C.P.E.	Society of Canadian Painter-Etchers and Engravers.
C.S.G.A.	Canadian Society of Graphic Art.
C.S.P.W.C.	Canadian Society of Painters in Water Colour.
D.P.C.	*Development of Painting in Canada* [exhibition, A.G.T., 1945].
F.C.A.	Federation of Canadian Artists.

Imp.	Impression [prints].
M.M.F.A.	Montreal Museum of Fine Arts (formerly Art Association of Montreal).
N.G.C.	National Gallery of Canada, Ottawa.
O.C.A.	Ontario College of Art, Toronto (formerly the Ontario School of Art & Design, founded in 1876; in 1890 it became the Central Ontario School of Art & Design, lasting until 1912, when an Act was brought in creating the Ontario College of Art).
O.S.A.	Ontario Society of Artists.
P.O.S.A.	President, Ontario Society of Artists.
P.R.C.A.	President, Royal Canadian Academy of Arts.
Prov.	Provenance.
R.C.A.	Royal Canadian Academy of Arts; Royal Canadian Academician.
S.S.C.	Sculptors' Society of Canada.

ART GALLERY of ONTARIO
the Canadian Collection

Lily Osman ADAMS
(1865-1945)

BORN: Toronto.

DIED: 1945.

STUDY: Toronto Art School, under J. W. Beatty; Columbia University, New York, under Mr. Down; Art Students' League, New York, under John Carlsen.

W. W. ALEXANDER (1870-1948)

BORN: William Walker Alexander, Toronto, August 9, 1870.

DIED: Toronto, April 3, 1948.

STUDY: Toronto, Central Ontario School of Art and Design; Art Students' League, Toronto; in the studio of G. A. Reid, Toronto; in 1880s at Pennsylvania Academy of Fine Arts, Philadelphia, under Thomas Eakins.

SOCIETIES: Art Students' League, Toronto, founder member, 1886, Pres. 1903; Society of Graphic Art, founder in 1906, Pres. 1908-09; Arts and Letters Club, Toronto [where affectionately known as "Billy Alec"]; Mahlstick Club.

Engraver, etcher, designer.

Frederick ALEXIE
(active, first quarter,
20th century)

A Tsimsyan half-breed from Port Simpson, B. C., belonging to the "Gillodzar Tribe..., whose territories are not far from the canyon border of the Skeena River. His clan is the Killer-Whale, and his native name — Great-Female Deer (Weeksem'wacn)." In 1945 he was "an old man in his 80's."

2482

TRILLIUMS

Pastel on paper, $11^3/_4$" x $13^7/_8$" [sight].
Signed (lower right): L. O. ADAMS.

EXHIBITIONS: [?] *R.C.A.*, 1928-29, no. 2; [?] *R.C.A.*, 1931, no. 2; [?] *C.N.E.*, 1932, no. 542.

Bequest of Ambia L. Going, 1938.

2483

COSMOS, STILL LIFE

Water colour on paper, 8" x $9^7/_{16}$".
Signed (lower left): L. O. ADAMS.

Bequest of Ambia L. Going, 1938.

51

THAMES TRAFFIC   1913

Etching, Imp.: 6" x $8^7/_8$". Paper: $10^1/_2$" x $13^1/_2$".
Signed and dated (lower right, in pencil): W. W. Alexander 1913.

EXHIBITIONS: *O.S.A.*, 1913, no. 92.

NOTE: Permanent loan from C.N.E. Association, 1913-66.

Gift of the Canadian National Exhibition Association, 1966.

1988

BRIDGE AT TWILIGHT

Aquatint, Imp.: $10^5/_8$" x $7^5/_8$". Paper: $14^1/_8$" x $9^7/_8$".
Signed (lower right, in pencil): Will W. Alexander.
Numbered and inscribed (lower left, in pencil): 4/20 To — B H — 1920.

PROV.: Sir Edmund Walker, Toronto.

EXHIBITIONS: *C.P.E.*, 1919, no. 1; Vancouver, *B. C. Art League*, 1921, no. 2; *R.C.A.*, 1922, no. 244; London, *British Empire Exhibition*, 1924, no. FF.27, and Canadian section of fine arts, no. 1; A.G.T.... Eaton...Simpson, *Exhibition and sale...for the benefit of André Lapine*, 1934, Simpson, no. 92.

Gift of Sir Edmund Walker Estate, 1926.

2763

INDIAN VILLAGE OF PORT SIMPSON

Water colour on paper, $12^3/_{16}$" x $19^7/_8$" [sight].
Inscribed (across bottom): Drawing by Frederick Alexcee Port Simpson. B.C.

Inscribed (on reverse, in ink): Purchased by A. Y. Jackson Sept. 1926/ from Pat Phillipson. Prince Rupert./Frederick Alexcee [sic] is a Port Simpson/Indian. father was an Iroquois who/probably went west with the. H. B. Co./He is an expert wood carver has/also made lantern

Wood carver, primitive painter, illustrator, maker of coloured slides [to illustrate Indian stories], and fisherman.

[See Marius Barbeau, "Frederick Alexie, a primitive", *Canadian Review of Music and Art*, vol. 3 (Dec., 1944 - Jan., 1945), pp. 19, 21-22].

slides probably/picked up some knowledge of drawing/from survey-ors. but no tuition of/any kind.

PROV.: Pat Phillipson, Prince Rupert; A. Y. Jackson, Manotick, Ontario.

NOTES: Port Simpson is located in the vicinity of the Skeena River, not far from Prince Rupert, B. C.

EXHIBITIONS: A.G.T., *Canadian West Coast Art*, 1928, no. 118 (one of two paintings by Alexee [sic], depicting "native houses and totem poles of Port Simpson"; lent by A. Y. Jackson).

REFERENCES: *Canadian Review of Music and Art*, vol. 3 (Dec., 1944-Jan., 1945), p. 21 (tells how the author and A. Y. Jackson visited Port Simpson together in 1926, where Jackson bought "a water colour sketch showing a few Tsimsyan houses with totem poles…").

Gift of A. Y. Jackson, 1944.

John Martin ALFSEN (1902-   )

BORN: Long Rapids, Michigan, December 23, 1902.

LIVES: Toronto. Came to Canada in 1915.

STUDY: Ontario College of Art, under Arthur Lismer, J. W. Beatty, and Frederick Varley; Art Students' League, New York, under Henry Hayes Miller, 1925-29; L'Académie Royale des Beaux-Arts d'Anvers, Belgium; France, sculpture, under Antoine Bourdelle.

SOCIETIES: C.G.P.; O.S.A., 1939; A.R.C.A., 1942; R.C.A., 1959; C.S.G.A., 1956.

TEACHING: Toronto, Ontario College of Art, since 1929.

AWARDS: Canada Council grants in 1958 and 1963.

2792

THE CELLIST   **1925**

Crayon on paper, 13$\frac{1}{8}$" x 9$\frac{1}{2}$" [sight].
Signed (lower right): J M Alfsen.

PROV.: the artist.

EXHIBITIONS: *C.S.G.A.*, 1929, no. 90; [?] *R.C.A.*, 1932, special section "Exhibition by young Canadians", John Alfsen, Carl Schaefer, no. 324; A.G.T., *Drawings*, 1963, p. 1.

Purchase, 1945.

2791

BOY'S FIGURE   **c. 1937**

Pencil on paper, 11$\frac{1}{4}$" x 6$\frac{3}{4}$" [sight].
Signed (lower right): Alfsen.

PROV.: the artist.

EXHIBITIONS: A.G.T., *Drawings*, 1963, p. 1.

Purchase, 1945.

2728

BILLY   **1937**

Oil on canvas, 14$\frac{1}{4}$" x 12$\frac{1}{4}$".
Signed (lower right): ALFSEN.

PROV.: the artist.

EXHIBITIONS: A.G.T., and Ontario Department of Education, 1951, no. 7.

Purchase, 1943.

2791   **Boy's Figure**

2522

GIRL'S HEAD   **1937/38**

Oil on canvas, 14¼" x 12¼".

EXHIBITIONS: Yale, 1944; *D.P.C.*, 1945, no. 220; A.G.T., and Ontario Department of Education, 1951, no. 6; A.G.O. [circulating exhibition], *Canadian paintings of the 1930s*, 1967-68, no. 1.

REFERENCES: A.G.T., *Accessions, 1938*, reprod.; *Canadian Art*, vol. II (March, 1945), p. 94 (reprod.).

Gift of E. M. Walker, 1938.

2522   **Girl's Head**

2793

SELF PORTRAIT   **1945**

Pencil on paper, 13⅛" x 9½" [sight].

PROV.: the artist.

Purchase, 1945.

3

51/44   **Clown Alley**

51/44

CLOWN ALLEY   **1951**

Oil on canvas, 36" x 50".

NOTES: Permanent loan from C.N.E. Association, 1952-65.

EXHIBITIONS: *C.N.E.*, 1951, no. 3; St. Catharines, *The Figure Form*, 1963 (Dec. 6-29) [no catalogue].

REFERENCES: Harper (1966), p. 332, fig. 302 (reprod.), p. 333 (says done while the artist was spending the winter with the Ringling Brothers circus in Florida).

Gift of the Canadian National Exhibition Association, 1965.

Ralph ALLEN (1926-   )

BORN: Raunds, Northamptonshire, England, December 6, 1926.

LIVES: Kingston, Ontario. Came to Canada in 1957.

STUDY: Sir John Cass College of Art, London, 1948-50; Slade School of Fine Art, London, 1950-54, under Sir William Coldstream, Henry Moore, Graham Sutherland and John Piper.

Worked at the Beaux-Arts Gallery in London, 1955-57.

TEACHING: Since 1957, Queen's University where he is now Associate Professor of Art (since 1966), and also Director of the Agnes Etherington Art Centre.

AWARDS: Canada Council Scholarship for creative studies, 1959.

60/58

PORTRAIT   **1960**

Oil on canvas board, 43⅞" x 29⅞".
Signed and dated (lower right): Allen 60.

PROV.: the artist.

EXHIBITIONS: *O.S.A.*, 1961, no. 2 (reprod.).

Gift from the McLean Foundation, 1961.

60/58   **Portrait**

Edmund ALLEYN (1931-   )

BORN: Quebec, June 9, 1931.

LIVES: Paris.

STUDY: Quebec, Ecole des Beaux-Arts, under Jean-Paul Lemieux.

Influenced by Goodridge Roberts, Alfred Pellan, and by the works of Nicolas de Staël.

AWARDS: Grand Prize by Concours Artistiques of the Province of Quebec, 1955; Canadian Government award, 1955, to study in Paris; Royal Society of Canada Bursary, 1956, for further study in Paris.

64/18

TRIBAL CELEBRATION   1962

Gouache on paper, 19^1/$_2$" x 24^3/$_4$" [sight].
Signed and dated (lower left centre): Alleyn. 62.

PROV.: [Roberts Gallery, Toronto].

EXHIBITIONS: Roberts Gallery, *Edmund Alleyn*, 1964 (Sept. 22-Oct. 3) [no catalogue].

Purchase, 1964.

64/18   **Tribal Celebration**

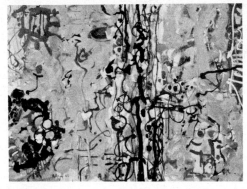

Henry ALMEIDA

BORN: Caracas, Venezuela.

LIVES: Toronto. Came to Canada in 1957.

STUDY: Under his father, an artist and professor of art in Venezuela; did some modelling in Mexico at the Academia San Carlos; in England, at St. Martin's School of Art, London, and at Willesden Technical College.

61/57

LANDSCAPE IN GREYS   1961

Monotype, 15^1/$_8$" x 21^1/$_8$" [sight].
Signed and dated (lower right, in ink): H. Almeida 61.

PROV.: [Picture Loan Society, Toronto].

Gift from the McLean Foundation, 1962.

Franklin ARBUCKLE (1909-   )

BORN: George Franklin Arbuckle, Toronto, February 17, 1909.

LIVES: Toronto.

STUDY: Toronto, Ontario College of Art, 1928-30, under F. S. Haines, Franz Johnston, J. E. H. MacDonald, J. W. Beatty and F. S. Challener.

SOCIETIES: O.S.A., 1933; A.R.C.A., 1936; R.C.A., 1943; P.R.C.A., 1960-64.

Landscape and figure painter, illustrator.

50/9

ST. LAWRENCE RIVER BARN   1950

Oil on canvas, 30^1/$_8$" x 40^1/$_{16}$".
Signed (lower left): FRANKLIN/ARBUCKLE.
Inscribed (on reverse, top of frame): C N E/"QUEBEC BARN" FRANKLIN ARBUCKLE.

PROV.: the artist.

EXHIBITIONS: *C.N.E.*, 1950, no. 1; *R.C.A.*, 1954, no. 4, p. 4 (reprod.); Stratford, *Canada on canvas*, 1963; Charlottetown, *The Academy in Retrospect*, 1966, no. 3 (as St. Lawrence River Basin [sic]; reprod.).

REFERENCES: *Star Weekly Magazine*, Toronto (April 12, 1958), on cover (reprod. in colour, erroneously as "Coach House").

Gift from the Fund of the T. Eaton Co. Ltd. for Canadian Works of Art, 1950.

50/9   St. Lawrence River Barn

Louis ARCHAMBAULT
(1915-   )

BORN: Montreal, 1915.

LIVES: Montreal.

STUDY: Montreal, Ecole des Beaux-Arts, from 1936.

SOCIETIES: A.R.C.A., 1966.

TEACHING: Ecole du Meuble, Montreal, 1945, and at the Montreal Museum of Fine Arts, School of Art and Design, c. 1947; since 1949 instructor in sculpture at the Ecole des Beaux-Arts, Montreal.

AWARDS: First prize for sculpture at the Concours Artistiques of the Province of Quebec in both 1948 and 1950; 1953-54 Canadian Government Fellowship to study in Paris and Venice; Canada Council fellowship for research, 1959 and 1962.

Commissioned in 1957 to make a ceramic wall for the Canadian pavilion at the Brussels International and Universal Exposition, 1958.

Sculptor, ceramist.

52/7

NIGHT AND DAY   **1948**

Terracotta, mounted on steel, 24" high, 17" wide.
Signed and dated (inside back, lower left): A.48.

PROV.: the artist [AGT, 1952].

EXHIBITIONS: A.G.T., *Archambault and Pellan*, 1952, no. 5; Brussels, 1958.

REFERENCES: Ross (1958), p. 34 (reprod.), p. 41; A.G.T., *Painting and sculpture* (1959), p. 89 (reprod.).

Gift from the John Paris Bickell Bequest Fund, 1952.

52/7   **Night and Day**

H. J. ARISS (1917-   )

BORN: Herbert Joshua Ariss, Guelph, Ontario, September 29, 1917.

LIVES: London, Ontario.

STUDY: Toronto, Western Technical School; Ontario College of Art; and with S. G. Moyer and Archibald Barnes.

SOCIETIES: O.S.A., 1958; C.S.P.W.C., 1956.

TEACHING: H. B. Beal Technical School, London, Ontario, since 1947.

AWARDS: Canada Council fellowship to Spain and France, 1960-61.

Painter, illustrator.

2729

ON FATIGUE   1942

Charcoal on paper, $15^7/_8$" x $19^{15}/_{16}$" [sight].
Signed and dated (lower right): Ariss/42.

PROV.: the artist [HH, 1942].

EXHIBITIONS. University of Toronto, Hart House, *Canadian Armed Forces art exhibition*, 1942, no. 103.

Purchase, 1943.

Caroline H. ARMINGTON (1875-1939)

BORN: Caroline Helena Wilkinson, Brampton, Ontario, September 11, 1875; married Frank Armington in Paris.

DIED: New York, October 25, 1939.

STUDY: Toronto, studio of J. W. L. Forster; Julian Academy, Paris, under Henri Royer, F. Schommer and Paul Gervais; Académie de la Grande Chaumière; and under Lucien Simon.

First went to Paris in 1900. In Winnipeg, together with husband, taught art, 1901-05; thereafter returning to France where they established permanent residency.

Etcher, painter of landscape and portraits.

161

PLACE DE LA RÉPUBLIQUE   1918

Etching, Imp.: $10^1/_8$" x 13". Paper: $12^5/_8$" x $15^5/_{16}$".
Signed (lower right, in pencil): Caroline H. Armington.
Inscribed (lower right): CAROLINE H. ARMINGTON. 1918.
Inscribed (lower left): THE BRITISH ARMY AND NAVY LEAVE CLUB/ PLACE DE LA REPUBLIQUE./PARIS FRANCE.

NOTES: Permanent loan from C.N.E. Association, 1921-66.

REFERENCES: *Saturday Night* (April 6, 1929), Women's section, p. 17.

Gift of the Canadian National Exhibition Association, 1966.

Frank M. ARMINGTON (1876-1941)

BORN: Frank Milton Armington, Fordwich, Ontario, July 28, 1876.

DIED: New York, September 23, 1941.

STUDY: Toronto, studio of J. W. L. Forster; Paris, Académie Julian, with Benjamin Constant, Jean-Paul Laurens, and Henri Royer; Académie de la Grande Chaumière.

First went to Paris in 1899. In Winnipeg, together with his wife, taught art, 1901-05. Returning to France, 1905, they established permanent residency there.

TRAVEL: Algeria, 1913-14.

Painter, etcher.

1987

LUDGATE HILL

Etching, Imp.: $20^7/_8$" x $14^7/_8$". Paper: 25" x $18^3/_4$".
Signed (lower right, in pencil): Frank M. Armington.
Inscribed (lower right): Ludgate Hill, London.
Inscribed (lower left, in pencil): To Sir Edmund Walker C.V.O./a souvenir from the etcher.

PROV.: Sir Edmund Walker, Toronto.

Gift of Sir Edmund Walker Estate, 1926.

1323

LA CARAVANE **1914**

Oil on canvas, $39^3/_8$" x $51^1/_4$".
Signed and dated (lower left): Frank M. Armington/1914.
Inscribed (on reverse, upper right): "La Caravane"/Par/Frank M. Armington.

PROV.: the artist [AGT, 1929].

EXHIBITIONS: New York, Durand-Ruel Galleries, *Frank M. Armington, and Caroline Armington*, 1929, no. 1; A.G.T., *French paintings...and Frank M. Armington*, 1929, p. 9, no. 1; *C.N.E.*, 1939, no. 5.

REFERENCES: *L'Art and Les Artistes* (June, 1927), p. 304 (reprod.); A.G.T., *Bulletin and Annual Report* (March, 1931), p. 9.

Gift of Friends of the Artist, 1930.

251

PÉNICHES SUR LA SEINE, PARIS **1915**

Lithograph, Imp.: $12^3/_4$" x $9^{11}/_{16}$". Paper: $14^1/_8$" x $11^1/_4$".
Signed and dated (lower, in pencil): Frank M. Armington 15.
Numbered (lower left, in pencil): 24/50.
Inscribed (lower right): Péniches sur la Seine, Paris.
Inscribed (lower left): 15/A.

NOTES: Permanent loan from C.N.E. Association, 1924-66.

EXHIBITIONS: *C.N.E.*, 1924, no. 514.

REFERENCES: Duval (1952), pl. 12 (reprod., as Fishing Boats, The Seine).

Gift of the Canadian National Exhibition Association, 1966.

William ARMSTRONG
(1822-1914)

BORN: Dublin, County Wicklow, Ireland, July 28, 1822.

DIED: Toronto, June, 1914. Came to Canada (Toronto) in 1851.

STUDY: Mostly self-taught, though he did some architectural drawing in Dublin, and trained with Ed. Newman. About 1857-58 he was associated with the firm of Armstrong, Beere and Hime, "photographists", "civil engineers and draughtsmen".

Was employed with the Grand Trunk Railway. In 1879, as chief engineer with the Sir Garnet Wolseley expedition to the North-West, he made many sketches. In 1880s he gave up his engineering career to dedicate his full time to art.

TEACHING: Drawing master at the Ontario

52/49

NIPIGON RIVER, LAKE SUPERIOR **1865**

Water colour on cardboard, $19^{11}/_{16}$" x $28^7/_8$".
Signed and dated (lower right): Armstrong/1865.

PROV.: [?] H. L. Hime, Toronto; Maurice W. Hime, Glendale, California.

Gift of Maurice W. Hime, 1953.

School of Art (Normal School); also taught at Jarvis Collegiate.

Civil engineer turned artist; painter of landscapes and Indian life in Ontario, Quebec, Manitoba and the Rockies.

Caven ATKINS (1907-   )

BORN: Ernest Cavin Atkins, London, Ontario, February 25, 1907.

LIVES: Whereabouts unknown; was living in Detroit, 1946.

STUDY: Winnipeg School of Art, under L. L. Fitzgerald.

SOCIETIES: C.S.P.W.C., Pres. 1943-45; C.G.P.; F.C.A.; C.S.G.A.

2724

ARC WELDER BY NIGHT   1942

Water colour on paper, 10$^7/_8$" x 15$^5/_{16}$" [sight].
Signed and dated (lower right): Atkins 42.

PROV.: the artist [OSA, 1943].

NOTES: War Record painting, done in July, 1942.

EXHIBITIONS: *O.S.A.*, 1943, no. 7 [one of two].

Purchase, 1943.

2723

LAUNCHED HULL BY NIGHT   1942

Water colour on paper, 15$^1/_4$" x 21$^7/_8$" [sight].
Signed and dated (lower left): ATKINS 42.

PROV.: the artist [OSA, 1943].

NOTES: War Record painting, done in August, 1942.

EXHIBITIONS: *O.S.A.*, 1943, no. 9.

REFERENCES: A.G.T., *Accessions 1943*, reprod.

Purchase, 1943.

2723   **Launched Hull by Night**

W. E. ATKINSON (1862-1926)

BORN: William Edwin Atkinson, Toronto, March 22, 1862.

DIED: Toronto.

STUDY: Toronto, Central Ontario School of Art and Design, 1881, under J. A. Fraser and Robert Harris; Pennsylvania Academy of Fine Arts, Philadelphia, 1883-84, under Thomas Eakins; Paris, Julian Academy, 1889-90, under Bouguereau and Ferrier; also Academy Delance, Paris, 1890.

SOCIETIES: O.S.A., 1892, resigned, 1907; A.R.C.A., 1894, resigned, then reinstated as associate, 1918; Canadian Art Club, founder member, 1907.

89

THE AFTERNOON THAW 1916

Oil on canvas, 33$\frac{1}{8}$" x 49".
Signed and dated (lower right): W. E. Atkinson - 1916.

NOTES: Permanent loan from C.N.E. Association, 1917-65.

EXHIBITIONS: *R.C.A.*, 1916, no. 3; *C.N.E.*, 1917, no. 116; *C.N.E.*, 1939, no. 7; *O.S.A.*, 1947, no. 153 (as After Thaw).

Gift of the Canadian National Exhibition Association, 1965.

Archibald G. BARNES (1887-)

BORN: Archibald George Barnes, London, England, March 19, 1887.

LIVES: Toronto. Came to Canada (Toronto) in 1931.

STUDY: St. John's Wood Art School, under Orchardson; Royal Academy Schools, London, under John Singer Sargent, Sir William Orpen.

SOCIETIES: England, Royal Society of Portrait Painters, and Royal Institute; O.S.A., 1932; A.R.C.A., 1933; R.C.A., 1935.

TEACHING: Toronto, Ontario College of Art, from 1935.

Portrait painter.

128

INTERIOR

Oil on canvas, 30" x 30".
Signed (lower right): Barnes.

NOTES: Permanent loan from C.N.E. Association, 1921-65.

EXHIBITIONS: *C.N.E.*, 1921, no. 9; Toronto, *Eaton's* Fine Art Galleries, *Barnes, and Heming*, 1923, no. 13; Ottawa, *Central Canada Exhibition*, 1926, no. 2 (reprod.); A.G.T., *Summer*, 1935, no. 101.

Gift of the Canadian National Exhibition Association, 1965.

128 Interior

Allan BARR (1890-1959)

BORN: Robert Allan Barr, Chiswick, London, England, January 10, 1890.

DIED: Toronto, August 14, 1959. Came to Canada (Kingston) in 1922; settled in Toronto 1923.

STUDY: London School of Art, 1907-11, under Frank Brangwyn, John M. Swan, and George W. Lambert; Regent Street Polytechnic, 1908-10, in the evenings.

SOCIETIES: O.S.A., 1927; A.R.C.A., 1928.

Portrait painter; also still life, landscape.

895

PORTRAIT OF MRS. ALLEYNE SUTHERLAND   **1927-28**

Oil on canvas, 40" x 30⅛"
Signed and dated (upper right): ALLAN·BARR·/1927-28·

PROV.: the artist [OSA, 1928].

EXHIBITIONS: *O.S.A.*, 1928, no. 7, p. 16 (reprod.); *C.N.E.*, 1928, no. 332; N.G.C., *Annual*, 1929, no. 5; A.G.T., *Summer*, 1935, no. 45; A.G.T., *Loan Exhibition*, 1935, no. 82 (erroneously cites exhibitions 1921, 1923); Stratford, *Faces of Canada*, 1964, reprod.

REFERENCES: *Canadian Magazine*, vol. 72 (Nov. 1929), p. 5 (reprod.).

Gift from the Reuben and Kate Leonard Canadian Fund, 1928.

895   **Portrait of Mrs. Alleyne Sutherland**

69

THE TRESTLE BRIDGE   **1915**

Etching, Imp.: 14¹³/₁₆" x 9³/₁₆". Paper: 17³/₈" x 10".
Signed and dated (lower right, in pencil): Cyril H Barraud/15.
Numbered (lower left, in pencil): 2 / [sic].

NOTES: Permanent loan from C.N.E. Association, 1915-66.

EXHIBITIONS: A.G.T., *Canadian prints*, 1949.

Gift of the Canadian National Exhibition Association, 1966.

Cyril H. BARRAUD (1877-   )

BORN: Barnes, England.

LIVES: Presumably in England, where he remained following the War. Came to Canada (Manitoba) in 1913.

STUDY: In England.

SOCIETIES: Gilbert Garrett Sketch Club, London; Manitoba Society of Arts and Crafts, 1914.
Served with the Cameron Highlanders, Winnipeg; official Canadian war artist, 1917.

Etcher.

163

EVENING ON THE YPRES-POPERINGHE ROAD   **1917**

Etching, Imp.: $8^5/_8$" x $14^7/_8$". Paper: $12^5/_8$" x 19".
Signed (lower right, in pencil): Cyril H Barraud.

NOTES: Permanent loan from the C.N.E. Association, 1921-66.

EXHIBITIONS: London, Royal Academy, *Canadian War Memorials Exhibition*, 1919, no. 298 (as Evening [on the Ypres-Poperinghe Road near the Asylum]; dated November 1, 1917; "On the western outskirts of Ypres. This corner was just in view from a Hun observation post through the greater part of the time the Canadians held the salient."); Ottawa, *Canadian War Memorials Exhibition* [2nd portion], 1920, no. 298.

REFERENCES: Canadian War Records Office, *Art and War* (n.d.), non-colour plate VII (reprod.), facing page (described as above [see Exhibition, 1919]); Godenrath, *Lest We Forget* (1934), p. 29 fig. 10 (reprod.).

Gift of the Canadian National Exhibition Association, 1966.

162

MONT DES CATS   **1917**

Etching, Imp.: $7^1/_8$" x $11^5/_{16}$". Paper: $11^1/_4$" x $16^7/_8$".
Signed (lower right, in pencil): Cyril H Barraud.

NOTES: Mont des Cats is situated in northern France, about two miles from the Belgian frontier, some twelve miles southwest of Ypres. At its foot lies Godewaersvelde, and on top a modern convent of Trappist monks. [see Baedeker's *Northern France*, 1909. p. 17]. The monastery was used as a hospital during World War I, and was almost ruined in the spring of 1918.

Permanent loan from the C.N.E. Association, 1921-66.

EXHIBITIONS: London, Royal Academy, *Canadian War Memorials Exhibition*, 1919, no. 293 (as Mont des Cats [from near Godewaers-velde]; dated October, 1917; "A Trappist Monastery used as a hospital by our men, now entirely ruined. This hill formed one of the chain of hills from Mount Kemmel to Cassel, and in this connection was of special interest in the Hun advance through Bailleul of 1918".); Ottawa, *Canadian War Memorials Exhibition* [2nd portion], 1920, no. 293.

REFERENCES: Godenrath, *Lest We Forget* (1934), p. 23, fig. 6 (reprod.); Duval (1952), pl. 13 (reprod.; erroneously dated 1912).

Gift of the Canadian National Exhibition Association, 1966

167

PLACE ST. BERTIN, POPERINGHE   **1917**

Etching, Imp.: 12" x 8".
Signed (lower right, in pencil): Cy[ ]il H Barraud.
Inscribed (right centre, on sign): ALL TRAFFIC/FOR YPRES/ ELVER-DINGHE/RENINGHELST.

NOTES: Poperinghe, Belgium, is situated six miles west of Ypres. The church of St. Bertin dates from about 1300.

Permanent loan from the C.N.E. Association, 1921-66.

EXHIBITIONS: London, Royal Academy, *Canadian War Memorials Exhibition*, 1919, no. 257 (dated October 18, 1917; says "up to this time Poperinghe had not been very heavily shelled, this church [Church of St. Bertin] only having been hit once."); Ottawa, *Canadian War Memorials Exhibition* [2nd portion], 1920, no. 257.

Gift of the Canadian National Exhibition Association, 1966.

Maxwell BATES (1906-   )

BORN: Maxwell Bennett Bates, Calgary, Alberta, December 14, 1906.

LIVES: Victoria, B. C.

STUDY: Calgary, Provincial Institute of Technology and Art, under Lars Haukness, 1926-27; in association with his father in architecture; Brooklyn Museum art school, under Max Beckmann and Abraham Rattner, 1949-50.

Went to England in 1931 to study architecture and painting; worked there 1934-39 as an architect; served in the war, and was captured at Dunkirk, thereafter prisoner-of-war in Germany, 1940-45. Returned to Calgary in 1946.

SOCIETIES: A.R.C.A., 1961; C.S.P.W.C., 1951; C.S.G.A., 1947; Alberta Society of Artists; B. C. Society of Artists; F.C.A., 1947; C.G.P.; Calgary Arts Club.

Architect, painter of figures, street scenes and landscapes, and theatrical designer.

52/14

ALBERTA ROAD   **1948**

Oil on canvas, $16^3/_8$" x $19^3/_4$".
Signed and dated (lower right): MAXWELL BATES 1948.

Gift of A. Y. Jackson, 1952.

52/14   **Alberta Road**

Aba BAYEFSKY (1923-   )

BORN: Toronto, April 7, 1923.

LIVES: Toronto.

STUDY: Toronto, Central Technical School, 1937-42; Paris, Académie Julian.

SOCIETIES: A.R.C.A., 1958; C.S.P.W.C., 1956; C.G.P., 1957, Pres. 1962-63; C.S.G.A., 1949, Pres. 1956-57; F.C.A., 1947-53, Pres. Ontario Region, 1949-53.

2720

PARK BENCH   **c. 1942**

Oil on canvas, $29^1/_4$" x $24^1/_4$".
Inscribed (on reverse): Park Scene Abbey.

PROV.: the artist [AGT, 1943].

EXHIBITIONS: A.G.T., *Painters under Twenty*, 1943; Yale, 1944.

Gift from the Albert H. Robson Memorial Subscription Fund, 1943.

Painted with "Studio" Group, Toronto, 1941-43.

TEACHING: Toronto, Ontario College of Art, since 1956.

Commissioned to execute mural entitled *Out of Bondage* for Beth El Synagogue, Don Mills, 1962.

Official war artist with the R.C.A.F., 1944.

Painter of figures, social subjects.

Harold BEAMENT (1898-   )

BORN: Thomas Harold Beament, Ottawa, July 23, 1898.

LIVES: Montreal.

STUDY: Law at Osgoode Hall for a time, but left to attend Ontario College of Art, 1922, studying under J. W. Beatty.

SOCIETIES: A.R.C.A., 1936; R.C.A., 1946; P.R.C.A. 1964 to the present; Pen and Pencil Club, Montreal, 1952.

TEACHING: Montreal Museum of Fine Arts, school of art; Nova Scotia College of Art, Halifax, from 1962.

TRAVEL: Extensively, painting in Europe, the Arctic and the West Indies.

Official Canadian War Artist with the Navy, 1943-46.

Landscape and marine painter.

J. W. BEATTY (1869-1941)

BORN: John William Beatty, Toronto, May 30, 1869.

DIED: Toronto, October 4, 1941.

STUDY: Toronto, Central Ontario School of Art and Design, 1894, under J. W. L. Forster, and G. A. Reid; Paris, Julian Academy, 1900, under J.-P. Laurens, and Benjamin Constant; London, Chelsea Polytechnic, under E. Borough Johnson.

SOCIETIES: O.S.A., 1901 [elected while still in Paris]; A.R.C.A., 1903; R.C.A., 1913; Arts and Letters Club, Toronto, Pres. 1912-13.

TEACHING: Toronto, Ontario College of Art, 1912-41.

1948
ROWING CLUB   1923

Cliche verre, Imp.: $7^3/_4$" x $8^3/_8$". Paper: $8^7/_{16}$ x $8^7/_8$".
Signed and dated (lower right, in pencil): Harold Beament/23.

EXHIBITIONS: A.G.T., *Exhibition of graphic art*, 1924, no. 18.

Gift of the Artist, 1924.

1947
PINE TREE AND RIVER   1924

Cliche verre, Imp.: $7^3/_8$ x $9^5/_{16}$.
Signed (lower right, in pencil): Harold Beament.
Inscribed and dated (lower right): H B 24.

Gift of the Artist, 1924.

304
THE BEECH WOODS

Oil on canvas, 35" x $40^1/_4$".
Signed (lower left): J. W. BEATTY.

NOTES: Permanent loan from the C.N.E. Association, 1926-65.

EXHIBITIONS: *O.S.A.*, 1926, no. 29; *C.N.E.*, 1926, no. 172, p. 35 (reprod.); A.G.T., *Summer*, 1935, no. 46; A.G.T., *Loan exhibition*, 1935, no. 83; A.G.T., *Memorial...Gagnon, Beatty*, 1942, no. 117 (dated between 1919 and 1926), p. 14 (reprod. in colour); *C.N.E.*, 1949, no. 121.

REFERENCES: Robson (1932), p. 97 (reprod. in colour); *Canadian Forum*, vol. 22 (Nov., 1942), p. 241 (reprod.); Laing Fine Art Galleries, *Pictures for lasting pleasure* (1943), p. 7 (reprod.); Hoover, *Beatty* (1948), p. 26; A.G.T., *Painting and sculpture* (1959), p. 37 (reprod. in colour); Kilbourn (1966), p. 35 (reprod. in colour).

Gift of the Canadian National Exhibition Association, 1965.

TRAVEL: England, France, Belgium, Holland and Spain, 1906-08.

First trip to northern Ontario, 1909.

Official war artist for the Canadian War Memorials, 1917-18.

Landscape painter.

304   **The Beach Woods**

216

THE MILL, MEADOWVALE

Drypoint, Imp.: $6^7/_8$" x $8^7/_8$". Paper: $10^1/_4$" x $13^1/_2$".
Signed (lower right, in pencil): J. W. Beatty.
Inscribed (lower left, in pencil): The Mill Meadowvale.

NOTES: Permanent loan from the C.N.E. Association, 1922-66.

Meadowvale is situated approximately 30 miles northwest of Toronto.

EXHIBITIONS: *C.N.E.*, 1922, no. 365; A.G.T., *Memorial…Gagnon, Beatty*, 1942, no. 153.

Gift of the Canadian National Exhibition Association, 1966.

2458

AUTUMN, ALGONQUIN PARK

Oil on canvas, $28^1/_8$" x 40".
Signed (lower left): J. W. BEATTY.

PROV.: [Galleries of J. Merritt Malloney, Toronto].

EXHIBITIONS: Toronto, Galleries of J. Merritt Malloney, Beatty, 1938, no. 22.

REFERENCES: Colgate (1943), p. 81 (says presented to the Gallery by a group of Beatty's students, as a "memorial" to him); Hoover, *Beatty* (1948), p. 36.

Gift of The Students of the Ontario College of Art, 1938.

2476

OTONABEE RIVER AND TREES

Oil on panel, $10^1/_2$" x $13^7/_8$".
Signed (lower right): J. W. BEATTY.
Inscribed (on reverse): To my very dear friend Miss Going/a souvenir of the happy hours/that I have spent with the family/J. W. Beatty/22nd/9 / 31 [drawing of lens].

NOTES: The Otonabee River flows in the area of Peterborough, Ontario.

REFERENCES: Hoover, *Beatty* (1948), p. 20.

Bequest of Ambia L. Going, 1938.

53/14

SPRING BREAK-UP, ALGONQUIN PARK

Oil on panel, $8^1/_4$" x $10^1/_4$" [sight].
Signed (lower right): J W BEATTY.

PROV.: Estate of the artist; [Laing Galleries, Toronto].

Gift from the Fund of the T. Eaton Co. Ltd. for Canadian Works of Art, 1953.

50/21

SKETCH IN SPAIN   c. 1906-09

Oil on canvas board, $6^{1}/_{4}$" x $9^{3}/_{8}$".
Signed (lower right): J. W. BEATTY.
Inscribed (on reverse): J. W. BEATTY to A. Y. Jackson/"Sketch in Spain"/probably Toledo?

Gift of A. Y. Jackson, 1951.

53/41

BARGE   1907

Oil on canvas board, $6^{1}/_{4}$" x $9^{3}/_{8}$".
Signed and dated (lower right): J. W. BEATTY 07.

EXHIBITIONS: [?] Toronto, Jenkins Gallery, *Beatty*, 1924, no. 28 (as Barge, Seine River).

Gift of Mary Wrinch Reid, 1954.

53/41   **Barge**

2478

BEECH TRUNKS   1920

Oil on panel, 10" x $13^{3}/_{8}$" [sight].
Signed and dated (lower right): J. W. BEATTY. 20.

Bequest of Ambia L. Going, 1938.

2477

FROZEN LAKE, NORTHERN ONTARIO   1928

Oil on canvas, 18" x $24^{1}/_{4}$".
Signed and dated (lower right): J. W. BEATTY. 28.

EXHIBITIONS: *O.S.A.*, 1929, no. 14.

Bequest of Ambia L. Going, 1938.

51/46

BAIE ST. PAUL   **1929**

Oil on panel, 10$^1/_{16}$" x 13$^3/_4$".
Signed and dated (lower right): J. W. BEATTY 29.

PROV.: [Laing Galleries, Toronto]; Stanford E. Dack, Toronto and
San Francisco.

NOTES: Two labels on reverse: one from artist's studio; the other from
Laing Galleries. Both give title as *Easter Time, Baie St. Paul*.

EXHIBITIONS: [?] Calgary, 1929, no. 7; A.G.T., *Benefit...Lapine*,
1934, no. 100; [?] Toronto, Galleries of J. Merritt Malloney, *Beatty*,
1938, no. 44.

Gift of Stanford E. Dack, 1952.

51/46   **Baie St. Paul**

F. M. BELL-SMITH (1846-1923)

BORN: Frederick Marlett Bell-Smith, London,
England, September 26, 1846.

DIED: Toronto, June 23, 1923. Came to Canada in 1866; lived in Montreal, working as a
photographer until 1871; in Hamilton, 1871-74,
and 1879-81; in Toronto, 1874-79, and after
1910.

STUDY: London, South Kensington Art School,
under Alexander Harrison and others; Paris,
Colarossi, 1896; Paris, under Courtois and
Dupain.

SOCIETIES: A.R.C.A., 1880, R.C.A., 1886;
O.S.A., 1872, P.O.S.A. 1905-08; Royal British
Colonial Society of Artists, London, 1908;

80

NEAR TOWER BRIDGE

Oil on canvas, 18" x 24".
Signed (lower left): F M BellSmith.

NOTES: Permanent loan from C.N.E. Association, 1916-65.

EXHIBITIONS: [?] Toronto, Provincial Art Gallery, 1897, no. 78; [?]
O.S.A., 1897, no. 113; *R.C.A.*, 1915, no. 14 (as New [sic] Tower
Bridge), p. 9 (reprod.); *O.S.A.*, 1916, no. 8; *C.N.E.*, 1916, no. 330,
p. 66 (reprod.).

REFERENCES: MacTavish (1925), betw. pp. 16 and 17 (reprod.).

Gift of the Canadian National Exhibition Association, 1965.

Society of Canadian Artists, Montreal, 1867;
Palette Club, Toronto, 1892; New Water
Colour Society, Toronto, 1900.

TEACHING: London, Ontario, 1881-88; Director of Fine Arts, Alma College, St. Thomas, 1881-90, and 1897-1910; Director, Toronto Art School, 1889-91.

Painter, photographer, illustrator.

80   Near Tower Bridge

52/45   The Beach
Colour reproduction, p. 533

18

99

THAMES BARGES OFF GREENWICH

Oil on canvas, 39⁷/₈" x 27".
Signed (lower right): F M Bell Smith.

NOTES: Permanent loan from the C.N.E. Association, 1919-65.

The buildings in the background are those of the Royal Naval College at Greenwich.

EXHIBITIONS: *O.S.A.*, 1947, no. 142 (dated between 1872 and 1882).

Gift of the Canadian National Exhibition Association, 1965.

2842

ALBERT CANYON, B. C.

Water colour on paper, 19" x 13¹/₄".
Signed (lower left): F M Bell Smith.
PROV.: W. R. Milligan, Toronto; Mrs. W. R. Milligan, Toronto.

NOTES: The Albert Canyon, through which foams the Illecillewaet River, is situated about halfway between Glacier and Revelstoke.

EXHIBITIONS: *C.S.P.W.C.*, 1951, no. 1.

Purchase, 1946.

2481

THAMES NEAR GREENWICH

Oil on canvas, 18¹/₄" x 24³/₈".
Signed (lower left): F M Bell Smith.

NOTES: Formerly entitled *London River (with barges);* title changed, 1966, to correspond with label on reverse [cf.].

Label on reverse, mostly obliterated, reads: Royal Canadian Academy/ .../[   ]ames near Greenwich.

Bequest of Ambia L. Going, 1938.

52/45

THE BEACH   1888

Water colour on paper, 13³/₈" x 20¹/₂" [sight].
Signed and dated (lower right): F. M. *Bell-Smith 1888*.

PROV.:J. P. Tisdall, Toronto (until 1934); Dr. F. F. Tisdall, Toronto (1934-1949); Mrs. F. F. Tisdall (1949-1953).

NOTES: The beach here is believed to be that at Scarborough, Ontario, with the Scarborough bluffs in the background. [see ref. Harper (1966)].

REFERENCES: Duval (1954), pl. 15 (reprod.); Harper (1966), p. 185, fig. 164 (reprod. in colour as The Beach, Scarborough), p. 188.

Gift of Mrs. F. F. Tisdall, 1953.

Charles-Ernest de BELLE
(1873-1939)

BORN: Budapest, Hungary, May 17, 1873.

DIED: Montreal, 1939. Came to Canada (Montreal), in 1912.

STUDY: Antwerp, about 1885-89, drawing and painting; Paris, studio of Munkacsy (Hungarian painter), 1889; England, where he shared a studio with Augustus John at the Nettleship Studio, Fitzroy Street, 1893.

Was also a friend of Whistler.

SOCIETIES: A.R.C.A., 1919.

Painter of portraits and figure pieces.

63/32

THREE WOMEN

Pencil and water colour on paper, $5^5/_8$" x $5^7/_8$" [sight].
Signed (lower right) [monogram]

PROV.: Mrs. Bess Hamilton, Doon, Ontario.

EXHIBITIONS: [?] *C.N.E.*, 1922, no. 215 (The Three Graces); [?] A.A.M., *Charles De Belle*, 1923 (Nov.), no. 19 (The Three Maids); [?] *R.C.A.*, 1932, no. 45 (Trio; pastel).

Purchase, 1964.

101

1919

Oil and pencil on canvas, $48^1/_4$" x $48^1/_4$".
Signed (lower left) [monogram]

NOTES: Permanent loan from C.N.E. Association, 1919-65.

Label on reverse reads: Art Association of Montreal/30th Spring Exhibition 1913/*Meditation*/C De Bell [sic]/705 St. Hubert

EXHIBITIONS: *R.C.A.*, 1918, no. 40 (reprod.); *C.N.E.*, 1919, no. 49, on frontispiece (reprod.).

Gift of the Canadian National Exhibition Association, 1965.

101   **1919**

Léon BELLEFLEUR (1910-   )

BORN: Montreal, February 8, 1910.

LIVES: Montreal.

STUDY: Montreal, Ecole Normale, and evening classes at the Ecole des Beaux-Arts, about 1929, but mainly self-taught; later, studied engraving in Paris, 1954, with Johnny Friedlaender, and in 1958-59, lithography at the Atelier Desjobert, Paris.

He was influenced for a time by Pellan, working in the manner of surrealist.

SOCIETIES: C.G.P.; C.S.G.A.; Association des artistes non-figuratifs, Montreal; Contemporary Arts Society, Montreal, 1945-48.

AWARDS: Canada Council fellowship, 1958, to study in Paris.

51/66

CLAMEUR DES SIGNES EN FEU   **1949**

Oil on canvas, 23½" x 19½".
Signed and dated (lower right): L BELLEFLEUR 1949.

PROV.: [Galerie Agnes Lefort, Montreal].

EXHIBITIONS: *C.N.E.*, 1952, no. 94.

Gift from the John Paris Bickell Bequest Fund, 1952.

51/66   **Clameur des signes en feu**
Colour reproduction, p. 547

57/21

MÉDITERRANÉE   **1957**

Gouache on cardboard, 20¹³/₁₆" x 26⅝" [sight].
Signed and dated (lower right): L·BELLEFLEUR·1957.

PROV.: the artist.

EXHIBITIONS: A.G.T., *Four Canadians*, 1957, no. 5.

REFERENCES: A.G.T., *Painting and sculpture* (1959), p. 86 (reprod.).

Gift from the McLean Foundation, 1958.

John A. E. BENNETT (1919-   )

BORN: John Alfred Everest Bennett, Diss, Norfolk, England, March 29, 1919.

LIVES: Toronto. Came to Canada as a child.

STUDY: Largely self-taught.

SOCIETIES: O.S.A., 1951; C.S.P.W.C.; Canadian Society for Education through Art.

TEACHING: Toronto, Northern Secondary School, drawing and painting, since 1946.

1942-46 served with Canadian Army overseas, painting whenever possible in Cornwall, Scotland, Ireland, Normandy, Belgium and Holland.

Painter of landscape, figure and still life.

Roloff BENY (1924-   )

BORN: Wilfred Roloff Beny, Medicine Hat, Alberta, January 7, 1924.

LIVES: Rome, Italy.

STUDY: Banff School of Fine Arts; University of Toronto; University of Iowa, 1945-46, graphic techniques under the engraver Mauricio Lasansky and others; New York University.

SOCIETIES: C.S.P.W.C.; C.G.P.

TRAVEL: Extensively painting and photographing in Europe, Africa, the Near and Far East.

AWARDS: Guggenheim Fellowship, 1952; prize at the Brooklyn International Museum for his colour engravings, *Ecclesiastes* [cf.].

Painter, photographer, illustrator, and printmaker.

2848

TRAINING GROUND, ALDERSHOT   1945

Water colour on paper, 14⅞" x 21⅝" [sight].
Signed (lower left): John Bennett.

PROV.: the artist [AGT, 1946].

NOTES: Aldershot, Hampshire, located some 10 miles southwest of London, is the site of a well-known British Military Camp, established in 1854.

The artist painted this while stationed at Aldershot during the last war.

EXHIBITIONS: A.G.T., *Bennett*, 1946, no: 4.

REFERENCES: Duval (1954), pl. 77 (reprod.).

Purchase, 1946.

2848   **Training Ground, Aldershot**

49/53

PRAIRIE DIMENSIONS   1947

Oil on canvas, 42" x 34⅛".
Signed (on reverse, at top): BENY.

PROV.: the artist.

EXHIBITIONS: *C.G.P.*, 1947-48, no. 5; *C.N.E.*, 1949, no. 91; Toronto, Eaton's Fine Art Galleries, *Beny retrospective*, n.d. [c. 1950-51], no. 17 (reprod.); Knoedler, *Beny*, 1951, no. 8; St. Catharine's, *Contemporary Canadian paintings*, 1953, no. 1.

REFERENCES: *R.A.I.C. Journal*, vol. 25 (Jan., 1948), p. 21 (reprod.); *Canadian Art*, vol. V (Spring, 1948), p. 193 (reprod.).

Gift from the Albert H. Robson Memorial Subscription Fund, 1950.

NOTES: [see Notes, acc. no. 48/19].

EXHIBITIONS: Florence, *Beny*, 1949, no. 6; Toronto, Eaton's Fine Art Galleries, *Beny Retrospective*, n.d. [c. 1950-51], no. 51; Knoedler, *Beny*, 1951, no. 28.

REFERENCES: *Art Digest*, vol. 24 (May 15, 1950), p. 17; *Art News*, vol. 52 (Jan., 1954), p. 76.

Gift from the Albert H. Robson Memorial Subscription Fund, 1949.

Aleksandre BERCOVITCH (1893-1951)

BORN: Cherson, near Odessa, Russia, March 15, 1893.

DIED: Montreal, January, 1951. Came to Canada (Montreal) in 1926.

STUDY: Palestine, Art School of "Bezabel" under Schatz; Leningrad, at the Academy of Art, under Carov; Munich, at the Academy of Art, under Stook.

Soon after the Revolution of 1917 in Russia, he went to Turkestan, settled in Achibaud, and there organized an art school.

SOCIETIES: Contemporary Arts Society, Montreal.

Painter of portraits, landscapes, flowers and still lifes.

2587

NEGRESS   1935

Oil on canvas, $36^3/_4$" x $23^5/_8$".
Signed, dated and inscribed (lower right): A Bercovitch 1935/ MONTREAL.

PROV.: the artist.

EXHIBITIONS: [?] *O.S.A.*, 1938, no. 15; [?] A.A.M., *Summer exhibition by contemporary Montreal artists*, 1939, no. 5; A.G.T., *Bercovitch, Daly, Pepper, and Winter*, 1942, erroneously dated 1939; *D.P.C.*, 1945, no. 207.

REFERENCES: Shoolman, and Slatkin (1942), pl. 715 (reprod.); A.G.T., *Painting and sculpture* (1959), p. 76 (reprod.).

Purchase, 1942.

2587   **Negress**

William von Moll BERCZY
(1748-1813)

BORN: Wilhelm Albrecht Ulrich Berczy, Baron von Moll, Saxony, Germany, 1748.

DIED: On a trip to New York, 1813. Came to Canada (Markham, Ontario) in 1794, as a settlement agent (colonist), turning to painting for a livelihood about 1801.

STUDY: University of Leipzig in Saxony, probably under the neo-classical painter, Adam Friedrich Oeser, Director of the Leipzig Academy; also at University of Jena.

TRAVEL: Extensively in Europe; spent most of his youth in Vienna; 1785-90 in Italy; 1790 to London, where he acted as agent to an English association owning land in the Genesee Valley, N. Y., in bringing out German settlers in 1792. In 1794 he brought the settlers to Upper Canada, and placed them on land in Markham Township, north of York (Toronto).

Painted portraits in Toronto in 1795; turned to full time professional painting about 1801-03.

From about 1805 lived chiefly in Montreal, but spent time in Quebec and Toronto also.

Colonist and artist, doing pastel miniatures principally, but also oil portraits, and some figure pieces, historical and religious.

55/19
SIR JAMES CRAIG (1748-1812)

Pastel on paper, 8$^{15}/_{16}$" x 7$^{7}/_{8}$" (oval).

NOTES: Sir James Craig was Governor-in-Chief of Canada 1807-11. From 1763, when he entered the British army, until 1806, he served in many parts of the world, including the American Revolution (he was wounded at the battle of Bunker's Hill), South Africa, India, the Mediterranean. In 1797 he was created a K.C.B. Died in London, Jan. 12, 1812. [see *Macmillan Dictionary of Canadian Biography*, 1963, p. 159].

REFERENCES: *Canadian Art*, vol. XIV (Winter, 1957), p. 57 (reprod.); André, *Berczy* (1967), between p. 120 and 121 (reprod.).

Gift of George E. Kingsford, 1955.

55/19 **Sir James Craig (1748-1812)**

60/21
LE SOIR AU COUCHANT

1960

Oil on canvas, 26$^{3}/_{8}$" x 36".
Signed and dated (lower left): S. Bergeron. 60.

PROV.: [Roberts Gallery, Toronto].

EXHIBITIONS: Toronto, Roberts Gallery, *Four Canadian Painters, Bobak, Bergeron, Palmer, Picher*, 1960 (Nov. 4-17) [no catalogue].

Gift from the McLean Foundation, 1961.

Suzanne BERGERON
(1930-   )

BORN: Causapscal, in the Gaspé Peninsula, P.Q., June 23, 1930.

LIVES: Paris.

STUDY: Ecole des Beaux-Arts, Quebec, diploma, 1953, under Jean-Paul Lemieux; in Paris, associated with those of the "Ecole de Paris".

AWARDS: Prize at Concours Artistiques de la Province de Québec, 1955, for study in Paris; in Paris, 1956, awarded "Le Prix de la Ville de Paris"; 1957, Canadian Government scholarship; 1963, Canada Council fellowship, to Paris again.

Landscape painter in abstract.

60/21   **Le soir au couchant**

Eric BERGMAN (1893-1958)

BORN: H. Eric Bergman, Dresden, Germany, November 10, 1893.

DIED: Winnipeg, February 8, 1958. Came to Canada in 1913, and went to Winnipeg, after a brief stay in Toronto.

STUDY: No formal training.

From 1914 until his death, worked in the Art Studios of Bridgens Ltd., in Winnipeg as a commercial artist.

In 1922 met with F. H. Brigden and W. J. Phillips and through association with them began to pursue art non-commercially, painting in northern Manitoba, Lake-of-the-Woods area, Eastern Ontario, and the Rocky Mountains.

Executed his first wood-engraving in 1926.

SOCIETIES: C.S.P.W.C., 1935; C.P.E., 1935; Manitoba Society of Artists.

Landscape painter, draughtsman, wood-engraver.

2133

THE WHITE MORNING

Wood-engraving, Imp.: $4^3/_8$" x $4^9/_{16}$". Paper: $8^3/_4$" x $9^3/_4$".
Signed (lower right, in pencil): H. E. Bergman.
Inscribed and numbered (lower left, in pencil): The White Morning 4/75.

Inscribed (lower right) [monogram].

PROV.: the artist [CSGA, 1933].

EXHIBITIONS: *C.S.G.A.*, 1933, no. 271; New York, *World's Fair*, 1939, section CSGA, no. 9.

Purchase, 1933.

2134

SPIRITS OF THE PAST   1932

Wood engraving, Imp.: $5^9/_{16}$" x $6^7/_8$". Paper: $9^{11}/_{16}$" x $10^1/_4$";
Signed (lower right, in pencil): H. E. Bergman.
Inscribed and numbered (lower left, in pencil): Spirits of the Past 4/75.

Inscribed (lower left) [monogram].

PROV.: the artist [CSGA, 1933].

EXHIBITIONS: *C.S.G.A.*, 1933, no. 268, p. 12 (reprod.); New York, *World's Fair*, 1939, section CSGA, no. 8; A.G.T., *Canadian prints*, 1949.

REFERENCES: *Studio*, vol. CXII (Dec., 1936), p. 324 (reprod.); Duval (1952), pl. 33 (reprod.; dated 1932).

Purchase, 1933.

George Théodore BERTHON
(1806-1892)

BORN: Royal Palace of Vienna, May 3, 1806, son of René Théodore Berthon (1777-1859), court painter to Napoleon I.

DIED: Toronto, January 18, 1892. Came to Canada in 1841; settled in Toronto, 1844.

STUDY: Under his father, and is said to have been apprenticed to portraiture under Jacques-Louis David.

Left his family in 1827 to go to England, where he entered the household of Sir Robert Peel, to teach Peel's daughters drawing and French.

SOCIETIES: O.S.A., 1876 (in 1891 elected a life member); R.C.A., 1880 (nominated a founder member, "but failed to qualify" [see Colgate (1943), p. 16]).

Portraitist [Portrait of Sir John Beverley Robinson, in collection of Osgoode Hall, is considered his masterpiece.].

LOAN   The Three Robinson Sisters
Colour reproduction, p. 529

59/13

QUEEN ELIZABETH REPRIMANDING THE COUNTESS OF ESSEX

Oil on canvas, $60^5/_{16}$" x $60^3/_8$".

PROV.: Augustus Berthon, son of the artist; William P. Playter; [his daughter] Mrs. Richard L. Mudge, Toronto.

NOTES: The Countess of Essex, the former Frances Walsingham, was first married to Sir Philip Sidney, in 1583. Widowed in 1586, she married secondly Robert Devereux, Earl of Essex, in 1590. [see G. B. Harrison, *Life and death of Robert Devereux, Earl of Essex*, New York, 1937, pp. 45-6].

The painting is based on a story surrounding the ring held here by Queen Elizabeth. It seems the Queen gave a ring to Essex, one of her favourites, who in turn gave it to his wife. When the Queen saw it she was enraged and proceeded to reprimand Essex' wife.

According to information furnished by the previous owner of the painting, the artist used Lady Falconbridge [wife of Sir William Glenholme Falconbridge, whom she married in 1873], and his own youngest daughter by his second marriage as models for the figures of Queen Elizabeth and the Countess of Essex respectively.

Purchase, 1960.

LOAN

THE THREE ROBINSON SISTERS   1846

Oil on canvas, $44^1/_8$" x 33".

PROV.: The Robinson Family, Toronto.

NOTES: The sitters, three daughters of Mr. and Mrs John Beverley Robinson (later Sir John and Lady Robinson), are identified as follows, from left to right: "Augusta, who was married to the son [James McGill Strachan] of Bishop Strachan on 31st October 1844; Louisa, who married George William Allan of Moss Park, Toronto...on 16th April, 1846; and Emily who on the same day as her sister, Louisa, was married to Captain, afterwards General Sir J. H. Lefroy, all of whom left descendants in Canada". [see reference, Colgate *Berthon*, 1942].

The painting was a gift to Mrs. Robinson from her three sons-in-law on April 16, 1846, the day her daughters Emily and Louisa were married.

EXHIBITIONS: *O.S.A. retrospective*, 1922, no. 10 (lent by Mrs. Christopher Robinson); A.G.T., *Loan exhibition of portraits*, 1927, no. 154 (lent by C. C. Robinson, Toronto); A.G.T., *Toronto centennial historical exhibition*, 1934, no. 134 (lent by J. Beverley Robinson, Toronto); *D.P.C.*, 1945, no. 43 (lent by J. Beverley Robinson), p. 19 (reprod.); *C.N.E.*, A tribute to women, 1960, reprod.; N.G.C., *300 years of Canadian art*, 1967, no. 104, p. 67 (reprod.).

REFERENCES: Hammond (1930), p. 11; Colgate, *Berthon* (1942), pp. 9-10 (identifies the sitters [see Notes, above]), p. 20, opp. p. 6 (reprod.); Colgate (1943), p. 14-16 (reprod.; collection of J. Beverley Robinson); *Saturday Night*, vol. 60 (Jan. 13, 1945), p. 4 (reprod.); McInnes (1950), p. 36; *Saturday Night* (Sept. 3, 1955), p. 35 (reprod.);

Hubbard (1960), pl. 41 (reprod.); Hubbard (1963), p. 53, pl. 82 (reprod.); Brieger, Vickers and Winter, *Art and Man,* III (1964), p. 155, fig. 172 (reprod.).

Lent by Mr. and Mrs. J. B. Robinson, 1944.

52/35

PORTRAIT OF LADY ROBINSON WITH HER DAUGHTER MARY 1847

Oil on canvas, 43$^1/_2$" x 33$^1/_2$".
Signed and dated (lower right): G. T. Berthon/1847.

PROV.: Mrs. R. A. Laidlaw, Toronto.

NOTES: Lady Robinson (d. 1865), the former Emma Walker of Harlesden, Middlesex, was the wife of Sir John Beverley Robinson (1791-1863), Chief Justice of Upper Canada. They were married in London, England in 1817; he was created Baronet of the United Kingdom in 1854.

Mary Amelia, the fourth and youngest daughter of the Robinsons, was born in 1831. In 1863 she married the Hon. Donald MacInnes (1824-1900) of Hamilton, Ontario.

[see Burke's *Peerage,* 1949, p. 1706; and *Macmillan Dictionary of Canadian Biography,* 1963, p. 638].

EXHIBITIONS: Vancouver, *Images,* 1966, no. 32; M.M.F.A., *The painter and the new world,* 1967, no. 110 (reprod.).

REFERENCES: A.G.T., *Accessions 1952-53,* reprod.; A.G.T., *Painting and sculpture* (1959), p. 50 (reprod.); *Antiques,* vol. XCII (July, 1967), p. 34 (reprod.).

Gift of the Cayley Sisters, Great-Granddaughters of Lady Robinson, 1953.

52/35   Portrait of Lady Robinson with her Daughter Mary

50/70   **Self Portrait**

André BIELER (1896-   )

BORN: Lausanne, Switzerland, October 8, 1896.

LIVES: Kingston, Ontario. Lived in Paris until 1908 when he came to Canada (Montreal).

STUDY: Switzerland, under his uncle Ernest Biéler; Paris, Ecole des Beaux-Arts and the Académie Ranson, under Maurice Denis and Paul Sérusier; New York, at the Art Students' League, under Eugene Speicher, Charles Rosen and George Bellows.

Between 1926-36 he painted in the Gaspé; then settled at Ste. Famille on the Ile d'Orléans; later at St. Sauveur in the Laurentians.

SOCIETIES: O.S.A., 1937; A.R.C.A., 1942, R.C.A., 1955; C.S.P.W.C.; C.G.P., charter member, 1933; C.S.G.A.; F.C.A., 1942, Pres. 1942-44.

TEACHING: Resident artist and professor of art, Queen's University, Kingston, from 1936 to 1963, when he retired.

Painter of landscapes and figure pieces in water colour and oils.

50/70

SELF PORTRAIT   **1890**

Oil on cardboard, 22$\frac{1}{2}$" x 18" [sight].
Signed and dated (lower left): Berthon 1890.
Inscribed (on reverse, lower right): Painted by himself in 1890/at the age of 84 years.

EXHIBITIONS: A.G.T., *Toronto centennial historical exhibition*, 1934, no. 23 (lent by Miss [Claire] Berthon, Toronto, daughter of the painter), p. 10 (reprod.).

REFERENCES: Colgate, *Berthon* (1942), p. 13; Harper (1966), p. 137, fig. 124 (reprod.; erroneously dated 1839).

Gift of G. T. Berthon, 1951.

50/19

SOIR D'HIVER   **1932**

Oil on panel, 9$\frac{7}{8}$" x 13".
Signed and dated (lower right): A B.32'.

NOTES: Label on reverse from an art exhibition at the Manoir Richelieu, n.d., list no. 11. [?].

Gift of A. Y. Jackson, 1951.

50/19   **Soir d'hiver**

2469

ELECTION DAY, ST. ADÈLE 1938

Water colour on paper, 18¹/₄" x 23¹/₄" [sight].
Signed (lower left): André Biéler.

PROV.: the artist [CSPWC, 1938].

EXHIBITIONS: London, Tate, 1938, no. 29 (lent by the artist);
C.S.P.W.C., 1938, no. 23; New York, *World's Fair*, 1939, section
CSPWC and SSC, no. 11; Kingston, *Biéler retrospective*, 1963, no. 29;
A.G.O. [circulating exhibition], *Canadian paintings of the 1930s*,
1967-68, no. 2.

REFERENCES: *Art News*, vol. XXXVII (Oct. 8, 1938), p. 7 (reprod.);
Studio, vol. 125 (Apr., 1943), p. 122 (reprod.); Barbeau (1946), p. 25
(reprod.; erroneously accredited to N.G.C. collection); Duval (1954),
pl. 46 (reprod.); Hubbard (1963), p. 113.

Purchase, 1938.

2469   **Election Day, St. Adèle**

2597

GATINEAU MADONNA 1940

Water colour on paper, 18¹/₄" x 21⁵/₁₆" [sight].
Signed and dated (lower left): André Biéler 40.

PROV.: the artist [CSPWC, 1942].

NOTES: An almost identical version of the same subject, oil on board,
41¹/₂" x 36", signed, lower right, is in the collection of the National
Gallery of Canada, accession no. 4610, and is catalogued and illustrated in their *Catalogue of the Canadian School*, 1960, p. 18.

EXHIBITIONS: Brooklyn, N.Y., *International water color exhibition, 11th Biennial*, 1941, no. 184 (reprod.); *C.S.P.W.C.*, 1942; Andover, Mass., 1942, no. 1; Yale, 1944; *D.P.C.*, 1945, no. 198.

REFERENCES: *Art Digest*, vol. 15 (Apr. 15, 1941), p. 5 (reprod.); *Saturday Night*, vol. 57 (July 11, 1942), p. 4 (reprod.): A.G.T., *Painting and sculpture* (1959), p. 79 (reprod.).

Purchase, 1942.

52/51

A. Y. JACKSON   **1949**

Pen and ink on paper, 8" x 5".
Signed and dated (lower right): A B. 49.
Inscribed (across bottom): A. Y. Jackson at Canmore Alta 1949./ ANDRE BIELER.

NOTES: For biography of sitter, see A. Y. Jackson, p. 205

Gift of Professor André Biéler, 1953.

B. C. BINNING (1909-   )

BORN: Bertram Charles Binning, Medicine Hat, Alberta, February 10, 1909; moved at an early age to Vancouver.

LIVES: Vancouver.

STUDY: Vancouver School of Art, under F.H. Varley and C. H. Scott; New York, Art Students' League, 1939, under Kuniyoshi and others; London, under Henry Moore; New York, under Ozenfant.

SOCIETIES: A.R.C.A., 1954, R.C.A., 1966; C.G.P., 1948; C.S.G.A., 1940; B. C. Society of Artists, 1935; F.C.A.

TEACHING: Instructor, Vancouver School of Art, 1938-48; Head of the Art Department, and Curator of the Art Gallery at University of British Columbia, since 1949.

Best known for his drawings until 1948, when he first exhibited paintings.

Draughtsman, painter, architectural designer.

2849

VIEW FROM GLENEAGLES   **1944**

Pen and ink on paper, 17³/₈" x 23¹/₂"" [sight].
Signed and dated (left centre): B. C. Binning 44.

PROV.: the artist [AGT, 1946].

EXHIBITIONS: A.G.T. *Binning*, 1946, no. 30.

REFERENCES: Duval (1952), pl. 91 (reprod.).

Purchase, 1946.

2850

ARBUTUS TREE   **1945**

Pen and ink on paper, 17¹/₂" x 23¹/₂" [sight].
Signed and dated (lower left): B. C. Binning/45.

PROV.: the artist [AGT, 1946].

EXHIBITIONS: A.G.T., *Binning*, 1946, no. 36.

Purchase, 1946.

50/59

SQUALLY WEATHER   **1948-50**

Oil on paper board, 32" x 40¹/₂".
Signed and dated (lower centre): B. C. Binning — '48-'50.

PROV.: the artist [AGT, 1951].

EXHIBITIONS: A.G.T., *Binning — Cosgrove*, 1951, no. 14; *C.N.E.*, 1952, no. 95.

REFERENCES: A.G.T., *Painting and sculpture* (1959), p. 84 (reprod.).

Gift from the Albert H. Robson Memorial Subscription Fund, 1951.

50/58   **Ghost Ships**

50/59   **Squally Weather**

50/58

GHOST SHIPS   **1949**

Oil on paper board, 36" x 17".
Signed and dated (lower centre): B. C. Binning '49.

PROV.: the artist [AGT, 1951].

EXHIBITIONS: Vancouver, U.B.C., *Binning*, n.d. [?1950], no. 6;
Washington, 1950, no. 5 (lent by the artist); A.G.T., *Binning — Cos-
grove*, 1951 (erroneously said to be lent by N.G.C.); *Pittsburgh inter-
national*, 1952, no. 23; N.G.C., *Coronation*, 1953, no. 6 (reprod.);
Venice, *Biennale*, 1954, p. 207, no. 3, pl. 57 (reprod.); Australia, 1957,
no. 2, pl. 15 (reprod.); Brussels, 1958; Mexico, 1960, no. 150; A.G.T.,
Art and Engineering, 1965, no. 1A (reprod.); N.G.C., *300 years of
Canadian art*, 1967, no. 274, p. 163 (reprod.).

REFERENCES: *Canadian Art*, vol. IX (Christmas/New Year, 1951-52),
p. 77 (reprod.); *Canadian Art*, vol. X (Winter, 1953), p. 83; *Vogue*
(Apr. 15, 1955), p. 109 (reprod.); A.G.T., *News and Notes*, vol. 2
(Jan., 1958), reprod. and discussed; *Canada at Brussels, 1958* (1957),
p. 53 (reprod.); *Vie des Arts*, no. 11 (Summer, 1958), p. 28 (reprod.);
Hubbard (1960), pl. 121 (reprod.); Brieger, Vickers, and Winter, *Art
and Man*, III (1964), p. 175, fig. 197 (reprod.); Kilbourn (1966), p. 98
(reprod. in colour).

Gift from the Albert H. Robson Memorial Subscription Fund, 1951.

Zbigniew BLAZEJE (1942-   )

BORN: Barnaul, U.S.S.R., June 2, 1942.

LIVES: Toronto. Came to Canada following
World War II; lived in Brampton until 1962.

STUDY: Self taught.

Works in optical and kinetic traditions of
modern art.

66/15

STRUCTURAL 1965, NO. 16   **1965**

Fluorescent, acrylic and phosphorescent paint on canvas and wood,
plastic, 48" x 37" x 3⅜".

PROV.: the artist [AGT, 1966].

EXHIBITIONS: A.G.T., *Audio-Kinetic Environment*, 1966 (Jan. 19 -
Feb. 3) [no catalogue].

Gift from the McLean Foundation, 1966.

66/15 **Structural 1965, No. 16**

Ronald BLOORE (1925-   )

BORN: Ronald Langley Bloore, Brampton, Ontario, May 29, 1925.

LIVES: Toronto.

STUDY: University of Toronto, 1945-49; New York University, Institute of Fine Arts, 1949-51; St. Louis, Washington University, 1953; also in Brussels, Antwerp and at the University of London, Courtauld Institute, 1955-57.

SOCIETIES: F.C.A.

TEACHING: Has taught in several universities; director, Norman McKenzie Gallery of Regina College, Regina, Saskatchewan, 1958-66; director of art, York University, Toronto, since 1966.

AWARDS: Canada Council Senior Fellowship, 1962-63, to Greece.

62/20

DRAWING NO. 8, 1960   1960

Pen and ink on paper, $20^3/_8$" x 26".
Inscribed and dated (on reverse): July 9, 1960, Lac La Rouge.

PROV.: [Dorothy Cameron Gallery, Toronto].

EXHIBITIONS: A.G.T., *Drawings*, 1963, p. 1.

Gift from the McLean Foundation, 1963.

64/34

BLUE, GREEN AND WHITE PAINTING   1961

Oil on masonite, 48" x 48".
Inscribed and dated (on reverse, upper centre): TOP/BLOORE/PAINTING (Sigh)/July - Aug. 61/Regina/Univ of Sask/NMA Gallery.

PROV.: [Dorothy Cameron Gallery, Toronto].

NOTES: Awarded first prize for this painting at Vancouver Art Gallery, Women's Auxiliary exhibition, 1963 [cf].

64/34   **Blue, Green and White Painting**

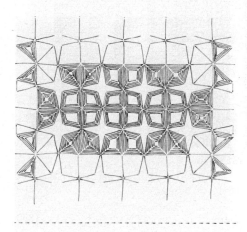

64/35   **Fanny Bay No. 2**

Bruno BOBAK (1923-   )

BORN: Brunislaw Jacob Bobak, Wawelowska, Poland, December 28, 1923.

LIVES: Fredericton, N.B. Came to Canada in 1927, living in various centres, until he settled with his family in Toronto in 1936.

STUDY: Central Technical School, Toronto, under Carl Schaefer and Elizabeth Wyn Wood, diploma, 1942; London, Central School of Arts and Crafts, and under John Farleigh; and at City and Guilds Art School.

SOCIETIES: A.R.C.A., 1959; C.S.P.W.C.;

EXHIBITIONS: A.G.T., *16th annual sale of Canadian art*, 1962, no. 10; Vancouver, *Women's Auxiliary 15th annual contemporary exhibition and sale*, 1962. [no catalogue in A.G.O. 1967; see press release from Vancouver Art Gallery, May 24, 1963]; Dorothy Cameron Gallery, and others, *Bloore*, 1965, no. e (in collection of Dorothy Cameron); Fredericton, *Saskatchewan Painters*, 1966.

REFERENCES: *Canadian Art*, vol. XXIII (Oct., 1966), p. 22 (reprod.).

Purchase, 1965.

61/62

SMALL WHITE CROSS   1962

Oil on masonite, 17⁵/₈" x 48".
Signed, inscribed and dated (on reverse): TOP/BLOORE/JAN 62/ REGINA.

PROV.: [Here and Now Gallery, Toronto].

EXHIBITIONS: Here and Now Gallery, *Bloore*, 1962 (Mar. 2-19) [no catalogue]; A.G.T., *Religious art*, 1963, no. 2; London, Tate, 1964, no. 95 (reprod.); Toronto, Dorothy Cameron Gallery, and others, *Bloore*, 1965, no. f; A.G.T., *Art and Engineering*, 1965, no. 2A (reprod.); Fredericton, *Saskatchewan Painters*, 1966.

REFERENCES: *Canadian Art*, vol. 10 (May, 1962), p. 176; *Canadian Art*, vol. XXIII (Oct., 1966), p. 23 (reprod.), p. 24.

Gift from the McLean Foundation, 1962.

64/35

FANNY BAY NO. 2   1964

Pen and ink on paper, 13" x 20¹/₈".

PROV.: [Dorothy Cameron Gallery, Toronto].

NOTES: Drawing related to symbols used in paintings of the same period.

Purchase, 1965.

50/57

CORNSTALKS   1950

Water colour on paper, 26³/₈" x 21⁷/₈".
Signed and dated (lower right): BOBAK/1950.

PROV.: the artist [CSPWC, 1951].

NOTES: Another version of the same subject, entitled simply *Corn*, water colour, 28¹/₂" x 20⁵/₈", signed and dated, lower left, BOBAK/ 1951, is in the collection of the National Gallery of Canada, accession no. 5804, and is catalogued and illustrated in their *Catalogue of the Canadian School*, 1960, p. 21.

EXHIBITIONS: *C.S.P.W.C.*, 1951, no. 22, p. 11 (reprod.); *C.S.P.W.C. travelling exhibition*, 1951, no. 4.

34

C.G.P.; C.P.E.; C.S.G.A.; B.C. Society of Artists.

TEACHING: Vancouver School of Art, until 1957; since 1960, resident artist, University of New Brunswick, Fredericton.

AWARDS: Canadian government fellowship to England, 1957-58.
Lived and worked in Vancouver, 1948-60.
Official Canadian war artist with the army, 1943-45.

REFERENCES: *Studio*, vol. 143 (April, 1952), p. 111 (reprod.); Duval (1954), pl. 88 (reprod.); *Canadian Art*, vol. XV (Jan., 1958), p. 25 (reprod.).

Gift from the Albert H. Robson Memorial Subscription Fund, 1951.

55/42

CRUMPLED LEAVES   **1954**

Linocut, Imp.: 15" x 16³/₄".
Signed (lower right, in pencil): Bruno J. Bobak.
Numbered (lower left, in pencil): 6/30.
Inscribed (lower centre, in pencil): "Crumpled Leaves".

EXHIBITIONS: *C.S.G.A.*, 1955, no. 6, on last page (announces this print to have been awarded one of the C. W. Jeffries [sic] Awards, made possible through the generosity of the Saracini Construction Co.; "the work purchased to be given later to two Canadian public galleries").

[NOTE: Impressions of this print have been exhibited also, London, Victoria and Albert Museum, 1956; Lugano, Switzerland, 1956.].

Gift of the Canadian Society of Graphic Art, 1956.

58/6

BIRDS IN GRASSES   **1956**

Two-colour linocut, 31¹/₁₆" x 12¹/₂".
Signed (lower right, in pencil): Bruno J. Bobak.
Numbered (lower left, in pencil): 13/15.
Inscribed (lower centre, in pencil): "Birds in Grasses".

PROV.: The Telegram, Toronto.

EXHIBITIONS: *C.S.G.A.*, 1956, no. 11 (reprod.; [purchased by The Telegram]).

[NOTE: Impressions of this print have been exhibited also, Lugano, Switzerland, 1956, reprod. pl. 16; Tokyo, *1st biennial*, 1957; Brussels, 1958; *A.F.A.*, 1959, reprod.].

REFERENCES: *Prisme des Arts*, no. 14 (Fall, 1957), p. 32 (reprod.); *Canada at Brussels, 1958* (1957), p. 53 (reprod.).

Gift from the Telegram Art Fund, 1958.

60/19   **Alders**

60/19

ALDERS   **1959**

Pastel on paper, 17¹/₂" x 23³/₄" [sight].
Signed (lower left): BRUNO/BOBAK.
Inscribed (lower left): D109.

PROV.: [Roberts Gallery, Toronto].

EXHIBITIONS: Roberts Gallery, *Four Canadian painters, Bobak, Bergeron, Palmer, Picher*, 1960 (Nov. 4-17) [no catalogue].

Gift from the McLean Foundation, 1961.

TOUCH OF FALL

1959

Pastel on paper, 17⅞" x 24" [sight].
Signed (lower right): BOBAK.
Inscribed (lower right): D81.

PROV.: [The Waddington Galleries, Montreal].

Gift from the McLean Foundation, 1961.

Molly Lamb BOBAK
(1922-   )

BORN: Molly Lamb, Vancouver, February 25, 1922, daughter of H. Mortimer Lamb.

LIVES: Fredericton, N.B.

In 1945, in London, she met and later married Bruno Bobak.

STUDY: Vancouver School of Art, under J. L. Shadbolt, graduating in 1942; also in London, San Francisco, and Chicago.

TEACHING: Vancouver School of Art, 1947-50; Fredericton, University of New Brunswick.

AWARDS: French government scholarship, for study in France, 1950-51; Canada Council fellowship, to work in Europe, 1960-61.

Joined C.W.A.C., 1942, becoming official war artist, 1944-46.

2738

REVEILLE (NO. 3)

1943

Pencil on paper, 15⅜" x 12".
Inscribed (sign on bed): Out of bounds/MEN AT/WORK.

PROV.: the artist.

REFERENCES: *New World Illustrated*, vol. 4 (Sept., 1943), p. 46 (reprod.); *Canadian Art*, vol. 18 (Jan., 1961), p. 14.

Purchase, 1943.

2739

DINNER IN THE KITCHEN (NO. 4)

1943

Pencil on paper, 15½" x 12".

PROV.: the artist.

Purchase, 1943.

2739   Dinner in the Kitchen (No. 4)

Paul-Emile BORDUAS
(1905-1960)

BORN: St. Hilaire, Quebec, November 1, 1905.

DIED: Paris, February 22, 1960, where he had lived and worked since 1955.

STUDY: Studied and worked with Ozias Leduc, about 1920; 1923, entered École des Beaux-Arts, Montreal; 1928, Paris, where he studied under Maurice Denis and Georges Desvallières at the Ecole des Arts Sacrés.

SOCIETIES: Founding member, Contemporary Arts Society, Montreal, 1939, and Pres. 1948. Leader of the *Automatistes* by 1947, a Montreal group who published their first manifesto in 1948, entitled *Refus Global*.

1953-54 in New York where he came under the influence of Franz Kline, and also showed an interest in the works of de Kooning, Gottlieb, Motherwell and Pollock.

TEACHING: Returned to Canada in 1930, and taught for some years in Montreal with the Catholic School Commission, and later at the Ecole du Meuble.

50/68   **Deux figures au plateau**

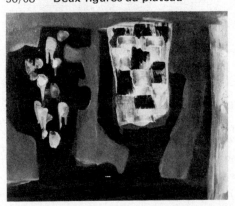

2740
C.W.A.C. BARRACKS (NO. 11)   **1943**

Pencil on paper, $15^1/_8$" x $11^3/_4$".

PROV.: the artist.

REFERENCES: *New World Illustrated*, vol. 4 (Sept., 1943), p. 46 (reprod.).

Purchase, 1943.

55/2
L'OISEAU DECHIFFRANT UN HIEROGLYPHE   **1943**

Oil on canvas, $18^5/_8$" x $22^1/_8$".
Signed and dated (lower right): Borduas/43.

PROV.: Gérard Lortie, Montreal, [Galerie Agnes Lefort, Montreal].

EXHIBITIONS: *D.P.C.*, 1945, no. 233 (lent by the artist); Albany, 1946, no. 65 (collection of the artist, reprod.); Australia, 1957, no. 3; M.M.F.A., and others, *Borduas*, 1962, no. 38, p. 18, under June 1955; London, Tate, 1964, no. 24; Hanover, N. H., Dartmouth College, *Borduas*, 1967, no. 3, fig. 2 (reprod.).

REFERENCES: Elie, *Borduas* (1943), p. 24, no. 19, pl. 19 (reprod.); *Canadian Art*, vol. XIV (Winter, 1957), p. 57 (reprod.).

Gift from J. S. McLean, Canadian Fund, 1955.

50/68
DEUX FIGURES AU PLATEAU   **1948**

Oil on canvas, $18^1/_2$" x $21^5/_8$".
Signed and dated (lower right): Borduas/48.

PROV.: the artist [AGT, 1951].

EXHIBITIONS: A.G.T., *Borduas and de Tonnancour*, 1951; Stratford, and St. John, N.B., *Ten decades, ten painters*, 1967, no. 41 (reprod.).

REFERENCES: *Canadian Art*, vol. IX (Christmas/New Year, 1951-52), p. 77 (reprod.); *Vie des Arts*, no. 19 (Eté, 1960), p. 24 (reprod.); M.M.F.A., and others, *Borduas*, 1962, p. 17, under June 1951 [not exhibited].

Gift from the Albert H. Robson Memorial Subscription Fund, 1951.

51/2
FLORAISON MASSIVE   **1951**

Oil on canvas, $25^3/_4$" x $31^7/_8$".
Signed and dated (lower right): Borduas/51.

PROV.: the artist [CNE, 1951].

EXHIBITIONS: *C.N.E.*, 1951, no. 17; *C.N.E.*, 1952, no. 96; M.M.F.A., and others, *Borduas*, 1962, no. 74, p. 17, under August 1951; Hanover, N. H., Dartmouth College, *Borduas*, 1967, no. 11, fig. 4 (reprod.).

51/2   **Floraison massive**

REFERENCES: A.G.T., *Painting and sculpture* (1959), p. 48 (reprod. in colour); *Vie des Arts*, no. 19 (Eté, 1960), p. 28 (reprod.); *Canadian painting in the twentieth century*, 1961, pl. 9 (reprod. in colour).

Gift from the Albert H. Robson Memorial Subscription Fund, 1951.

59/22

LES BOUCLIERS   **1953**

Oil on canvas, 32$^7/_{16}$" x 42$^1/_4$".
Signed and dated (lower right): Borduas/53.

PROV.: [Laing Galleries, Toronto, 1953-60].

EXHIBITIONS: M.M.F.A., and others, *Borduas*, 1962, no. 78; Hanover, N. H., Dartmouth College, *Borduas*, 1967, no. 12, fig. 5 (reprod.); Victoria, *Ten Canadians*, 1967, no. 49; Stratford, and St. John, N. B., *Ten decades, ten painters*, 1967, no. 43.

REFERENCES: *Vie des Arts*, no. 19 (Eté, 1960), p. 28 (reprod.).

Gift from the McLean Foundation, 1960.

59/22   **Les boucliers**
Colour reproduction, p. 548

57/20

ARDENTE CHAPELLE   **1954**

Water colour on paper, 22$^1/_4$" x 30$^1/_2$".
Signed and dated (lower right): Borduas/54.

PROV.: [Martha Jackson Gallery, New York].

REFERENCES: *Vie des Arts*, no. 23 (Eté, 1961), p. 17 (reprod.).

Gift from the McLean Foundation, 1958.

60/47

ABSTRACT IN BLUE **1959**

Oil on canvas, 36¹/₄" x 28⁷/₈".
Signed (on reverse, at top): Borduas.

NOTES: This painting was purchased from the Amsterdam exhibition by Mr. and Mrs. Zacks (Special Purchase Fund), for the Art Gallery of Toronto.

EXHIBITIONS: Amsterdam, *Borduas*, 1960-61, reprod., dated 1959; Hanover, N. H., Dartmouth College, *Borduas*, 1967, no. 28, fig. 9 (reprod.); Paris, Musée National d'Art Moderne, *Canada: art d'aujourd'hui*, 1968, no. 13.

Gift of Mr. and Mrs. S. J. Zacks, 1961.

60/47   **Abstract in Blue**

James BOYD (1928-   )

BORN: James Henderson Boyd, Ottawa, December 16, 1928.

LIVES: Ottawa.

STUDY: New York, National Academy of Design, 1953-57, under Robert Phillip; Art Students' League, under Bernard Klonis and Will Barnett; "Contemporaries" graphic work shop, under M. Ponce de Léon.

SOCIETIES: C.S.G.A., 1956.

TEACHING: Graphics at Municipal Art Centre, Ottawa, 1956-66;

Designer for the C.B.C.

64/26

THE MEGALITH **1963**

Single relief print and metal collage, Imp.: 15³/₄" x 13¹³/₁₆".
Signed (lower right, in pencil): James Boyd.
Inscribed and dated (lower left, in pencil): The Magalith/63.
Numbered (lower centre, in pencil): 1/1.

PROV.: [Isaacs Gallery, Toronto].

Gift from the Georgia J. Weldon Estate, 1965.

Marcel BRAITSTEIN
(1935-   )

BORN: Charleroi, Belgium, July 11, 1935.

LIVES: Montreal. Came to Canada in 1951.

STUDY: Montreal, Ecole des Beaux-Arts; Mexico, Instituto Allende, San Miguel.

TEACHING: Montreal Museum of Fine Arts, School of Art and Design; and Ecole des Beaux-Arts.

AWARDS: Canada Council grants to Mexico and Europe, 1959-61.

Sculptor, in welded metal and bronze.

Fritz BRANDTNER (1896-   )

BORN: Free City of Danzig, Prussia, July 28, 1896.

LIVES: Montreal. Came to Canada in 1928, and after some time in Winnipeg, settled in Montreal about 1934.

STUDY: Danzig, under Fritz August Pfuhle, at the University of Danzig, but largely self-taught. Influenced by German Expressionists.

SOCIETIES: C.S.P.W.C.; C.G.P.; C.S.G.A.; F.G.A.

TEACHING: University of Danzig, 1924-26; McGill University, Montreal; University of New Brunswick summer school.

40

60/60

STRUGGLE WITH FRUSTRATION   **1961**

Pen and ink on paper, 20" x 13".
Signed and dated (lower right): MB '61.

PROV.: the artist [AGT, 1961].

EXHIBITIONS: A.G.T., *Exhibition and sale of garden sculpture*, 1961, no. 65.

Canada Council Joint Drawings Purchade Fund, 1961.

60/60   **Struggle with Frustration**

2541

THE RIDERS   **1939**

Water colour on paper, $18^5/_8$" x $24^3/_8$" [sight].
Signed and dated (lower right): f. brandtner 39.

EXHIBITIONS: *C.S.P.W.C.*, 1939; New York, *World's Fair*, 1939, section CSPWC, and SSC, no. 16; [?] Elmira, N. Y., 1946, no. 23; A.G.T., *Fifty years of painting in Canada*, 1949, no. 74; Boston, 1949, no. 8, p. 29 (reprod.).

REFERENCES: *Saturday Night*, vol. 54 (June 10, 1939), p. 17 (reprod.); *Studio*, vol. 125 (Apr., 1943), p. 124 (reprod.); *Canadian Art*, vol. V (Spring, 1948), p. 168 (reprod.); *Studio*, vol. 143 (April 1952), p. 111 (reprod.).

Purchase, 1940.

2541　　**The Riders**

2598

SPY ROCK, LAURENTIANS   **1940**

Water colour on paper, $19^3/_8''$ x $26^5/_8''$ [sight].
Signed and dated (lower centre): f. brandtner. 40.

PROV.: the artist [CSPWC, 1942].

EXHIBITIONS: Brooklyn, N. Y., *International water color exhibition, 11th biennial,* 1941, no. 186; *C.S.P.W.C.,* 1942.

REFERENCES: Duval (1954), pl. 54 (reprod.).

Purchase, 1942.

2736

WELDERS WORKING ON A KILN   **1941**

Black chalk and ink, heightened with white, on paper, 18″ x $24^1/_{16}''$.
Signed and dated (lower right): f brandtner 41.

PROV.: the artist.

REFERENCES: *Canadian Art,* vol. I (Oct. - Nov., 1943), p. 25 (reprod.; as Welders working on a kiln, No. 3).

Purchase, 1943.

2712

SIXTEEN ISLANDS LAKE (NO. 1)   **1942**

Water colour on paper, $17^1/_2''$ x $23^3/_8''$ [sight].
Signed, dated and inscribed (lower right): f. brandtner 42./ sixteen island lake.

PROV.: the artist [CSPWC, 1943].

EXHIBITIONS: *C.S.P.W.C.,* 1943; *D.P.C.,* 1945, no. 195.

Purchase, 1943.

2712　　**Sixteen Islands Lake (No. 1)**

2718

CHRISTMAS 1942   1942

Linocut, Imp.: 9¹¹/₁₆" x 7¹/₄". Paper: 10¹/₂" x 7³/₄".
Signed and dated (lower right, in ink): F. brandtner 42.

Gift of the Artist, 1943.

Claude BREEZE (1938-   )

BORN: Claude Herbert Breeze, Nelson, B. C., October 9, 1938.

LIVES: Vancouver.

STUDY: University of Saskatchewan School of Art, Regina College, under Arthur McKay, Ronald Bloore, Roy Kiyooka, and Ken Lochhead; Vancouver School of Art, 1959.

AWARDS: Canada Council Junior Fellowship, 1964.

64/77

LOVERS IN THE LANDSCAPE (NO. 6)   1965

Polymer on canvas, 70" x 70".
Signed and dated (lower centre): Breeze/65.
Inscribed (on reverse, top of stretcher): LOVERS IN A LANDSCAPE #6./CLEAN WITH DAMP CLOTH ONLY/-PAINTED IN "AQUA-TEC"/-SIGNED LOWER CENTRE.

PROV.: the artist.

EXHIBITIONS: Montreal, *Expo 67*, 1967, Painting in Canada, no. 40 (reprod.).

Gift from Anonymous Fund and Matching Canada Council Grant, 1965.

64/77   **Lovers in the Landscape (No. 6)**

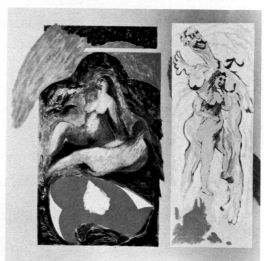

2166.1-18

TORONTO, OLD AND NEW   1934

Woodblocks, Paper: 4⁷/₁₆ x 6⁵/₁₆" each.
Signed (lower right, in pencil): CORRY WM. BRIGDEN 34.
Inscribed (lower left, in pencil): [title as it appears below].

PROV.: the artist.

NOTES: A portfolio of prints, in a folio, 14" x 10", inscribed on cover: TORONTO/OLD AND NEW/A/FOLIO/OF/PRINTS/BY/CORRY WM. /BRIGDEN.

Corry W. BRIGDEN (1912-   )

BORN: Corry William Brigden, Toronto, September 29, 1912.

LIVES: Mexico, part of the year, and the rest in Ontario's French River area.

STUDY: Toronto, Central Technical School, with Charles Goldhamer, Carl Schaefer and others.

TEACHING: Hamilton, Westdale Secondary

42

School, 1938-56; and Central Secondary School, 1956-59.

TRAVEL: 1955, to Italy, to study in Florence. 1943-45 served with the Royal Canadian Engineers.

Inscribed on first page: The prints in this portfolio are all artists'/proofs from hand-cut blocks. /The edition is limited to two hundred and/fifty copies of which this is *No. 10.*

The prints:

2166.1	The Home of Jesse Ketchum.
.2	Spadina Avenue Near the Crescent.
.3	College Avenue at Yonge Streets.
.4	Doel's Brewery.
.5	The First Post-Office.
.6	The Bishop's Palace.
.7	The College of Medicine.
.8	The Old Railway Station.
.9	Early Transportation.
.10	Toronto's Skyline.
.11	The Princes' Gate.
.12	The Art Gallery.
.13	Hart House.
.14	The Parliament Buildings.
.15	"Records of Man and Nature".
.16	Lower Bay Street.
.17	College and Yonge Sts. 1934.
.18	Yorkminster Baptist Church.

Purchase, 1934.

F. H. BRIGDEN (1871-1956)

BORN: Frederick Henry Brigden, London, England, April 9, 1871.

DIED: Bolton, Ontario, on a sketching trip, March, 1956. Came to Canada in 1872.

STUDY: Toronto, Central Ontario School of Art and Design, 1885-1890, under William Cruikshank and G. A. Reid; Toronto Art Students' League, 1890-1906; Woodstock, N. Y., summer of 1912, under John Carlson.

Worked at Brigdens, a commercial engraving firm run by his father, 1885-1941, when he retired to devote full time to painting.

SOCIETIES: O.S.A., 1898, P.O.S.A., 1927-31; A.R.C.A., 1934, R.C.A., 1939; C.S.P.W.C., founding member, 1926, First Pres. 1926-28; Toronto Art Students' League, 1890-1906; Mahlstick Club, Toronto, about 1899-1903; Graphic Arts Club, Toronto, founder member, 1903, Pres. 1926-30; Arts and Letters Club, Toronto, charter member, 1908.

Landscape painter, illustrator, commercial engraver.

60/14

AFTERNOON IN THE VALLEY

Oil on canvas, $36^3/_4$" x $44^1/_2$".
Signed (lower right): F. H. BRIGDEN.
Inscribed (on reverse of frame, upper left): AFTERNOON IN THE VALLEY/F. H. BRIGDEN O.S.A.

PROV.: Harry L. Sutherland, Toronto; Mrs. Walter L. Tarr, Cincinnati, Ohio.

EXHIBITIONS: *O.S.A.,* 1915, no. 9; *C.N.E.,* 1915, no. 117; Stratford, *Canada on canvas,* 1963.

Gift of Mrs. Walter L. Tarr, Cincinnati, in memory of her father, Harry L. Sutherland, 1961.

1325

ISLES OF GARGANTUA

Oil on canvas, $24^1/_8$" x $34^1/_8$".
Signed (lower left): F. H. BRIGDEN.

PROV.: the artist [OSA, 1930].

NOTES: Cape Gargantua is located on the northeast shore of Lake Superior.

EXHIBITIONS: *O.S.A.,* 1930, no. 22; London, Ont., *Milestones,* 1942, no. 39; *O.S.A.,* 1957, Brigden Memorial, no. 32.

Gift from the Friends of Canadian Art Fund, 1930.

1325   Isles of Gargantua

887   Down to Lake Superior

52/2   Summer Morning, Newtonbrook

53/7

NORTHERN ONTARIO FOREST   1920

Water colour on paper, 24" x 18" [sight].
Signed (lower left): F. H. BRIGDEN.

NOTES: According to artist this water colour was painted "from a sketch made while camping on northern shore of Lake Nipigon, in 1919."

Label on reverse reads: ONTARIO FOREST NORTH OF LAKE NIPIGON/1920/THE ARTIST.

Gift of F. H. Brigden, 1953.

887

DOWN TO LAKE SUPERIOR   1926

Water colour on paper, 17$^1/_2$" x 23$^1/_2$".
Signed (lower left): F. H. BRIGDEN.

PROV.: the artist [CSPWC, 1926].

EXHIBITIONS: *C.S.P.W.C.*, 1926, no. 535 (as On the Way to Lake Superior); A.G.T., *Summer*, 1935, no. 74; A.G.T., *Loan exhibition*, 1935, no. 221; New York, *World's Fair*, 1939, section CSPWC and SSC, no. 19.

REFERENCES: A.G.T., *Bulletin* (Nov., 1927), p. 12 (reprod.); Duval (1954), pl. 45 (dated 1926); C.S.P.W.C., *42nd annual exhibition* (1967), p. 9 (reprod. [not exhibited]).

Gift from the Reuben and Kate Leonard Canadian Fund, 1927.

53/5

WATERFALL IN LAKE SUPERIOR COUNTRY   1927

Water colour and pencil on cardboard, 8$^3/_4$" x 11$^5/_8$" [sight]
Signed (lower left): F. H. BRIGDEN.

NOTES: According to the artist: "Painted on location not far from Schreiber on the north shore, in 1927."

EXHIBITIONS: *O.S.A.*, 1957, Brigden memorial, no. 33.

Gift of F. H. Brigden, 1953.

53/2

SUMMER MORNING, NEWTONBROOK   1928

Oil on cardboard, 9$^1/_4$" x 11$^1/_2$".
Signed (lower left): F. H. BRIGDEN.
Inscribed (on reverse): Summer Morning, Newtonbrook.

NOTES: According to the artist: "Sketch on location looking east from my home on west side of Don Valley, 1928".

A painting of the same subject, for which this may have been a study, was exhibited at the *C.N.E.*, 1932, no. 89, entitled *Summer Morning in the Valley*, and illustrated.

44

EXHIBITIONS: [?] *O.S.A. little pictures*, 1928, no. 115 (as Summer Day, Newtonbrook).

Gift of F. H. Brigden, 1953.

53/4

THE GRAY CANYON   c. 1930

Water colour and pencil on paper, 8$^3/_4$" x 11$^{13}/_{16}$" [sight].
Signed (lower left): F. H. BRIGDEN.

NOTES: According to the artist, this water colour was "painted on location when camping at Agawa Canyon, about 1930".

Gift of F. H. Brigden, 1953.

53/3

A COUNTY BRIDGE IN AUTUMN   1933

Oil on panel, 8$^3/_8$" x 10$^1/_2$".
Signed (lower right): F. H. BRIGDEN.
Inscribed (on reverse): A County Bridge/in Autumn.

NOTES: According to the artist, this is a "sketch on location, The German Mills Creek, a tributary of the Don near Newtonbrook, 1933".

EXHIBITIONS: A.G.O. [circulating exhibition], *Canadian paintings of the 1930s*, 1967-68, no. 3.

Gift of F. H. Brigden, 1933.

53/1

LAURENTIAN FARM IN MARCH   1941

Oil on panel, 9" x 11".
Signed (lower left): F. H. BRIGDEN.
Inscribed (on reverse): Laurentian Farm in March.

NOTES: Sketch on location near Gray Rocks.

EXHIBITIONS: *O.S.A.*, 1957, Brigden Memorial, no. 35.

Gift of F. H. Brigden, 1953.

53/6

THE PEYTO GLACIER   1948

Water colour on paper, 11$^7/_8$" x 13$^5/_8$" [sight].
Signed (lower left): F. H. BRIGDEN.

NOTES: According to the artist this water colour was "painted from a point on the Banff-Jasper highway when in camp with the Alpine Club of Canada, in 1948".

EXHIBITIONS: [?] *C.S.P.W.C.*, 1949, p. 2 (Peyto Glacier, Canadian Rockies); *O.S.A.*, 1957, Brigden Memorial, no. 34.

Gift of F. H. Brigden, 1953.

Leonard BROOKS (1911-   )

BORN: Frank Leonard Brooks, London, England, November 7, 1911.

LIVES: San Miguel de Allende, Mexico, since about 1948. Came to Canada (Toronto) in 1912.

STUDY: Mostly self-taught, having spent only six months at Ontario College of Art, in 1929; Mexico, Escuela Universitaria de Bellas Artes, 1947.

SOCIETIES: O.S.A., 1939; A.R.C.A., 1939; C.G.P.; C.P.E.; Arts and Letters Club, Toronto.

TRAVEL: England, France, and Spain, 1932-34; Europe, 1961.

Official Canadian war artist with the Royal Canadian Navy, 1944-45.

Painter of landscape, landscape with figures, still life; muralist, etcher, lithographer.

Archibald BROWNE (1866-1948)

BORN: Joseph Archibald Browne, Liverpool, England, February 8, 1866, of Scottish parents; grew up in Blantyre, Scotland.

DIED: Cornwall, Ontario, November 7, 1948. Came to Canada in 1888.

STUDY: Scotland, under Macaulay Stevenson; otherwise no formal training.

SOCIETIES: O.S.A., 1907, resigned 1908; A.R.C.A., 1898, R.C.A., 1919; Canadian Art Club, founder member, 1907; Arts and Letters Club, Toronto, founder member, 1908; Pen and Pencil Club, Montreal, 1923.

Lived in Toronto until about 1923, when he moved to Montreal, and in 1927 moved to Lancaster, Ontario.

Landscape painter.

2877

MARITIME VILLAGE   1946

Gouache on paper, 22½" x 30 9/16.
Signed and dated (lower left): LEONARD BROOKS/46.

PROV.: the artist [CSPWC, 1947].

EXHIBITIONS: *C.S.P.W.C.*, 1947, p. 2.

Purchase, 1947.

100

SILVERY DAY ON THE ST. LAWRENCE   1918

Oil on canvas, 24⅞" x 36".
Signed and dated (lower left): Archibald Browne. 1918.

NOTES: Permanent loan from the C.N.E. Association, 1919-65.

EXHIBITIONS: *C.N.E.*, 1919, no. 22, p. 11 (reprod.); *C.N.E.*, 1939, no. 33.

Gift of the Canadian National Exhibition Association, 1965.

100   **Silvery Day on the St. Lawrence**

Franklin BROWNELL
(1856-1946)

BORN: Peleg Franklin Brownell, New Bedford, Mass., July 27, 1856.

DIED: Ottawa, 1946. Came to Canada (Ottawa) in 1886.

STUDY: Boston Museum of Fine Arts, under T. W. Dewing; Paris, Académie Julian, under Tony Robert-Fleury, W. A. Bouguereau, and later under Léon Bonnat.

SOCIETIES: O.S.A., 1906, resigned in 1907; A.R.C.A., 1894, R.C.A., 1895, resigned and retired in 1915; Canadian Art Club, founding member, 1907.

TEACHING: Head of the Ottawa Art School, 1886-1937, when he retired from teaching.

TRAVEL: Visited the West Indies for a period, about 1911-12.

Landscape and landscape with figures painter.

68

BY WARD MARKET, OTTAWA

Oil on canvas, 16¼" x 21⅛".
Signed (lower right): — F brownell —.
Inscribed (on reverse, lower left): F. brownell.

NOTES: Permanent loan from C.N.E. Association, 1915-65.

EXHIBITIONS: *O.S.A.*, 1915, no. 8 (reprod.); *R.C.A.*, 1915, no. 27; *C.N.E.*, 1915, no. 124, p. 44 (reprod.); Ottawa, *Central Canada Exhibition*, 1926, no. 8; [?] N.G.C., *Canadian painting*, 1935, no. 15.

Gift of the Canadian National Exhibition Association, 1965.

68   **By Ward Market, Ottawa**

2131

VIEW OF MOUNT NEVIS FROM ST. KITTS   1911

Oil on canvas, 16⅛" x 24⅛".
Signed and dated (lower right): Fb — 11.

PROV.: Mrs. R. Leonard, St. Catharines, Ontario.

NOTES: St. Kitts (St. Christopher) is one of the Leeward Islands, and Nevis a neighbouring island.

EXHIBITIONS: A.G.T., *Loan exhibition*, 1935, no. 87.

Gift of Mrs. R. Leonard, 1933.

2131   **View of Mount Nevis from St. Kitts**

Blair BRUCE (1859-1906)

BORN: William Blair Bruce, Hamilton, Ontario, October 10, 1859.

DIED: Stockholm, November 17, 1906.

STUDY: Hamilton Art School, 1877, then entered architect's office; Paris, Julian Acad-

54/9

STUDY OF A CHILD

Oil on cardboard, 12¾" x 9¹/₁₆" [sight].

PROV.: Mrs. Reginald Allworth, Hamilton, Ontario.

Gift from the John Paris Bickell Bequest Fund, 1954.

emy, 1881, under Robert-Fleury and Bouguereau.

Lived in Sweden and Paris; returned to Canada
only once, in 1886.

Landscapes, marines, portraits, mythological
subjects.

54/10   **Portrait of the Artist's Wife
Caroline**
Colour reproduction, p. 534

54/10

PORTRAIT OF THE ARTIST'S WIFE CAROLINE   1890

Oil on canvas, $29^9/_{16}$ x $12^3/_4$".
Signed and dated (lower left): W. Blair Bruce 1890.

NOTES: Mrs. Bruce was the former Caroline Benedicks, a young
Swedish sculptress of titled family. She and the artist first met at Grez,
a favourite sketching haunt, and in 1888 were married in Paris.

EXHIBITIONS: Stratford, *Faces of Canada*, 1964, reprod.; Hamilton,
Some artists who have lived and worked in Hamilton, 1967, no. 11
(reprod.).

REFERENCES: Harper (1966), p. 233 (reprod.).

Gift of Mrs. Reginald Allworth, Hamilton, 1954.

William BRYMNER (1855-1925)

BORN: Greenoch, Scotland, December 14, 1855.

DIED: Wallasey, Cheshire, England, June 18, 1925. Came to Canada as a child, in 1857, and settled in the Eastern Townships.

STUDY: Architecture, in Ottawa; Paris, Julian Academy, 1878, under Bouguereau and Tony Robert-Fleury, where he returned to painting; also in Paris with Carolus-Duran.

Returned to Canada in 1885.

SOCIETIES: O.S.A., 1886; A.R.C.A., 1883, R.C.A., 1886, P.R.C.A., 1909-1917; Canadian Art Club, 1910; Pen and Pencil Club, Montreal, 1890.

1916 created a C. M. G. [Companion of St. Michael and St. George].

TEACHING: Director of art classes at the Art Association of Montreal, 1886-1921.

64/1

NUDE WOMAN

Oil on panel, $9^{15}/_{16}$" x $13^7/_{16}$".
Inscribed (on reverse, upper left, in ink): Wm BRYMNER.

PROV.: Mrs. Bess Hamilton, Doon, Ontario.

Purchase, 1964.

4

CARITA   1910

Oil on canvas, $32^1/_2$" x $24^3/_4$".
Signed and dated (lower left): Wm Brymner. 10.

NOTES: Permanent loan from C.N.E. Association, 1911-65.

EXHIBITIONS: *C.N.E.*, 1911, no. 96, p. 22 (reprod.); *C.N.E.*, 1915, no. 252; Ottawa, *Central Canada Exhibition*, 1926, no. 11; A.G.T., *Works by Senior painters in Canada*, 1937, no. 11.

REFERENCES: O.S.A., *Annual report*, 1912, p. 6.

Gift of the Canadian National Exhibition Association, 1965.

4   Carita

Irving BURMAN (1928-   )

BORN: Toronto, July 1, 1928.

LIVES: Toronto.

STUDY: Self taught.

Painted fairly regularly until 1957, when he turned to sculpture.

Painter, draughtsman, sculptor.

64/42

REACHING FORM NO. 2   1964

Bronze, $9^1/_2$" x $14^1/_4$".

PROV.: [Helene-Arthur Galleries, Toronto].

NOTES: One of six casts.

Anonymous gift, 1965.

64/42   **Reaching Form No. 2**

Dennis BURTON (1933-   )

BORN: Lethbridge, Alberta, December, 1933.

LIVES: Toronto.

STUDY: Toronto, Ontario College of Art, 1952-56, under Jock Macdonald and others; University of Southern California, Los Angeles, with Frances de Erdeley; with Rico Lebrun in 1955; with Ben Shahn at Skowhegan School, Maine, 1959.

TEACHING: Toronto's New School of painting and sculpture.

AWARDS: Royal Canadian Academy Scholarship, 1955; Canada Council award, 1961.

Has carried out several mural commissions, including one for Edmonton airport, 1963.

Worked at graphic design for television, 1957-60, 1966.

Painter, sculptor.

64/83

MOTHER, EARTH, LOVE   **1965**

Oil and acrylic copolymer on canvas, 60" x 80".
PROV.: [Isaacs Gallery, Toronto].

EXHIBITIONS: Saint John, and Edmonton, *Burton 1959-65*, 1966, no. 17.

REFERENCES: *Canadian Art*, vol. XXII (Sept., 1965), p. 34 (reprod. in colour); Kilbourn (1966), p. 92 (reprod. in colour); *Vie des Arts*, no. 44 (Autumn, 1966), p. 66.

Gift from the Junior Women's Committee Fund, 1965.

For monotype by Burton, see "Toronto 20", p. 453–457

64/83   **Mother, Earth, Love**

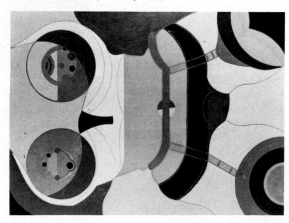

Jack BUSH (1909-   )

BORN: Jack Hamilton Bush, Toronto, March 20, 1909.

LIVES: Toronto.

64/29

VILLAGE PROCESSION   **1946**

Oil on masonite, 24" x 30$\frac{1}{8}$".
Signed (lower right): Bush.

STUDY: Art Association of Montreal, 1927-28, under Adam Sherriff Scott, and Edmond Dyonnet; Toronto, Ontario College of Art, under F. S. Challener, J. W. Beatty, and J. E. H. MacDonald.

SOCIETIES: O.S.A., 1943; A.R.C.A., 1946; C.S.P.W.C., 1942, Pres. 1945-46; C.G.P.; C.S.G.A.; Painters Eleven, 1953.

Painter, illustrator, advertising artist.

64/29   **Village Procession**

56/6   **Theme Variation no. 2**

PROV.: Rolph-Clark-Stone Limited, Toronto.

NOTES: Sketch for the painting made from notes on train passing the village of Gelert [near Minden], Ontario, October, 1945; painting executed January, 1946.

Awarded Rolph-Clark-Stone prize at O.S.A. exhibition, 1946.

EXHIBITIONS: *O.S.A.*, 1946, no. 15, p. 14 (reprod.).

REFERENCES: *Canadian Review of Music and Art*, vol. 5 (Feb., 1946), p. 19 (reprod.), p. 20; *Canadian Art*, vol. III (Summer, 1946), p. 177 (reprod.); A.G.T., *Programme 1946-47*, p. 6 (illustrates artist with his prize-winning painting).

Gift from the Georgia J. Weldon Estate, 1965.

2871

ACROSS THE VALLEY   **1946**

Water colour on paper, $12^1/_{16}$" x $15^7/_8$".
Signed (lower right): Bush.
Inscribed (on reverse, in pencil): "Across the Valley"/Toronto/Feb. 1946/Jack H. Bush/Toronto.

PROV.: the artist [CSPWC, 1947].

EXHIBITIONS: *C.S.P.W.C.*, 1947, p. 2.

Purchase, 1947.

51/64

THE OLD TREE   **1951**

Oil on masonite, 17" x 22".
Signed (lower right): Bush.

PROV.: [Roberts Gallery, Toronto].

EXHIBITIONS: [?] *O.S.A.* 1951, no. 11A; Roberts Gallery, *Bush*, 1952, no. 8.

REFERENCES: *Saturday Night*, vol. 67 (Mar. 29, 1952), p. 20.

Gift from the John Paris Bickell Bequest Fund, 1952.

56/6

THEME VARIATION NO. 2   **1955**

Water colour and chalk on paper, 30" x 40".
Signed and dated (lower right): Bush 55.

PROV.: the artist [CSPWC, 1956].

EXHIBITIONS: *C.S.P.W.C.*, 1956, no. 11; Brooklyn, N. Y., *20th Biennial International water colour exhibition*, 1959, no. 13.

Gift from J. S. McLean, Canadian Fund, 1956.

62/67   **Trophy**

58/70   **Water Colour 120**
Colour reproduction, p. 550

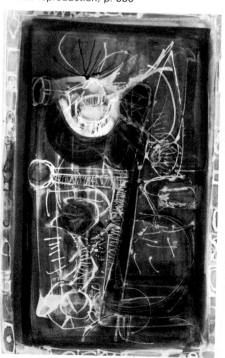

62/67

TROPHY   **1955-56**

Oil on masonite, 49⁵/₈″ x 32″.
Signed (lower left centre): Oscar Cahén.

PROV.: Estate of the artist; [Jerrold Morris International Gallery, Toronto].

EXHIBITIONS: [?] London, Ont., *Four man show, Bush, Cahen, de Tonnancour, and Borduas*, 1955 (March) [no catalogue]; O.S.A., 1959, *Cahen memorial*, no. 15 (dated 1955-56); Jerrold Morris International Gallery, *Cahen*, 1963 (May 18 - June 5) [no catalogue].

REFERENCES: Kilbourn (1966), p. 104 (reprod. in colour).

Purchase, 1963.

58/70

WATER COLOUR 120   **1956**

Water colour with rubber resist on paper board, 26¹/₁₆″ x 16⁷/₈″ [sight].
Signed and dated (lower right): Oscar Cahen 56.

PROV.: Mrs. Oscar Cahén, Toronto.

EXHIBITIONS: O.S.A., 1959, *Cahen memorial*, no. 37.

REFERENCES: *C.S.P.W.C. 41st exhibition*, 1966-67 (reprod.; [not exhibited]).

Bequest of Col. William C. Michell, 1959.

58/71

WATER COLOUR 131-12   **1956**

Ink and water colour with rubber resist on paper board, 29¹/₄″ x 39⁵/₈″ [sight].
Inscribed (on reverse): WC-131-12.

PROV.: Mrs. Oscar Cahén, Toronto.

EXHIBITIONS: O.S.A., 1959, *Cahen memorial*, no. 35.

Bequest of Col. William C, Michell, 1959.

58/69

UNTITLED   **1956**

Oil on masonite, 23″ x 33¹/₈″.

PROV.: Mrs. Oscar Cahén, Toronto.

NOTES: Unfinished work on the artist's easel, November 26, 1956.

EXHIBITIONS: O.S.A., 1959, *Cahen memorial*, no. 24.

Bequest of Col. William C. Michell, 1959.

Ghitta CAISERMAN-ROTH
(1923-   )

BORN: Montreal, March 2, 1923.

LIVES: Montreal.

STUDY: Montreal, under Alexander Bercovitch; New York, Parsons School of Design; New York Art School under Moses Soyer; and at New York, Art Students' League.

SOCIETIES: A.R.C.A., 1956; C.G.P.; C.S.G.A.

AWARDS: Canada Council Senior Fellowship, 1962.

Since about 1963 has exhibited under the name Caiserman-Roth.

Frank CARMICHAEL
(1890-1945)

BORN: Franklin H. Carmichael, Orillia, Ont., May 4, 1890.

DIED: Toronto, October 24, 1945. Moved to Toronto in 1911; joined firm of Grip Ltd.

STUDY: Ontario College of Art, with William Cruikshank and G. A. Reid; Toronto Technical School with Gustav Hahn; and Académie Royale des Beaux-Arts, Antwerp, 1913-15, under Isidor Opsomer, and G. Van der Veben.

SOCIETIES: O.S.A., 1917, P.O.S.A. 1937-41; A.R.C.A., 1935; R.C.A., 1938; C.S.P.W.C., founding member, 1926, Pres. 1932-34; Group of Seven, original member, 1919; C.G.P., founding member, 1933.

TEACHING: Toronto, Ontario College of Art, 1932-45.

53/49

FRIENDS   1953

Colour lithograph, Imp.: $21\frac{1}{4}$" x $11\frac{5}{8}$".
Signed and dated (lower right, in pencil): Ghitta Caiserman '53.
Inscribed (lower left, in pencil): Friends.
Numbered (lower centre, in pencil): 5/8/1 [?].

PROV.: the artist [CSGA, 1954].

EXHIBITIONS: *C.S.G.A.*, 1954, no. 11.

REFERENCES: *Canadian Art*, vol. XII (Winter, 1955), p. 56 (reprod.).

Gift from J. S. McLean, Canadian Fund, 1954.

2880

SILVERY TANGLE   1921

Oil on canvas, 40" x $47\frac{1}{8}$".
Signed and dated (lower right): FRANK/CARMICHAEL/192[1].

PROV.: Estate of the artist [AGT, 1947].

EXHIBITIONS: A.G.T., *Group of Seven*, 1921, no. 2; *C.N.E.*, 1921, no. 134; Winnipeg, *Canadian art of today*, 1921, no. 78; Worcester, Mass., 1924, no. 3; London, *British Empire Exhibition*, 1925, Canadian section of fine arts, p. 6 (lent by the artist); London, Whitechapel Art Gallery, 1925, no. 44; Manchester, 1926, no. 92; N.G.C., *Retrospective...Group of Seven*, 1936, no. 14 (lent by the artist); A.G.T., *Carmichael memorial*, 1947, no. 19 (erroneously dated 1941); Washington, 1950, no. 11; Hamilton, *Inaugural*, 1953-54, no. 6, pl. 5 (reprod.); Vancouver, *Group of Seven*, 1954, no. 3 (reprod.); Vancouver, *Images*, 1966, no. 87; N.G.C., [travelling exhibition], *Canadian painting 1850-1950*, 1967-68, no. 49, p. 27 (reprod.).

REFERENCES: A.G.T., *50th anniversary* (1950), p. 33 (reprod.); *R.A.I.C. Journal*, vol. 27 (Jan., 1950), p. 27 (reprod.).

Gift from the Albert H. Robson Memorial Subscription Fund, 1947.

2880   **Silvery Tangle**

305　Jackfish Village

305

JACKFISH VILLAGE　1926

Water colour and pencil on paper, 20" x 22⅝₁₆".
Signed and dated (lower right): FRANK/CARMICHAEL/1926.

NOTES: Permanent loan from C.N.E. Association, 1926–65.

Jackfish Village is situated on the north shore of Lake Superior.

EXHIBITIONS: *C.S.P.W.C.*, 1926, no. 538; *C.N.E.*, 1926, no. 491, p. 59 (reprod.); Paris, 1927, no. 20; N.G.C., *Annual*, 1927, no. 26; A.G.T., *Summer*, 1935, no. 75; A.G.T., *Loan exhibition*, 1935, no. 222; New York, *World's Fair*, 1939, section CSPWC and SSC, no. 24; London, Ont., *Group of Seven*, 1946, no. 4 (reprod.); A.G.T., *Carmichael memorial*, 1947, no. 24; Edmonton, *Group of Seven*, 1955 [no catalogue; see Edmonton Museum of Arts, *Bulletin* (Jan., 1955), p. 2]; Victoria, *Group of Seven*, 1955, no. 42.

REFERENCES: Housser (1926), opp. p. 204 (reprod.), p. 217; *American Magazine of Art*, vol. XXV (July, 1932), p. 15 (reprod.); Buchanan (1945), pl. 74 (reprod.); Duval (1954), pl. B (reprod. in colour).

Gift of the Canadian National Exhibition Association, 1965.

64/15　Port Coldwell II

64/15

PORT COLDWELL II　1926

Pencil on paper, 8" x 10".
Inscribed and dated (lower right): Port Coldwell 1926.
Stamped (lower right): ESTATE/OF/FRANKLIN/CARMICHAEL

PROV.: Estate of the artist; [Galerie Dresdnere, Toronto].

EXHIBITIONS: Galerie Dresdnere, *Frank Carmichael, retrospective*, 1964, no. 9.

Purchase, 1964.

1278

SNOW CLOUDS　1927

Water colour and chalk on paper, 14¹⁵₁₆" x 20¼" [sight].
Signed and dated (lower right): FRANK/CARMICHAEL/1927.

PROV.: the artist.

EXHIBITIONS: *C.S.P.W.C.*, 1927, no. 18; A.G.T., *Exhibition of Canadian sculpture…recent accessions*, 1928, no. 8; A.G.T., *Summer*, 1935, no. 77, p. 23 (reprod.); A.G.T., *Carmichael memorial*, 1947, no. 25.

REFERENCES: A.G.T., *Bulletin* (Nov., 1928), p. 18 (reprod.); Brooker, *Yearbook 1928-29* (1929), p. 77; C.S.P.W.C., *42nd annual exhibition* (1967), p. 8 (reprod. [not exhibited]).

Gift from the Reuben and Kate Leonard Canadian Fund, 1928.

1328 **Bay of Islands**
Colour reproduction, p. 543

1328

BAY OF ISLANDS **1930**

Water colour on paper, 17½" x 21½" [sight].
Signed and dated (lower right): FRANK/CARMICHAEL/1930.

PROV.: the artist [AGT, 1930].

EXHIBITIONS: A.G.T., *Group of Seven*, 1930, no. 6, p. 2 (reprod.); A.A.M., *Group of Seven*, 1930, no. 6; A.G.T., *Summer*, 1935, no. 76; A.G.T., *Loan exhibition*, 1935, no. 223; N.G.C., *Retrospective...Group of Seven*, 1936, no. 17; New York, *World's Fair*, 1939, section CSPWC and SSC, no. 23; Rio de Janeiro, 1944, no. 23; London, Ont., *Group of Seven*, 1946, no. 5; A.G.T., *Carmichael memorial*, 1947, no. 29; *C.S.P.W.C.*, 1951, no. 6; N.G.C. [travelling exhibition], *Canadian painting 1850-1950*, 1967-68, no. 50.

REFERENCES: A.G.T., *Bulletin* (Apr., 1930), reprod.; A.G.T., *Bulletin and annual report* (Mar., 1931), p. 4 (reprod.); *Studio*, vol. CXIV (Aug., 1937), p. 61 (reprod.); *Canadian Art*, vol. VIII (Spring, 1951), p. 98 (reprod.); Duval (1954), pl. 32 (reprod.); A.G.T., *Painting and sculpture* (1959), p. 69 (reprod.); *artscanada*, vol. XXIV (Jan., 1967), p. 11 (reprod.).

Gift from Friends of Canadian Art Fund, 1930.

2883

LANDSCAPE, NORTH SHORE, LAKE HURON **1938**

Water colour on paper, 11½" x 13⅜".

PROV.: Estate of the artist [AGT, 1947].

NOTES: According to Mr. Joachim Gauthier, Toronto, a sketching partner of the artist, Carmichael did not sketch in Algoma. In this water colour, the hills are definitely those behind Carmichael's cottage on Cranberry Lake, painted in the summer of 1938.

EXHIBITIONS: A.G.T., *Carmichael memorial*, 1947, no. 44 [?].

Purchase, 1947.

2881

NORTH SHORE OF LAKE HURON **1940-41**

Oil on panel, 11¾" x 16".

PROV.: Estate of the artist [AGT, 1947].

NOTES: According to Mr. Gauthier [see Notes, acc. no. 2883], Carmichael did not sketch on size 12" x 15" [sic] until 1939 (previously using 10" x 12"). Mr. Gauthier says this was painted in 1940-41, in the vicinity of Cranberry Lake, or perhaps the Charleton or McGregor Bay region.

EXHIBITIONS: A.G.T., *Carmichael memorial*, 1947, no. 45 [?]; Vancouver, *Group of Seven*, 1954, no. 7.

Purchase, 1947.

2882   Hills of Cranberry Lake

2882

HILLS OF CRANBERRY LAKE   1941

Oil on panel, 11$^{13}/_{16}$" x 16".
Signed and dated (lower right): FRANK/CARMICHAEL/1941.
Inscribed (on reverse, in pencil): The Valley — 50.00 O.S.A. SP 1943/
Frank Carmichael/21 Cameron Ave./Lansing.

PROV.: Estate of the artist [AGT, 1947].

NOTES: This sketch was first exhibited under the title *The Valley*.
According to Mr. Gauthier [see Notes, acc. no. 2883], this sketch depicts the view from the top of Carmichael's cottage on Cranberry Lake.

EXHIBITIONS: [?] *O.S.A. little pictures*, 1943 [not verified; information from inscription on reverse]; A.G.T., *Carmichael memorial*, 1947, no. 45 [?]; A.G.T., and Ontario Department of Education, 1951, no. 32; Vancouver, *Group of Seven*, 1954, no. 6; Port Arthur, *Group of Seven and Lake Superior*, 1964, no. 3 (erroneously dated 1943).

Purchase, 1947.

M. Emily CARR (1871-1945)

BORN: Victoria, B. C., December 13, 1871.

DIED: Victoria, B. C., March 2, 1945.

STUDY: San Francisco School of Art, 1889 - c.'95; London, at Westminster School of Art, c. 1899-1904; Paris, at Colarossi, and sketching in Brittany, 1910-11.

In 1927, at her first exhibition in the East, she came in contact with the Group of Seven, and particularly Lawren Harris.

SOCIETIES: C.G.P., founding member, 1933; B. C. Society of Artists.

Wrote several books, among which her autobiography, *Growing Pains*, published by Oxford University Press in 1946.

2844

INSIDE A FOREST

Oil on paper board, 33$^{3}/_{4}$" x 23$^{7}/_{16}$".
Signed (lower left): M. EMILY CARR.

PROV.: Estate of the artist; [Dominion Gallery, Montreal].

EXHIBITIONS: A.G.O. [circulating exhibition], *Canadian paintings of the 1930s*, 1967-68, no. 4.

REFERENCES: *Saturday Night*, vol. 61 (Nov. 3, 1945), p. 5 (reprod.); A.G.T., *50th anniversary* (1950), p. 32 (reprod.); *R.A.I.C. Journal*, vol. 27 (Jan., 1950), p. 26 (reprod.).

Purchase, 1946.

2545

INDIAN HOUSE AND TOTEMS, SKIDEGATE   c. 1912

Water colour on paper, 25$^{15}/_{16}$" x 17$^{7}/_{8}$" [sight].
Signed (lower left): Emily Carr.

PROV.: the artist [AGT, 1940].

NOTES: Skidegate is situated on the Queen Charlotte Islands.

EXHIBITIONS: A.G.T., *Carr, Harris, Brandtner, and Comfort*, 1940, as Indian House and carvings, Skidgate [sic].

Purchase, 1940.

2705

GUYASDOMS D'SONOQUA

c. 1927

Oil on canvas, 39½" x 25¾".
Signed (lower left): M. EMILY CARR.

PROV.: The Emily Carr Trust Collection.

NOTES: D'Sonoqua means "wild woman of the woods". [see ref. Carr (1941), p. 51].

EXHIBITIONS: New York, National Arts Club, 1945 (March - June) [no catalogue]; N.G.C., and A.G.T., *Carr*, 1945, no. 32; New York, Riverside Museum, *Canadian women artists*, 1947, no. 10; Dallas, 1958; University of Toronto, Hart House, *Carr*, 1963 (Sept. 16 - Oct. 13) [no catalogue]; University of Waterloo, *Carr*, 1967, reprod.

REFERENCES: Emily Carr, *Klee Wyck* (1941), opp. p. 48 (reprod. in colour); A.G.T., *Accessions — 1942*, reprod.; *New World Illustrated*, vol. II (Feb., 1942), p. 24 (reprod. in colour); McRae (1944), p. 45 (reprod.); *Saturday Night*, vol. 60 (Jan. 13, 1945), p. 5 (reprod.); *Quill and Quire*, vol. 11 (Nov., 1945), p. 43 (reprod.); *Studio*, vol. CXXIX (Apr., 1945), p. 98 (reprod. in colour).

Gift from the Albert H. Robson Memorial Subscription Fund, 1942

2705   **Guyasdoms d'Sonoqua**

2420

KISPIAX VILLAGE **1929**

Oil on canvas, $36^1/_8$" x $50^3/_4$".
Signed, dated and inscribed (lower right): M. EMILY CARR./
KISPIAX. 1929.

PROV.: the artist [AGT, 1937].

NOTES: Kispiax is located about 200 miles inland, northeast of Prince
Rupert, near Hazelton, B. C.

EXHIBITIONS: A.G.T., *Group of Seven*, 1930, no. 22; A.A.M., *Group
of Seven*, 1930, no. 22; A.G.T., *Carr*, 1937 (Apr.) [no catalogue];
A.G.T., *Carr*, 1943 (Feb.), p. 2; N.G.C., and A.G.T., *Carr*, 1945, no. 25
(says exhibited Paris, International Exposition, 1937 [lent but not
actually hung]), pl. 8 (reprod.); M.M.F.A., and others, *Native arts of
the Pacific Northwest*, 1951 [no catalogue]; C.N.E., 1952, no. 64;
University of Waterloo, *Carr*, 1967, reprod.

REFERENCES: *Canadian Forum*, vol. XXI (Dec., 1941), p. 277
(reprod.); *Canadian Art*, vol. V (Spring, 1948), on cover (reprod. in
colour); *Canadian Art*, vol. XI (Winter, 1954), p. 44 (reprod.); A.G.T.,
Painting and sculpture (1959), p. 45 (reprod. in colour).

Purchase, 1937.

2420   **Kispiax Village**

2419

WESTERN FOREST **c. 1931**

Oil on canvas, $50^1/_2$" x $36^1/_8$".
Signed (lower right): M EMILY CARR.

PROV.: the artist [AGT, 1937].

EXHIBITIONS: A.G.T., *Carr*, 1937 (Apr.) [no catalogue]; A.G.T.,
Carr, 1943 (Feb.), p. 3; N.G.C., and A.G.T., *Carr*, 1945, no. 40;
A.G.T., and Toledo, Ohio, *Two cities collect*, 1948, no. 5 (reprod.;
dated about 1931); University of Toronto, Hart House, *Carr*, 1963
(Sept. 16 - Oct. 13) [no catalogue]; University of Waterloo, *Carr*,
1967, reprod.

REFERENCES: *Canadian Forum*, vol. XXI, (Mar., 1942), p. 382 (reprod.); *Saturday Night*, vol. 61 (Nov. 3, 1945), p. 4 (reprod.); *Maclean's Magazine*, vol. 69 (June 9, 1956), p. 40 (reprod. in colour).

Purchase, 1937.

2418

STUDY IN MOVEMENT   **1936**

Oil on canvas, 27″ x 44″.
Signed (lower left): EMILY CARR.
Inscribed (on reverse, upper right): STUDY IN MOVEMENT/ M. EMILY CARR/316 BECKLEY ST./VICTORIA B.C.

PROV.: the artist [AGT, 1937].

EXHIBITIONS: A.G.T., *Carr*, 1937 (Apr.) [no catalogue]; A.G.T., *Carr*, 1943 (Feb.), p. 5; N.G.C., and A.G.T., *Carr*, 1945, no. 61; *D.P.C.*, 1945, no. 189; Owen Sound, *Thomson and the Group of Seven*, 1967, no. 40; University of Waterloo, *Carr*, 1967, reprod.

REFERENCES: A.G.T., *Bulletin and annual report* (April, 1938), reprod.; *Maritime Art*, vol. 3 (July/Aug., 1943), p. 170 (reprod.); Colgate (1943), p. 191 (reprod.); *Saturday Night*, vol. 60 (Jan. 13, 1945), p. 5 (reprod.); *Maclean's Magazine*, vol. 64 (Jan. 1, 1951), p. 13 (reprod. in colour); *Canadian painting in the twentieth century* (1961), pl. 6 (reprod. in colour).

Purchase, 1937.

2419   **Western Forest**
Colour reproduction, p. 544

2418   **Study in Movement**

A. J. CASSON (1898-   )

BORN: Alfred Joseph Casson, Toronto, May 17, 1898.

LIVES: Toronto.

STUDY: Hamilton Technical School, under John S. Gordon, for a short time, 1912; Toronto, Central Technical School, about 1916-18, under Alfred Howell; and in the early

1320

AUTUMN

Water colour on paper, 14″ x 16″.
Signed (lower right): A. J. CASSON

PROV.: the artist.

EXHIBITIONS: Rio de Janeiro, 1944, no. 25.

Gift from the Reuben and Kate Leonard Canadian Fund, 1929.

1920s at Ontario College of Art, under Harry Britton.

Met and worked with Franklin Carmichael in 1919-20.

SOCIETIES: O.S.A., 1923, P.O.S.A. 1941-46; A.R.C.A., 1926, R.C.A., 1939, P.R.C.A. 1948-52; Group of Seven, 1926; C.G.P., founding member, 1933; C.S.P.W.C., founder member, 1926; C.P.E., for several years around 1922-23; C.S.G.A., early member, around 1920; Arts and Letters Club, 1921; National Academy of Design, New York.

Painter of landscapes and flowers.

220

ORIENTAL POPPIES

Colour woodblock, Imp.: $7\frac{1}{16}$" x $7\frac{1}{2}$".
Signed (lower right, in pencil): A J Casson.
Numbered (lower left, in pencil): 7/50.

NOTES: Permanent loan from C.N.E. Association, 1922-66.

EXHIBITIONS: *C.N.E.*, 1922, no. 458; *R.C.A.*, 1922, no. 247; London, *British Empire Exhibition*, 1924, Canadian section of fine arts, no. 31.

Gift of the Canadian National Exhibition Association, 1966.

60/15

BIRCHES IN WINTER   **1924**

Oil on cardboard, $9\frac{1}{4}$" x 11".
Signed (lower right): A. J. CASSON.
Inscribed and dated (on reverse): Birches in Winter - 1924/A J Casson.

PROV.: [Roberts Gallery, Toronto].

EXHIBITIONS: Roberts Gallery, *Casson, early oil sketches 1917-32*, 1960 (Sept. 30 - Oct. 3) [no catalogue].

Gift from the McLean Foundation, 1961.

60/15   **Birches in Winter**

51/84

LIME KILN, ELORA   **1926**

Oil on cardboard, $9\frac{1}{2}$" x $11\frac{3}{8}$".
Signed (lower left): A. J. CASSON.
Inscribed and dated (on reverse): Elora — Lime Kiln — 1926/ A J Casson.

PROV.: the artist.

NOTES: Elora is situated northwest of Guelph, Ontario.

Gift from the Fund of the T. Eaton Co. Ltd. for Canadian Works of Art, 1952.

1283

HILLSIDE VILLAGE **1927**

Water colour on paper, 20$\frac{1}{2}$" x 17$\frac{1}{4}$" [sight].
Signed (lower right): A. J. CASSON.

PROV.: the artist [CNE, 1928].

EXHIBITIONS: *C.S.P.W.C.*, 1927, no. 21; N.G.C., *Annual*, 1928, no. 28; *C.N.E.*, 1928, no. 398 (reprod.); A.G.T., *Exhibition...recent accessions*, 1928, no. 9; A.G.T., *Summer*, 1935, no. 78; New York, *World's Fair*, 1939, section CSPWC and SSC, no. 26; London, Ont., *Group of Seven*, 1946, no. 37.

REFERENCES: *R.A.I.C. Journal*, vol. V (Oct., 1928), pp. 372, 373 (reprod.); A.G.T., *Bulletin* (Nov., 1928), p. 12 (reprod.); Brooker, *Yearbook 1928-29* (1929), p. 77; Duval, *Casson* (1951), p. 28 (dated 1927), pp. 63, 34 (reprod.); A.G.T., *Painting and sculpture* (1959), p. 69 (reprod.).

Gift from the Reuben and Kate Leonard Canadian Fund, 1928.

60/17

NEAR CREDIT FORKS **1927**

Oil on cardboard, 9$\frac{1}{4}$" x 11$\frac{1}{4}$".
Signed (lower right): A. J. CASSON

PROV.: [Roberts Gallery, Toronto].

EXHIBITIONS: *O.S.A. small pictures*, 1927, no. 26 (as Credit Forks); [?] *O.S.A. little pictures*, 1928, no. 130 (as Near Credit Forks); Roberts Gallery, *Casson, early oil sketches*, 1917-32, 1960 (Sept. 20 - Oct. 3) [no catalogue].

Gift from the McLean Foundation, 1961.

60/16

LAKE ROSSEAU **1927**

Oil on cardboard, 9$\frac{5}{16}$" x 11$\frac{5}{16}$".
Signed (lower right): A. J. CASSON.
Inscribed and dated (on reverse): Lake Rosseau — 1927/ A J Casson.

PROV.:[Roberts Gallery, Toronto].

EXHIBITIONS: Roberts Gallery, *Casson, early oil sketches 1917-32*, 1960 (Sept. 20 - Oct. 3) [no catalogue].

Gift from the McLean Foundation, 1961.

51/78

NEAR ROCKWOOD **1927**

Oil on cardboard, 9$\frac{1}{4}$" x 11$\frac{1}{4}$".
Signed (lower right): A. J. CASSON.
Inscribed and dated (on reverse): Near Rockwood/October 1927/ A J Casson.

PROV.: the artist.

NOTES: Rockwood is situated northeast of Guelph, Ontario.

EXHIBITIONS: [?] *O.S.A. small pictures*, 1927 (Dec.), no. 25 (as Rockwood); Vancouver, *Group of Seven*, 1954, no. 15.

Gift from the Fund of the T. Eaton Co. Ltd. for Canadian Works of Art, 1952.

1305

OLD MILL AT CHELTENHAM   **c. 1928**

Oil on fibre board, $9^5/_{16}$" x $11^5/_{16}$".
Signed (lower right): A. J. CASSON.

NOTES: Permanent loan from C.N.E. Association, 1929-65.

EXHIBITIONS: *C.N.E.*, 1929, no. 541; A.G.T., and Ontario Department of Education, 1951, no. 34.

Gift of the Canadian National Exhibition Association, 1965.

51/83

LAKE SUPERIOR   **1928**

Oil on cardboard, $9^3/_8$" x $11^3/_{16}$".
Signed (lower right): A. J. CASSON.
Inscribed and dated (on reverse): Lake Superior –/1928.

PROV.: the artist.

NOTES: Entered as no. 6 in the *Group of Seven and Lake Superior* exhibition, 1964, at Lakehead College, Port Arthur, but not actually exhibited.

EXHIBITIONS: Vancouver, *Group of Seven*, 1954, no. 17.

Gift from the Fund of the T. Eaton Co. Ltd. for Canadian Works of Art, 1952.

51/83   **Lake Superior**

VILLAGE OF ALTON **1929**

Oil on cardboard, 9³/₈″ x 11¹/₈″.
Signed (lower right): A. J. CASSON.
Inscribed and dated (on reverse): Village of Alton —/September—1929.

PROV.: the artist.

NOTES: Alton is situated just south of Orangeville, Ontario.

Gift from the Fund of the T. Eaton Co. Ltd. for Canadian Works of Art, 1952.

1327

CREDIT FORKS **c. 1930**

Water colour on paper, 16⁷/₈″ x 20³/₁₆″ [sight].
Signed (lower right): A. J. CASSON.

PROV.: the artist.

EXHIBITIONS: A.G.T., *Group of Seven*, 1930, no. 25; A.A.M., *Group of Seven*, 1930, no. 25; A.G.T., *Summer*, 1935, no. 79; A.G.T., *Loan exhibition*, 1935, no. 224 (dated c. 1929); C.S.P.W.C., 1951, no. 7.

REFERENCES: Duval, *Casson* (1951), p. 28 (dated 1930), p. 35 (reprod.), p. 63; C.S.P.W.C., *42nd Annual Exhibition* (1967), p. 6 (reprod. [not exhibited]).

Gift from Friends of Canadian Art Fund, 1930.

1327   **Credit Forks**
Colour reproduction, p. 543

51/81

PARRY SOUND **1930**

Oil on cardboard, $9^3/_8$" x $11^1/_8$".
Signed (lower left): A. J. CASSON.
Inscribed and dated (on reverse): Parry Sound —/October - 1930/ A J Casson.

PROV.: the artist.

EXHIBITIONS: [?] *C.N.E.*, 1931, no. 604; N.G.C., *Retrospective...Group of Seven*, 1936, no. 27 (lent by the artist); Vancouver, *Group of Seven*, 1954, no. 16; A.G.O. [circulating exhibition], *Canadian paintings of the 1930s*, 1967-68, no. 5.

Gift from the Fund of the T. Eaton Co. Ltd. for Canadian Works of Art, 1952.

51/82

RAIN, WILBERFORCE **1942**

Oil on cardboard, $9^7/_{16}$" x $11^1/_4$".
Signed (lower right): A. J. CASSON.
Inscribed and dated (on reverse): Rain- Wilberforce/1942.

PROV.: the artist.

NOTES: Wilberforce is situated north of Peterborough and west of Bancroft, Ontario.

Gift from the Fund of the T. Eaton Co. Ltd. for Canadian Works of Art, 1952.

51/85

MILL AT WILBERFORCE **1942**

Oil on canvas board, $9^7/_{16}$" x $11^1/_4$".
Signed (lower left): A. J. CASSON.
Inscribed and dated (on reverse): Mill at Wilberforce/1942.

PROV.: the artist.

NOTES: Label on reverse indicates *C.G.P.*, 1947 [not in exhibition catalogue].

Gift from the Fund of the T. Eaton Co. Ltd. for Canadian Works of Art, 1952.

51/80

THUNDERSTORM, NORWAY CREEK, ALGONQUIN PARK **1944**

Oil on canvas board, $9^3/_8$" x $11^1/_4$".
Signed (lower right): A. J. CASSON.
Inscribed and dated (on reverse): Thunderstorm — /Norway Creek —/ Algonquin Park/1944.

PROV.: the artist.

Gift from the Fund of the T. Eaton Co. Ltd. for Canadian Works of Art, 1952.

2811   **Country Store**

2811

COUNTRY STORE   **1945**

Oil on insulite, 30" x 36".
Signed (lower right): A. J. CASSON.

PROV.: the artist [CGP, 1945].

NOTES: A preliminary drawing in pencil, 8" x 10¼", is in the Mc-
Michael Conservation Collection of Art, Kleinberg; illustrated in catalogue of the McMichael Collection, 1967, where it is dated 1928
[sic].

Entered as no. 14 in the R. C. A. exhibition, *The Academy in Retrospect*, 1966, at Confederation Art Gallery and Museum, Charlottetown, P.E.I., but the painting was unavailable for loan to that exhibition
and was replaced by Casson's *The Corners* [cf].

EXHIBITIONS: *C.G.P.*, 1945-46, no. 9; *C.N.E.*, 1948, no. 81.

REFERENCES: Duval, *Casson* (1951), frontispiece (reprod. in colour),
p. 29 (dated 1945), p. 64; *Saturday Night*, (Apr. 12, 1952), p. 20
(reprod. in colour).

Purchase, 1945.

58/50

JACK PINE AND POPLAR   **1948**

Oil on insulite, 30" x 36".
Signed (lower right): A. J. CASSON.

PROV.: Salada Tea Company, Toronto; Salada-Shirriff-Horsey Ltd.,
Toronto.

NOTES: In a press release, prepared for the donor at the time the gift
was made to the Art Gallery, the painting is dated 1948. "The painting
has never been exhibited and was purchased by the Salada organiza-
tion as soon as it had been painted... The actual scene is looking north
across McGregor Bay toward the Cloche Hills from Little Cloche
Island. This is at the east end of the North Channel between Mani-
toulin Island and the mainland."

EXHIBITIONS: Charlottetown, *The Academy in Retrospect*, 1966,
no. 15 (as Rock, Spruce and Poplar [sic]).

Gift of Salada-Shirriff-Horsey Limited, 1959.

58/60

THE CORNERS   **1958**

Oil on masonite, 18" x 35¼".
Signed (lower right): A. J. CASSON.
Inscribed (on label, on reverse): "The Corners"/A J Casson.

PROV.: [Roberts Gallery, Toronto].

EXHIBITIONS: Roberts Gallery, *Casson*, 1959 (Mar. 6-21) [no catalo-
gue]; Charlottetown, *The Academy in Retrospect*, 1966 [not entered
in catalogue; exhibited in place of *Country Store* (cf)].

Gift from the McLean Foundation, 1959.

F. S. CHALLENER (1869-1959)

BORN: Frederick Sproston Challener, Whetstone, Middlesex, England, July 7, 1869.

DIED: Toronto, September 30, 1959. Came to Canada in 1883.

STUDY: Toronto, Ontario School of Art, 1884-86, under G. A. Reid and William Cruikshank; Toronto Art Students' League, 1885-89.

SOCIETIES: O.S.A., 1890; A.R.C.A., 1891, R.C.A., 1899; Toronto Art Students' League, 1890-1906; Palette Club, Toronto, c. 1902; Arts and Letters Club, Toronto, founder member, 1908.

TEACHING: Toronto, Central Technical School, 1921-24; and Ontario College of Art, 1927-52, when he retired.

TRAVEL: England, Italy, Egypt and the Holy Land, 1898-99.

Lived in Toronto until 1907, when he moved to Conestoga, until 1917, then back to Toronto.

Worked for the Canadian War Memorials, 1917-18.

Muralist, historical painter and teacher.

62/22

BOY FISHING   1890

Oil on cardboard, 4" x 7⅞".
Signed and dated (lower right): F. S. CHALLENER. 1890.

PROV.: Mrs. Walter Bayley, Toronto.

Purchase, Dr. S. J. Streight Endowment, 1963.

65/72

LAMBTON MILLS   1891

Oil on canvas, 18½" x 13⅝".
Signed and dated (lower right): F. S. CHALLENER 1891.
Inscribed (on building, centre): J. G. ROGERS.

PROV.: Sidney J. Mendelson, Toronto; [Jerrold Morris International Gallery Ltd., Toronto].

EXHIBITIONS: O.S.A., 1891, no. 6 (reprod. sketch after the painting).

Purchase, 1966.

65/72   **Lambton Mills**
Colour reproduction, p. 535

70

121   **Nude**

638

PROFILE PORTRAIT OF G. A. REID   **1893**

Pencil on paper, 7¹/₄" x 5¹/₄" [sight].
Signed and dated (across top): F · S · CHALLENER · 22·2·1893 ·.

NOTES: For biography of sitter, see G. A. Reid, p 385.

Gift of G. A. Reid, 1922.

121

NUDE   **1910**

Pencil and chalk on paper, 9³/₁₆" x 6³/₁₆" [sight].
Signed (lower centre): Challener.

PROV.: the artist [CSGA, 1928].

EXHIBITIONS: *C.S.G.A.*, 1928, one of nos. 314, 317, 319; A.G.T.,
Drawings, 1963, p. 1.

REFERENCES: Duval (1952), pl. 11 (reprod.; dated 1910).

Purchase, 1928.

John CHAMBERS (1931-   )

BORN: London, Ontario.

LIVES: London, Ontario, since 1962.

STUDY: H. B. Beal Technical School, London,
Ontario; and from 1954 to 1959 at the Real
Academia de Bellas Artes de San Fernando,
Madrid.

Lived in Spain until 1961, teaching and
painting in the Castilian village of Chinchon,
south of Madrid.

AWARDS: State Prize for Painting at the Royal
Academy, Madrid, 1958; Canada Council
grant, 1965.

65/22

ANTONIO AND MIGUEL IN THE U.S.A.   **1965**

Oil on panel, 52¹/₄" x 49¹/₄".
Signed and dated (lower right): CHAMBERS 65.

PROV.: [Isaacs Gallery, Toronto].

NOTES: Antonio and Miguel are Spanish friends of the artist.

Drawing for the painting, pen and ink, 18¹/₄" x 16³/₄", signed and dated,
1964-65, exhibited in A.G.T., *Focus on drawings*, 1965, no. 17, is now
in the collection of Mr. and Mrs. G. Ciamaga, Toronto.

Pencil notation on reverse reads: Bea, dark land [sic].

EXHIBITIONS: New York, Forum Gallery, *John Chambers*, 1965
(Apr.) [no catalogue; see review, *Art News*, vol. 64 (May, 1965),
p. 56]; Windsor, *Some Canadians in Spain*, 1965, no. 23 (lent by The
Isaacs Gallery; reprod.); Isaacs Gallery, *John Chambers, new paintings*,
1965 (Oct. 28 - Nov. 17) [no catalogue]; N.G.C., *300 years of Canadian art*, 1967, no. 358, p. 213 (reprod.).

REFERENCES: *Canadian Art*, vol. XXIII (April, 1966), p. 45 (reprod.);
Canadian Art, vol. XXIII (July, 1966), p. 21 (reprod. in colour), p. 25;
Reid, *Chambers* (1967), p. 12 (reprod.); *L'Oeil*, no. 148 (April, 1967),
p. 38 (reprod.).

Purchase, 1966.

65/22 **Antonio and Miguel in the U.S.A.**
Colour reproduction, p. 556

Georges CHAVIGNAUD (1865-1944)

BORN: Near Brest, Brittany, France, September 24, 1865.

DIED: Meadowvale, Ontario, May 4, 1944. Came to Canada (Toronto) in 1884.

STUDY: Paris, Collège Charlemagne; Brussels, under Prof. Isidore Verheyden; and in Antwerp, under Jacob Smets, 1903-04.

SOCIETIES: O.S.A., 1900, resigned in 1917.

TEACHING: Principal of the Victoria School of of Art, Halifax, 1912-16.

Landscape and marine painter.

51/33

COAST SCENE WITH FISHING BOATS

Water colour on paper, 23" x 31³/₈" [sight].
Signed (lower right): G. Chavignaud —.

NOTES: A work, very similar in subject and composition, entitled *On the rise of the tide — Dutch fishing boats at Heyst on Sea* was exhibited *O.S.A.*, 1912, no. 36, and reproduced in catalogue.

Bequest of John Paris Bickell, 1952.

51/33 **Coast Scene with Fishing Boats**

72

Paraskeva CLARK (1898-   )

BORN: Petrograd, U.S.S.R., October 28, 1898.

LIVES: Toronto. Came to Canada (Toronto) in 1931.

STUDY: Leningrad, 1916-18 privately under Ilya Zeidenberg; 1918-21 in the Free Art Studios (formerly Imperial Academy of Fine Arts), Leningrad, under Vassily Shuhaeff, and Kuzma Petrov-Vodkin.

SOCIETIES: O.S.A., 1954; A.R.C.A., 1956, R.C.A., 1965; C.S.P.W.C., 1937, Pres. 1948-50; C.G.P., 1936; C.S.G.A., 1938, resigned 1941; F.C.A.

Painter of landscape, figures and still life.

2588   **Snow in the Backyards**

2535

SWAMP 1939

Oil on canvas, 30" x 20".
Signed and dated (lower left): paraskeva clark/39.

PROV.: the artist [CGP, 1939].

EXHIBITIONS: *C.G.P.*, 1939; New York, National Arts Club, 1945 (March - June) [no catalogue]; Richmond, Va., 1949, no. 16; *C.N.E.*, 1949, no. 128.

REFERENCES: *Maritime Art*, vol. 2 (Dec., 1941), p. 51 (reprod.).

Gift from the Albert H. Robson Memorial Subscription Fund, 1939.

2588

SNOW IN THE BACKYARDS 1940

Oil on canvas, $20\frac{1}{4}$" x $24\frac{3}{16}$".
Signed and dated (lower left): paraskeva clark/40.

PROV.: the artist [CGP, 1942].

NOTES: Label on reverse from Addison Gallery, Andover, Mass., 1942, giving title as *Winter Landscape*. [not in catalogue].

EXHIBITIONS: *C.G.P.*, 1942, no. 12, p. 8 (reprod.); *C.N.E.*, 1950, no. 72; M.M.F.A., Gallery XII, *Paraskeva Clark and Henri Masson*, 1954-55 [no catalogue]; Stratford, *Canada on canvas*, 1963; A.G.O. [circulating exhibition], *Canadian paintings of the 1930s*, 1967-68, no. 6.

REFERENCES: *Maritime Art*, vol. 2 (Apr. - May, 1942), p. 122 (reprod.); A.G.T., *Painting and sculpture* (1959), p. 74 (reprod.).

Purchase, 1942.

47/2

BUILDING CLIFTON ROAD 1947

Oil on canvas, 30" x $20\frac{1}{8}$".
Signed and dated (lower left): paraskeva/clark/47.

PROV.: the artist [CGP, 1947].

EXHIBITIONS: *C.G.P.*, 1947-48, no. 19.

Purchase, 1947.

CLAYES, Des, see DES CLAYES

CLEMENCE, see UNKNOWN 19th century, acc. nos. 2833-2836

F. S. COBURN (1871-1960)

BORN: Frederick Simpson Coburn, Upper Melbourne, P. Q., March 18, 1871.

DIED: Upper Melbourne, May 25, 1960.

STUDY: Montreal, Conseil des Arts et Manufactures, under C. S. Stevenson; New York, Carl Hecker School of Art; Berlin, Royal Academy, under Ehrentraut and Skarbina; in Munich; in Paris, under Gérôme; London, Slade School under Prof. Henry Tonks; and Antwerp, Institut Supérieur des Beaux-Arts, under de Vriendt.

SOCIETIES: A.R.C.A., 1920, R.C.A., 1927; Pen and Pencil Club, Montreal, 1933.

Illustrator of novel and verse, until 1914, when he took up painting; also etcher, and engraver on wood.

Alan C. COLLIER (1911-   )

BORN: Alan Caswell Collier, Toronto, March 19, 1911.

LIVES: Toronto.

STUDY: Ontario College of Art, 1929-33, with J. W. Beatty, Franklin Carmichael, J. E. H. MacDonald, and others; New York, Art Students' League, 1937-39, under Howard Trafton.

Lived in New York from 1937 to 1942.

SOCIETIES: O.S.A., 1952, P.O.S.A. 1958-61; A.R.C.A., 1956, R.C.A., 1960.

TEACHING: Toronto, Ontario College of Art, 1955-66.

169

THE ROLLWAY   1921

Oil on canvas, 14¼" x 26³/₁₆".
Signed and dated (lower right): – F. S. COBURN – 21 –.

NOTES: Permanent loan from the C.N.E. Association, 1921-65.

EXHIBITIONS: *C.N.E.*, 1921, no. 126; A.G.T., *Loan exhibition*, 1935, no. 91; Stratford, *Canada on canvas*, 1963.

REFERENCES: O.S.A., *Annual report*, 1922, p. 6.

Gift of the Canadian National Exhibition Association, 1965.

169   The Rollway

60/46

ABANDONED - DAWSON CITY, YUKON TERRITORY   1960

Pen and ink on paper, 14³/₈ x 11³/₈"[sight].
Signed and inscribed (lower left): ALAN COLLIER/DAWSON CITY, Y. T.

Inscribed (top of store front): WINAUTS/STORE.

PROV.: [Roberts Gallery, Toronto].

EXHIBITIONS: Roberts Gallery, *Collier*, 1961 (Feb. 24 - Mar. 9) [no catalogue].

Canada Council Joint Drawings Purchase Fund, 1961.

63/48

THE LAND THAT LISTENS   1963

Oil on masonite, 16" x 36".
Signed (lower right): ALAN C. COLLIER.

PROV.: [Roberts Gallery, Toronto].

EXHIBITIONS: Roberts Gallery, *Collier*, 1963 (Apr. 4-17) [no catalogue].

Purchase, 1964.

63/48 **The Land that Listens**

Alex COLVILLE (1920-   )

BORN: David Alexander Colville, Toronto, August 24, 1920. Grew up in Amherst, Nova Scotia.

LIVES: Sackville, N. B.

STUDY: Sackville, Mount Allison University school of art under Stanley Royle, 1938-42.

TEACHING: Mount Allison University, Sackville, N.B., 1946-63.

Official war artist 1944-46.

57/42 **Elm Tree at Horton Landing**
Colour reproduction, p. 550

2865

THREE HORSES   **1946**

Oil on canvas, $20^1/_{16}$" x $26^1/_8$".
Signed and dated (lower right): ALEX COLVILLE 46.
Inscribed (on stretcher, in pencil): WHITE LEAD 22 JUN 46.

PROV.: the artist [RCA, 1946].

EXHIBITIONS: *R.C.A.*, 1946, no. 20; *C.N.E.*, 1949, no. 34; St. John, N.B., *Colville*, 1951, no. 8.

Purchase, 1946.

2865 **Three Horses**

57/42

ELM TREE AT HORTON LANDING   **1956**

Oil on masonite, $47^7/_8$" x $35^7/_8$".
Signed and dated (lower right): ALEX COLVILLE 1956.
Inscribed (on reverse, upper left): ELM TREE AT HORTON LANDING/ ALEX COLVILLE 1956/OIL.

PROV.: [Laing Galleries, Toronto].

75

EXHIBITIONS: Laing Galleries, *Colville*, 1957 (Oct. 25 - Nov. 8) [no catalogue]; New York, Banfer Gallery, *Colville*, 1963, no. 8; London, Ont., *Magic Realism in Canadian painting*, 1966, no. 10.

REFERENCES: A.G.T., *Painting and sculpture* (1959), p. 83 (reprod.); *New York Times Book Review* (Sept. 23, 1962), Section 7, p. 1 (reprod.).

Gift from the McLean Foundation, 1958.

Charles COMFORT (1900-   )

BORN: Charles Fraser Comfort, Edinburgh, Scotland, July 22, 1900.

LIVES: Hull, Quebec. Came to Canada in 1912, settling in Winnipeg. In 1925 moved to Toronto.

STUDY: Winnipeg School of Art, with A. J. Musgrove, 1916-20; New York, Art Students' League, 1922-23, under Robert Henri, E. Allen Tucker, and Frank Vincent Dumond; Utrecht, Holland.

SOCIETIES: O.S.A., 1927; A.R.C.A., 1936, R.C.A., 1942, P.R.C.A. 1957-60; C.S.P.W.C., charter member, 1926, Pres. 1950-52; C.G.P., founder member, 1933; C.S.G.A., 1925; Fellow of the Royal Society of Artists, London, 1957; Arts and Letters Club, Toronto.

TEACHING: Toronto, Ontario College of Art, 1937; Associate Professor, Fine Arts Department, University of Toronto, 1938-60.
Director of the National Gallery of Canada, 1960-65.

AWARDS: Royal Society Fellowship, 1955-56, for study in The Netherlands.
Official war artist with the Army, 1943-46, painting in Italy and northern Europe.

Painter, muralist, designer and educator.

1685

LAKE McARTHUR

Oil on beaver board, $10^3/_{16}$" x 12".
Signed (lower right, in ink): COMFORT.

NOTES: Permanent loan from the C.N.E. Association, 1930-65.

EXHIBITIONS: *C.N.E.*, 1930, no. 364.

Gift of the Canadian National Exhibition Association, 1965.

866

RUE ST. PAUL, MONTREAL   c. 1927

Pencil on paper, $13^7/_8$" x 12" [sight].
Signed (lower right): Comfort.
Inscribed (lower right): Rue St. Paul.

PROV.: the artist [CSGA, 1927].

EXHIBITIONS: *C.S.G.A.*, 1927, no. 342.

Purchase, 1927.

For drawings to illustrate *Toronto's 100 Years*, 1934, see *Toronto's 100 Years*, p. 457-462.

50/10

LAKE SUPERIOR VILLAGE   1937

Oil on canvas, $42^1/_2$" x 70".
Signed and dated (lower right): COMFORT '37.
Inscribed (on roof, centre): NIPIG [   ] [   ]ANY.

PROV.: the artist.

NOTES: Painted from sketches made at Roseport, Ontario, on north shore of Lake Superior.

This painting awarded first prize, *Great Lakes Exhibition*, Buffalo, N. Y., 1938.

EXHIBITIONS: *C.G.P.*, 1937-38, no. 19; Buffalo, *Great Lakes Exhibition*, 1938-39, no. 154; New York, *World's Fair*, 1939, section CGP, no. 15; A.G.T., *Carr, Harris, Brandtner, and Comfort*, 1940; Quebec, *Exposition...O.S.A.*, 1944, no. 34; C.N.E., 1950, no. 6 (lent by the artist); Stratford, *Canada on canvas*, 1963.

REFERENCES: *Art News*, vol. 37 (Nov. 5, 1938), p. 8 (reprod.); *Saturday Night*, vol. 54 (Nov. 12, 1938), p. 26; *Art Digest*, vol. 13 (Nov. 15, 1938), p. 9 (reprod.); *Parnassus*, vol. 10 (Dec., 1938), p. 21 (reprod.); A.G.T., *Bulletin* (Nov./Dec., 1938), reprod.; A.G.T., *Bulletin* (Jan., 1939), says artist awarded First Prize for this painting, by the Patteran Society of Buffalo.

Gift from the Fund of the T. Eaton Co. Ltd. for Canadian Works of Art, 1950.

50/10   Lake Superior Village

2554

THE SILO   **1940**

Oil on panel, $12^1/_8$" x $15^{15}/_{16}$".

PROV.: the artist [OSA, 1940].

EXHIBITIONS: *O.S.A., small pictures*, 1940, p. 29, no. 230.

REFERENCES: *Farmer's Magazine* (Dec., 1948), p. 11 (reprod.); *Here and Now*, vol. II (June, 1949), p. 61, no. 10 (reprod.).

Purchase, 1940.

2870

HALIBURTON HIGHLANDS   **1946**

Water colour on paper, $15^1/_2$" x $22^{11}/_{16}$".
Signed and dated (lower right): Comfort '46.
Inscribed (on reverse, lower right, in pencil): "Haliburton Highlands"/ overlooking Eagle Lake in Haliburton County, Ontario./Painted on the "thanksgiving" week-end./13th October 1946/Comfort.

PROV.: the artist [CSPWC, 1947].

EXHIBITIONS: *C.S.P.W.C.*, 1947, p. 2.

Purchase, 1947.

2886

CAMPOBASSO IN THE MOLISE 1947

Oil on canvas, 24" x 30".
Signed and dated (lower right): COMFORT 47.
Inscribed (on reverse, in oil): "CAMPOBASSO IN THE MOLISE",
ITALY/CHARLES F. COMFORT R.C.A., O.S.A./ TORONTO.

PROV.: the artist [OSA, 1947].

EXHIBITIONS: *O.S.A.*, 1947, no. 30, p. 54 (reprod.); *C.N.E.*, 1947,
no. 122.

Purchase, 1947.

2886   **Campobasso in the Molise**

48/7

FLIGHT LIEUT. CARL SCHAEFER, R.C.A.F. 1948

Water colour on paper, 32³/₈" x 30³/₈" [sight].
Signed and dated (lower left): COMFORT '48.

PROV.: the artist.

NOTES: Label on reverse reads: "Flight-Lieut. Carl Schaefer, R.C.A.F."/
Official Canadian War Artist serving with/the Air Force. A water colour
portrait/against a background of the air field at/Middleton-St. George,
Durham, 428 Squadron,/No. 6 Bomber Group.

For biography of sitter, see Carl Schaefer, p. 410

EXHIBITIONS: *R.C.A.*, 1948, no. 34, p. 12 (reprod.); *C.G.P.*, 1949,
no. 12; *C.N.E.*, 1949, no. 5; Dallas, 1958; N.G.C. [travelling exhibition],
Canadian painting 1850-1950, 1967-68, no. 58.

REFERENCES: *Canadian Art*, vol. VII (Christmas/New Year, 1949-50),
p. 70 (reprod.); A.G.T., *50th anniversary* (1950), p. 35 (reprod.);
R.A.I.C. Journal, vol. 27 (Jan., 1950), p. 29 (reprod.); *Studio*,
vol. 143 (April, 1952), p. 110 (reprod.); A.G.T., *Painting and
sculpture* (1959), p. 71 (reprod.); *Canadian painting in the twentieth
century* (1961), pl. 8 (reprod. in colour); Harper (1966), p. 335;
C.S.P.W.C., *42nd Annual exhibition* (1967), p. 7 (reprod. [not
exhibited]).

*Gift from the Fund of the T. Eaton Co. Ltd. for Canadian Works of Art,
1948.*

48/7   **Flight Lieut. Carl Schaefer,
R.C.A.F.**

53/16

OUTER REEFS, GEORGIAN BAY   **1953**

Oil on canvas board, 11$^7/_8$" x 15$^7/_8$".
Signed and dated (lower centre): Comfort 53.

PROV.: the artist.

*Gift from the Fund of the T. Eaton Co. Ltd. for Canadian Works of Art,
1953.*

Ulysse COMTOIS (1931-   )

BORN: Granby, P. Q., 1931.

LIVES: Near Granby, P. Q.

STUDY: Montreal, Ecole des Beaux-Arts.

SOCIETIES: Association des artistes non-
figuratifs, Montreal.
Jointed the 'Automatiste' Group in 1953.

AWARDS: Canada Council grant, 1967.

Painter, sculptor.

65/19

DEUX RÉALITÉS   **1962**

Oil on canvas, 50" x 53$^7/_8$".
Signed and dated (lower left): COMTOIS '62.
Inscribed (on reverse): COMTOIS 1962/"DEUX REALITES".

PROV.: [Dorothy Cameron Gallery, Toronto].

Purchase, 1965.

65/20

UNTITLED BROWN AND RED   **1964**

Laminated wood, 18$^3/_4$" x 17$^3/_4$" x 13$^1/_2$".

PROV.: [Dorothy Cameron Gallery, Toronto].

Purchase, 1965.

65/20   **Untitled Brown and Red**

Nelson COOK (1817-1892)

BORN: Probably in or near Ballston Spa, N. Y.

DIED: Boston, Mass., July 29, 1892.

Worked in Toronto, 1835-37, and periodically thereafter; at Saratoga Springs, N.Y., 1841-44, and again 1857-59; at Rochester, N. Y., 1852 and 1857; also at Ballston Spa, and Buffalo.

Artist, poet and portrait painter.

64/13

PORTRAIT OF TIRZAH HOPKINS   1838

Oil on canvas, 29" x 25".

Signed and dated (on reverse): Nelson Cook, pinx^t,/Upper Canada/ 1838.

PROV.: F. A. Bestall, Sault Ste. Marie.

NOTES: Tirzah Hopkins [dates unknown] was the daughter of Caleb Hopkins (1787-1880), a representative of the Legislative Assembly of Upper Canada. This portrait was painted to mark the marriage of Miss Hopkins to Alan Poyntz Patrick [see pendant, acc. no. 64/14] in 1837.

Purchase, 1964.

64/13   **Portrait of Tirzah Hopkins**
Colour reproduction, p. 528

64/14   **Portrait of Alan Poyntz Patrick**

64/14

PORTRAIT OF ALAN POYNTZ PATRICK   1838

Oil on canvas, 29" x 25".
Signed and dated (on reverse): N. Cook, pinx^t./1838.

PROV.: F. A. Bestall, Sault Ste. Marie.

NOTES: Alan Poyntz Patrick [dates unknown] is said to have been directly descended from John Spencer, First Earl Spencer, who married the eldest daughter of the Rt. Hon. Stephen Poyntz of Midgham, Berks. in 1755. He was Chief Clerk of the House of Commons in the Upper Canada Legislature for thirty-seven years, followed by thirteen years in the federal government under Sir John A. MacDonald, until his retirement in 1879.

This portrait was painted to mark the marriage of Patrick to Miss Tirzah Hopkins [see pendant, acc. no. 64/13] in 1837.

Purchase, 1964.

Edwy COOKE (1926-　　)

BORN: Edwy Francis Cooke, Toronto, March 10, 1926.

LIVES: Montreal.

STUDY: University of Toronto, Art and Archaeology; University of Iowa.

TEACHING: University of Toronto, 1951-59; Curator, Beaverbrook Fine Art Gallery, Fredericton, N. B., and teacher, University of New Brunswick, 1959-64; since 1964 has taught in Fine Arts Department, Sir George Williams University, Montreal.

Stanley COSGROVE (1911-　　)

BORN: Stanley Morel Cosgrove, Montreal, P. Q., December 23, 1911.

LIVES: La Tuque, P.Q., since 1962.

STUDY: Montreal, Ecole des Beaux-Arts, under Charles Maillard, 1927-31; 1935, School of the Art Association of Montreal, under Edwin Holgate; from 1939 to 1944, worked with Orozco in Mexico.

SOCIETIES: A.R.C.A., 1951; C.G.P.

TEACHING: Former professor, Ecole des Beaux-Arts, Montreal.

AWARDS: Province of Quebec prize for painting in 1939, and went to Mexico; 1953, Canadian government fellowship, for study in France.

Painter of figures, landscape, and still life.

52/27

GIANT NETS　　　　　　　　　　　　　　**1952**

Oil on masonite, 31" x 25".
Signed (lower left centre): COOKE.

PROV.: the artist [CGP, 1952-53].

EXHIBITIONS: C.G.P., 1952-53, no. 22.

Gift from the John Paris Bickell Bequest Fund, 1953.

52/27　　**Giant Nets**

50/67

STILL LIFE WITH RED CLOTH　　　　　　**1942**

Oil on masonite, $9^{15}/_{16}$" x 18".
Signed and dated (upper right): COSGROVE 42.

PROV.: the artist [AGT, 1957].

EXHIBITIONS: [?] A.A.M., *Cosgrove*, 1944, no. 17 (as Pitcher on a Red Cloth); A.G.T., *Binning-Cosgrove*, 1951, no. 7.

Gift from the Albert H. Robson Memorial Subscription Fund, 1951.

2790

STILL LIFE WITH WHITE VASE　　　　　**1943**

Oil on panel, $13^1/_2$" x $17^3/_8$".
Signed and dated (lower right): COSGROVE 43.
Inscribed (on reverse): "STILL LIFE".

PROV.: the artist.

NOTES: Reproduced in catalogue of exhibition, *A Tribute to Women*, 1960, held at C.N.E., but not actually exhibited. The *Still Life* exhibited,

2790   **Still Life with White Vase**

oil on masonite, 28½" x 36½", signed only, was lent by, and is still in the possession of Mr. and Mrs. Kenneth C. Young, Toronto.

EXHIBITIONS: A.A.M., *Cosgrove*, 1944, no. 58; A.G.T., *Binning-Cosgrove*, 1951.

REFERENCES: *Canadian Art*, vol. II (Dec., 1944), p. 64 (reprod.); A.G.T., *Painting and sculpture* (1959), p. 82 (reprod.).

Purchase, 1945.

2845

LANDSCAPE   **1943**

Oil on masonite, 18" x 24".
Signed and dated (lower left): 43 COSGROVE.

PROV.: the artist.

EXHIBITIONS: A.G.T., *Binning-Cosgrove*, 1951.

Purchase, 1946.

2845   **Landscape**

50/66

STUDY FOR A PAINTING   **1950**

Oil on paper, 35⅜" x 24¼" [sight].
Signed and dated (lower right): COSGROVE/50.

PROV.: the artist (AGT, 1951].

EXHIBITIONS: A.G.T., *Binning-Cosgrove*, 1951, no. 14.

REFERENCES: *Arts et Pensée*, no. 1 (Jan., 1951), p. 11 (reprod. in background of photo of the artist in his studio).

Gift from the Albert H. Robson Memorial Subscription Fund, 1951.

John W. COTTON (1869-1931)

BORN: John Wesley Cotton, Simcoe County, Ontario, October 29, 1869.

DIED: Toronto, November 24, 1931.

STUDY: Toronto, Art Students' League; Art Institute of Chicago; Palette and Chisel Club, Chicago; and in London, England.

SOCIETIES: O.S.A., 1914, resigned 1918, re-elected 1930; Toronto Art Students' League; Printmakers Society of California; Chicago Society of Etchers; Chicago Water Color Club; Palette and Chisel Club, Chicago.

Worked in England and Belgium, 1911-12; lived for a time in Glendale, California.

Etcher and painter.

143

ENTRANCE TO THE CHAPTER HOUSE AND CLOISTERS, VÉZELAY, FRANCE

Etching, Imp.: $8^{11}/_{16}$" x $6^3/_4$". Paper: $13^{13}/_{16}$" x $10^7/_8$".
Signed (lower right, in pencil): J Cotton
Inscribed (lower left, in pencil): NARTEX [sic]/CHURCH of the MADELINE [sic]/VESELAY [sic], FRANCE.

NOTES: Permanent loan from the C.N.E. Association, 1921-66.

Gift of the Canadian National Exhibition Association, 1966.

2408

THE BRINK OF THE VALLEY

Etching, Imp: $5^{15}/_{16}$" x $6^7/_8$". Paper: $9^3/_8$" x $10^7/_8$".
Signed (lower right, in pencil): J. Cotton.
Inscribed and numbered (lower left, in pencil): 3/50 The brink of the valley. Edition 50.

EXHIBITIONS: *C.P.E.*, 1929, no. 226; A.G.T., *Canadian prints*, 1949.

Gift of Mrs. J. W. Cotton, 1936.

2409

ACROSS THE CAMPUS, UNIVERSITY OF TORONTO

Etching, Imp.: $7^7/_8$" x 11". Paper: $10^3/_4$ x $14^1/_4$.
Signed (lower right, in pencil): J. Cotton.
Inscribed (lower left): [C]otton.
Numbered (lower left, in pencil): Edition 50, № 10.
Inscribed (lower centre): ACROSS THE CAMPUS   TORONTO UNIVERSITY   MEMORIAL TOWER.

Gift of Mrs. J. W. Cotton, 1936.

2410

THE DOORWAY, UNIVERSITY COLLEGE, UNIVERSITY OF TORONTO

Etching, Imp.: $10^7/_8$" x $7^{11}/_{16}$". Paper: $14^5/_{16}$" x $10^1/_2$".
Signed (lower right, in pencil): J. Cotton.
Inscribed (lower right): J Cotton.
Numbered (lower left, in pencil): 10/50.
Inscribed (lower centre): FAMOUS DOORWAY   TORONTO UNIVERSITY.

EXHIBITIONS: Toronto, Metropole Galleries, *Cotton*, 1912, no. 92.

Gift of Mrs. J. W. Cotton, 1936.

34

HAMPSTEAD HEATH

Aquatint, Imp.: $5^3/_4$" x $11^3/_4$".
Signed (lower right, in pencil): J. W. Cotton.

NOTES: Permanent loan from the C.N.E. Association, 1912-1966.

EXHIBITIONS: Toronto, Metropole Galleries, *Cotton*, 1912, no. 71; Winnipeg, R.C.A., 1912, no. 171; *C.N.E.*, 1912, no. 613 [under British artists].

Gift of the Canadian National Exhibition Association, 1966.

1949

PLACE DE LA DIGUE, BRUGES   1912

Etching, Imp.: $7^7/_8$" x $4^7/_8$". Paper: $11^3/_{16}$" x $8^{11}/_{16}$".
Signed and dated (lower right, in pencil): J. Cotton/-12.
Inscribed (lower left, in pencil): Place de la Digue, Bruges.

EXHIBITIONS: Toronto, Metropole Galleries, *Cotton*, 1912, no. 91.

Gift of the Artist, 1924.

35

"THE CASTLE", ST. IVES   1912

Etching, Imp.: $4^{15}/_{16}$" x $6^7/_8$". Paper: $7^7/_8$" x $10^1/_4$".
Signed and dated (lower right, in pencil): J. W. Cotton./12.
Inscribed (lower left, in pencil): "The Castle."

NOTES: Permanent loan from the C.N.E. Association, 1912-1966.
St. Ives is located in Cornwall, England.

EXHIBITIONS: Toronto, Metropole Galleries, *Cotton*, 1912, no. 74; *C.N.E.*, 1912, no. 620 [under British artists].

Gift of the Canadian National Exhibition Association, 1966.

54

FISH STREET, ST. IVES   1913

Etching, Imp.: $8^7/_8$" x $5^7/_8$". Paper: $11^5/_8$" x 9".
Signed and dated (lower right, in pencil): J Cotton/-13.

NOTES: Permanent loan from the C.N.E. Association, 1913-1966.

REFERENCES: Duval (1952), pl. 7 (reprod.; dated c. 1910 [sic]).

Gift of the Canadian National Exhibition Association, 1966.

1422

LELANT DOWNS, CORNWALL   1913

Etching, Imp.: $5^{13}/_{16}$" x $8^7/_8$". Paper: $9^3/_8$" x 15".
Signed and dated (lower right, in pencil): J. Cotton/13.
Inscribed (lower left, in pencil): Lelant downs, Cornwall,.

EXHIBITIONS: *O.S.A.*, 1913, no. 94.

Gift of Sir Edmund Walker Estate, 1926.

Walter J. COUCILL (1915-)

BORN: Walter Jackson Coucill, Camden, New Jersey, June 22, 1915.

LIVES: Toronto. Came to Canada (Toronto) in 1923, after living in England for five years.

STUDY: Toronto, Ontario College of Art.

SOCIETIES: Arts and Letters Club, Toronto. Served with the R.C.A.F. during World War II.

Commercial artist.

Graham COUGHTRY (1931-)

BORN: John Graham Coughtry, St. Lambert, P. Q., June 8, 1931.

LIVES: Toronto.

STUDY: Montreal, school of the Montreal Museum of Fine Arts; Toronto, Ontario College of Art, graduating 1953.

SOCIETIES: C.G.P.; C.S.G.A.

AWARDS: Scholarships for travel and study in Europe, 1951, 1953; Canada Council grants, 1959-60, 1965-66.

Painter, sculptor.

1188

THE GRANGE, ENTRANCE   1915

Aquatint, Imp.: $9^3/_4$" x $7^7/_{16}$". Paper: $17^1/_8$" x $12^1/_{16}$".
Signed and dated (lower right, in pencil): J. W. Cotton/17 May 1915.

PROV.: [unknown].

Accessioned, 1954.

2731

RAINY DAY, LACHINE   1942

Water colour on paper, $15^5/_{16}$" x $20^1/_4$".
Signed, dated and inscribed (lower right): W. J. Coucill/42./LACHINE.

PROV.: the artist [HH, 1942].

EXHIBITIONS: University of Toronto, Hart House, *Canadian Armed Forces art exhibition*, 1942, no. 355.

Purchase, 1943.

62/66

FIGURE ON A BED   1954

Oil on canvas, $30^3/_{16}$" x $40^1/_{16}$".
Signed and dated (lower left): COUGHTRY 54.

PROV.: Miss Theresa L. Cosgrove, Toronto.

EXHIBITIONS: University of Toronto, Hart House, *Coughtry-Snow*, 1955 (Jan.) [no catalogue].

Gift from the McLean Foundation, 1963.

62/66   **Figure on a Bed**

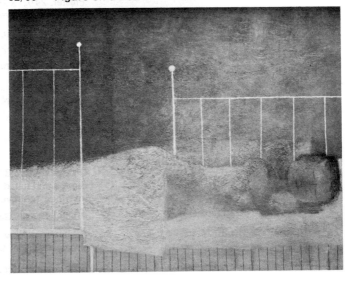

E. B. COX (1914-   )

BORN: Elford Bradley Cox, Botha, Alberta, July 16, 1914.

LIVES: Willowdale, Ontario.

STUDY: No formal art training.

SOCIETIES: O.S.A., 1951; A.R.C.A., 1961; S.S.C., 1961.

Sculptor.

51/87

ALABASTER FIGURE   1952

Alabaster, 10$\frac{1}{2}$" x 16$\frac{1}{2}$" x 10$\frac{3}{8}$".
Signed (underside): E. B. Cox.

PROV.: the artist [OSA, 1952].

EXHIBITIONS: *O.S.A.*, 1952, no. 108.

Gift from the John Paris Bickell Bequest Fund, 1952.

57/7

FACE OF THE MOON   1954

Green marble and abalone shell, Diam. 12$\frac{13}{16}$".

PROV.: the artist.

REFERENCES: A.G.T., *Painting and sculpture* (1959), p. 88 (reprod.).

Gift from the McLean Foundation, 1957.

57/7   **Face of the Moon**

60/59

PERUVIAN HEAD   1956

Red granite, 16$\frac{3}{4}$ x 13$\frac{1}{4}$" x 10$\frac{1}{2}$".

PROV.: the artist [AGT, 1961].

EXHIBITIONS: A.G.T., *Exhibition and sale of garden sculpture*, 1961, no. 9.

Gift from the McLean Foundation, 1961.

Julia CRAWFORD (1896-   )

BORN: Julia Tilley Crawford, Kingston, New Brunswick, April 18, 1896.

LIVES: St. John, N.B.

STUDY: New York, Pratt Institute, 1925-28.

SOCIETIES: C.S.P.W.C., 1940; Associate member, New York Water Color Club, 1937; Fellow of the International Institute of Art and Literature, 1960.

TEACHING: St. John Vocational School, 1928-44; Netherwood School of New Brunswick, 1944-57; and private classes in her studio since 1944.

William Nicol CRESSWELL (1822-1888)

BORN: Devonshire, England.

DIED: Seaforth, Ontario, 1888. Came to Canada and settled at Seaforth, Ontario, 1855.

STUDY: England, with W. E. Cook and Clarkson Stanfield, 1842-50.

SOCIETIES: O.S.A., 1874; R.C.A., charter member, 1880.

Pioneer landscape and marine painter.

2424
STILL LIFE   1937

Water colour on paper, $18\frac{1}{4}$" x $14\frac{7}{8}$" [sight].
Signed and dated (upper right): J Crawford '37.

PROV.: the artist [CSPWC, 1937].

EXHIBITIONS: *C.S.P.W.C.*, 1937, no. 31; New York, *World's Fair*, 1939, section CSPWC, and SSC, no. 33.

Gift from Friends of Canadian Art Fund, 1937.

52/24
LANDSCAPE WITH SHEEP   1878

Oil on canvas, $23\frac{3}{4}$" x $35\frac{3}{4}$".
Signed and dated (lower right): W. N. Cresswell./1878.

Gift of Misses Emily and Florence Cresswell, 1953.

52/24   **Landscape with Sheep**

52/23
SAN ANTONIA CANYON, CALIFORNIA   1887

Water colour on paper, 18" x $26\frac{1}{2}$" [sight].
Signed (lower right): W. N. Cresswell, R. C.A.

NOTES: According to correspondence from the donors, the artist painted this during a winter spent in California, the year before he died.

Gift of Misses Emily and Florence Cresswell, 1953.

52/23   **San Antonia Canyon, California**

168

PLOUGHING, LOWER ST. LAWRENCE

Oil on canvas, 37½″ x 63⅞″.
Signed (lower right): W. Cruikshank.

EXHIBITIONS: [?] *R.C.A.*, 1898, no. 21 [described in notes by F. S. Challener in A.G.O. Library as a large canvas with girl in blue skirt]; [?] *R.C.A., and O.S.A.*, 1901, no. 22; Buffalo, *Pan American Exposition*, 1901, no. 16 (lent by the artist; awarded medal [see ref. *The Farmer's Advocate*]); *C.N.E.*, 1903, no. 33; A.G.T., *Summer*, 1910; A.G.T., *William Cruikshank*, 1918-19, no. 1; *C.N.E.*, 1939, no. 56; *O.S.A.*, 1947, no. 149.

REFERENCES: *The Farmer's Advocate* (Dec. 16, 1901), p. 828 (reprod.; says the artist won a medal for the painting at the Pan-American exposition, Buffalo); MacTavish (1925), p. 134.

Permanent loan from the artist, accessioned, 1920.

168   **Ploughing, Lower St. Lawrence**

William CRUIKSHANK (1848-1922)

BORN: Broughty Ferry, Scotland, December 25, 1848.

DIED: Kansas City, Missouri, May 19, 1922. Came to Canada (Toronto) in 1857.

STUDY: Edinburgh, Royal Scottish Academy; London, Royal Academy School, under Leighton, Millais and others; Paris, Atelier Yvon.

SOCIETIES: A.R.C.A., 1884, resigned, re-elected, 1893, R.C.A., 1894; O.S.A., 1882; Toronto Etching Society, 1885; Toronto Art Students' League.

TEACHING: Toronto, Central Ontario School of Art, drawing, for some 25 years.

Moved to Kansas City, 1919.

Painter of portraits, landscape.

52/10

FRENCH INTERIOR

Oil on cardboard, 11″ x 8³/₈″
Signed (lower right): W Cruikshank.

PROV.: Mrs. J. H. Birkenshaw, Toronto.

Gift from the Fund of the T. Eaton Co. Ltd. for Canadian Works of Art, 1952.

52/10   **French Interior**

58/14

ANNE CRUIKSHANK

Oil on canvas, 38³/₄″ x 35¹/₂″.

NOTES: The sitter was sister of the artist, and one of his favourite models. She never married.

The sitter was also great-aunt to the donor.

EXHIBITIONS: Stratford, *Faces of Canada*, 1964; N.G.C., *300 years of Canadian art*, 1967, no. 159, p. 99 (reprod.).

REFERENCES: A.G.T., *Painting and sculpture* (1959), p. 49 (reprod.); Harper (1966), pp. 229, 232, fig. 207 (reprod. in colour).

Gift of Mrs. Charles B. Norris, Madison, Wisconsin, 1958.

58/13

DOROTHY

Oil on canvas, 34³/₈″ x 24³/₈″.
Signed (upper right): W. Cruikshank.
Inscribed (on reverse): W. Cruikshank.

EXHIBITIONS: *O.S.A.*, 1904, no. 23; *C.N.E.*, 1904, no. 76, opp. p. 10 (reprod.); [?] Hamilton, *R.C.A.*, 1909, no. 33; [?] A.G.T., *Summer*, 1910; [?] A.G.T., *William Cruikshank*, 1918-19, no. 8.

Gift of Mrs. Charles B. Norris, Madison, Wisconsin, 1958.

58/14   **Anne Cruikshank**
Colour reproduction, p. 535

403

LEAVES FROM SKETCH BOOK (115)

Pencil and/or pen and ink on paper, of varying sizes, ranging from
$5^{1}/_{4}$" x $7^{3}/_{8}$" to $8^{1}/_{2}$" x $10^{1}/_{2}$".

EXHIBITIONS: A.G.T., *Loan exhibition*, 1912, p. 30.

REFERENCES: *Canada and its provinces*, vol. 12 (1914), p. 630.

Gift of William Cruikshank, 1909.

1409

SELF PORTRAIT   **1887**

Crayon on paper, $23^{3}/_{4}$" x $17^{7}/_{8}$".
Signed, dated and inscribed (lower left): W. Cruikshank/Peterborough
14/1/87.

Gift of Thomas Symington, 1918.

1409   **Self Portrait**

57/41

QUEBEC LANDSCAPE   **c. 1910**

Oil on panel, 8" x $10^{1}/_{2}$".
Signed (lower right): W. Cruikshank.
Inscribed (on reverse): I painted this about 1910/ W. Cruikshank/
Sold to my friend Tom Symington/WC/March/1919.
Inscribed (on reverse): I have an option on this/Sept 12/11/W M
Boulton.
Inscribed (on reverse): I also have an option on this yours having
expired — /Morris — /May 18 — 1912.

PROV.: T. S. Symington, Toronto.

*Gift from the Fund of the T. Eaton Co. Ltd. for Canadian Works of
Art, 1958.*

Maurice CULLEN (1866-1934)

BORN: St. John's Newfoundland, June 6, 1866. Moved to Montreal, with family, 1870.

DIED: Chambly, P. Q., March 28, 1934.

STUDY: Montreal, Conseil des Arts et Manufactures (sculpture); Montreal, with sculptor Philippe Hébert, 1880s; Paris, Ecole des Beaux-Arts, under Elie Delaunay, 1889-92; at which time he turned from sculpture to painting; Paris, under Roll.

SOCIETIES: A.R.C.A., 1899, R.C.A., 1907; Associate of the Société Nationale des Beaux-Arts, 1895; Canadian Art Club, 1910-15; Pen and Pencil Club, Montreal, 1896.

TRAVEL: 1888-95, in Europe — during the 1890s was associated with Morrice in Venice and Brittany; 1900-02, in Europe and North Africa.

Painted for the Canadian War Memorials in France, Belgium and England in 1918.

Landscape painter.

51/48

WINTER NEAR MONTREAL

Oil on cardboard, $8^3/_8$" x $11^3/_4$".
Signed (lower right): M C.

NOTES: Formerly entitled *Birches in Winter*.

EXHIBITIONS: Kitchener, *Canadian classic*, 1959, no. 2.

Gift of Stanford E. Dack, 1952.

56/29

MORET, WINTER   1895

Oil on canvas, $23^1/_2$" x $36^1/_4$".
Signed and dated (lower left): Maurice Cullen/95.

PROV.: John Taylor, Montreal; Mrs. Allan Grant Urquhart, Montreal.

NOTES: Label formerly on reverse, now in A.G.O. accession file, reads: Lent to the exhibition [1956] by Mrs. Allan Grant Urquhart, daughter of the late Mr. John Taylor, who purchased the picture from the artist, when several of his paintings were shown at the old Art Gallery on Phillips Square, Montreal.

[The Art Association of Montreal, known since 1939 as The Montreal Museum of Fine Arts, was situated in Phillips Square from 1879 to 1912.]

EXHIBITIONS: Hamilton, and others, *Cullen*, 1956, no. 4 (lent by Mrs. Allan Grant Urquhart); Kitchener, *Canadian classic*, 1959, no. 5; London, Ont., *Canadian Impressionists*, 1965, no. 11.

REFERENCES: A.G.T., *Accessions 1956-57*, reprod.; A.G.T., *Painting and sculpture* (1959), p. 51 (reprod.).

Gift from J. S. McLean, Canadian Fund, 1957.

56/29   **Moret, Winter**
Colour reproduction, p. 536

799   **On the St. Lawrence**

2861   **Levis from Quebec**

799

ON THE ST. LAWRENCE   1897

Oil on canvas, 21$\frac{1}{8}$" x 28$\frac{5}{8}$".
Signed and dated (lower right): M Cullen/97.

PROV.: Mrs. F. C. Paul, Toronto [?].

NOTES: According to correspondence from William R. Watson, 1946, the painting was done out-of-doors, near Les Eboulements, Quebec.

EXHIBITIONS: A.G.T., *Loan exhibition*, 1935, no. 93; A.G.T., *Works by senior painters in Canada*, 1937, no. 29, on cover (reprod. in colour); Hamilton, and others, *Cullen*, 1956, no. 14 (says painted at Beaupré); Kitchener, *Canadian classic*, 1959, no. 1; Kitchener, *Cullen*, 1965, no. 19.

REFERENCES: Robson (1932), p. 75 (reprod. in colour); McRae (1944), p. 52 (reprod.); *Canadian Geographical Journal*, vol. XXXVIII (Mar., 1949), on cover (reprod. in colour).

Gift from the Reuben and Kate Leonard Canadian Fund, 1926.

2861

LEVIS FROM QUEBEC   1906

Oil on canvas, 30$\frac{3}{16}$" x 40$\frac{1}{4}$".
Signed and dated (lower right): M. Cullen/.06.

PROV.: Estate of the artist's widow; [Watson Art Galleries, Montreal].

EXHIBITIONS: Hamilton, and others, *Cullen*, 1956, no. 29; Kitchener, *Canadian Classic*, 1959, no. 3; Stratford, *Canada on canvas*, 1963; Kitchener, *Cullen*, 1965, no. 18; London, Ont., *Canadian Impressionists*, 1965, no. 12.

REFERENCES: A.G.T., *Accessions 1946-1947*, reprod.

Gift from the Albert H. Robson Memorial Subscription Fund, 1946.

54/3

THE LAST LOADS   1916

Oil on canvas, 45$\frac{1}{2}$" x 67$\frac{3}{4}$".
Signed and dated (lower right): M. Cullen/16.

PROV.: Estate of the artist; [Watson Art Galleries, Montreal].

NOTES: Also known under the titles, *Ice Cutters*, and *The Last Loads, Longueuil.*

EXHIBITIONS: Hamilton, *Inaugural*, 1953-54, no. 11 (lent by Watson Galleries); Hamilton, and others, *Cullen*, 1956, no. 49 (reprod.).

REFERENCES: Gour, *Cullen* (1952), opp. p. 6 (reprod.), p. 16; *Canadian Art*, vol. XIII (Winter, 1956), p. 254 (reprod.).

Gift of Reuben Wells Leonard Estate, 1954.

55/30

AT THE FRONT   1918

Oil on panel, 9$\frac{3}{4}$" x 14".
Inscribed (on reverse, lower right, in pencil): M Cullen.

PROV.: H. A. Cascadden, Toronto.

NOTES: Label on reverse reads: AT THE FRONT — 1918/Maurice Cullen/Collection of H. A. Cascadden.

EXHIBITIONS: Kitchener, *Canadian classic*, 1959, no. 4; Kitchener, *Cullen*, 1965, no. 20.

Gift from J. S. McLean, Canadian Fund, 1955.

130

HARVEST MOON   c. 1920

Oil on canvas, 24" x 32".
Signed (lower right): M. Cullen.

NOTES: Permanent loan from C.N.E. Association, 1921-65.

EXHIBITIONS: *R.C.A.*, 1920, no. 55; *C.N.E.*, 1921, no. 119; Kitchener, *Cullen*, 1965, no. 17.

REFERENCES: O.S.A., *Annual report*, 1922, p. 6.

Gift of the Canadian National Exhibition Association, 1965.

Greg CURNOE (1937-   )

BORN: London, Ontario, 1937.

LIVES: London.

STUDY: H. B. Beal Technical School, London, 1954, under Herb Ariss; summer, 1956, at Doon School of Art; Toronto, Ontario College of Art, 1957-60.

65/24   **Spring on the Ridgeway**

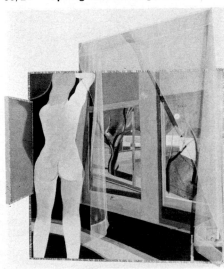

65/24

SPRING ON THE RIDGEWAY   1964

Oil on plywood, rayon/nylon [curtain], metal [window lifts], wood [yoyo], paper ["Admiral" radio], string.

OVERALL: 73⅝" x 73⅝".
Panel, left side: 36¼" x 27¹³/₁₆".
Inscribed (around border, beginning upper left): [drawing of hand] WHILE I WAS IN TORONTO LAST WEEK I KEPT THINKING OF YOU — FOUR LEAF CLOVER — CANKER — THE MONEY — MY HAND/S SHOULD BE TOUCHING YOU — SKINNING THE CAT — COLITIS — THE BREAKAWAY — WALKING OVER THE OLD KING STREET BRIDGE. UP/BECHER STREET TO THE V WHERE THE RIDGEWAY JOINS. TO YOUR ROOMING HOUSE ON THE NORTH SIDE — THE FLYING SAUCER —/ASTHMA — THE SLEEPER — WHY HAVE WE ARGUED ABOUT THIS 'PAINTING'? — AROUND THE WORLD AND BACK AGAIN — HAY FEVER — ZENITH?
Inscribed (on panel, left side, beginning upper left): ARO/UND THE WORLD TWICE — AROUND THE WO/RLD BACKWARDS — ROCK THE CRADLE — EATING SPAGHETTI —/OVER THE FALLS — WALK THE DOG — THE CR/EEPER — THREE LEAF CLOVER — AROUND THE WORLD —.
Inscribed (on window): A LOOP.

PROV.: [David Mirvish Gallery, Toronto].

EXHIBITIONS: David Mirvish Gallery, *Curnoe*, 1964 (Sept. 17-Oct. 6) [no catalogue]; Vancouver, *Curnoe*, 1966, no. 10.

Purchase, 1965.

For relief print by Curnoe, see "Toronto 20", 453-457

Gertrude Spurr CUTTS
(1858-1941)

BORN: Scarborough, Yorkshire, England, 1858; married artist William M. Cutts (1857-1943).

DIED: Port Perry, Ontario, July 21, 1941. Came to Canada about 1890.

STUDY: Scarborough School of Art, under Albert Strange; Lambeth School of Art, London; also in London, under E. H. Holder; Art Students' League, New York, under F. A. Bridgman, John Carlson and Birge Harrison.

SOCIETIES: O.S.A., 1891 [life member]; A.R.C.A., 1895.

67

MOUNTAIN SOLITUDE

Oil on canvas, 32" x 46¹/₄".
Signed (lower left): Gertrude Spurr-Cutts.

NOTES: Permanent loan from the C.N.E. Association, 1915-65.

EXHIBITIONS: *R.C.A.*, 1914, no. 52; *C.N.E.*, 1915, no. 137, p. 49 (reprod.); Ottawa, *Central Canada Exhibition*, 1926, no. 14; *C.N.E.*, 1939, no. 59.

Gift of the Canadian National Exhibition Association, 1965.

Jean DALLAIRE (1916-1965)

BORN: Jean-Philippe Dallaire, at Hull, Quebec, June 9, 1916.

DIED: France, December 1, 1965.

STUDY: Technical school in Hull, Quebec, 1934; in Toronto, at Central Technical School under Charles Goldhamer, Peter Haworth, and Elizabeth Wyn Wood (sculpture): school of the Boston Museum of Fine Arts; Paris, 1938, under Maurice Denis and André Lhote.

TEACHING: Ecole des Beaux-Arts, Quebec, for a time.

AWARDS: Province of Quebec prize for painting, 1938.

Interned in France during World War II, returning to Canada in 1945.

53/22

AU CASTEL DE LA MER   1953

Oil on canvas, 20¹/₈" x 24".
Signed and dated (lower right): 1953/Dallaire.
Inscribed (lower left): "AU CASTEL DE LA MER".

PROV.: [Dominion Gallery, Montreal].

EXHIBITIONS: Dominion Gallery, *Dallaire*, 1954 (Apr. 22 - May 8) [no catalogue]; N.G.C., *300 years of Canadian art*, 1967, no. 284, p. 173 (reprod.).

REFERENCES: *Canadian Art*, vol. XII, (Winter, 1955), p. 57 (reprod.); *Vie des Arts*, no. 45 (Winter, 1967), p. 34 (reprod.).

Gift from J. S. McLean, Canadian Fund, 1954.

53/22   **Au Castel de la Mer**

96

Kathleen DALY (1898-   )

BORN: Kathleen Frances Daly, Napanee, Ontario, May 28, 1898; widow of George Pepper, whom she married in 1929.

LIVES: Toronto

STUDY: Ontario College of Art, under Beatty, Reid, Lismer and J. E. H. MacDonald, graduating 1924; Paris, Académie de la Grande Chaumière, 1924-25; and in Paris, wood cuts under René Pottier, 1924-25.

SOCIETIES: O.S.A., 1935; A.R.C.A., 1947, R.C.A., 1961; C.G.P., 1934.

Portraits, landscape, drawing, some abstract painting, etching.

1324   Midwinter, Hull

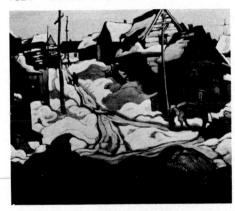

Sylvia DAOUST (1902-   )

BORN: Montreal, May 24, 1902.

LIVES: Montreal.

STUDY: Montreal, Ecole des Beaux-Arts; and in Europe, mostly France.

SOCIETIES: A.R.C.A., 1943, R.C.A., 1951; S.S.C.

TEACHING: Ecole des Beaux-Arts, Quebec, 1930-43; since 1943, sculpture in wood, Ecole des Beaux-Arts, Montreal.

AWARDS: Willingdon Arts Competition prize for sculpture, 1929, and a Quebec Provincial Government Scholarship, 1929, both of which were used for study in France; 1955-56, Royal Society of Canada scholarship, again for study in France; Allied Art Medallist, 1961.

Sculptor in wood.

1324

MIDWINTER, HULL   **1929**

Oil on canvas, 36" x 40".
Signed (lower right): K DALY.

PROV.: the artist [OSA, 1930].

EXHIBITIONS: *O.S.A.*, 1930, no. 46, p. 10 (reprod.); N.G.C., *Annual*, 1931, no. 59; Ottawa, Art Association, *Daly, and Pepper*, 1932 (May 9-14), no. 94; A.G.T., *Summer*, 1935, no. 31; A.G.T., *Loan exhibition*, 1935, no. 95.

REFERENCES: A.G.T., *Bulletin and annual report* (May, 1931), p. 6 (reprod.).

Gift from Friends of Canadian Art Fund, 1930.

2887

CHIEF SITTING EAGLE'S FAMILY   **1946**

Oil on canvas, 30" x 24".
Signed (lower right): K. Daly.

PROV.: the artist [OSA, 1947].

EXHIBITIONS: *O.S.A.*, 1947, no. 35; *C.N.E.*, 1949, no. 6; *C.N.E.*, 1952, no. 66.

Purchase, 1947.

53/18

MARIE A CANA   **1952**

Wood carving, 22½" high.
Signed and dated (on base, at back): Sylvia Daoust/52.

PROV.: the artist.

EXHIBITIONS: *R.C.A.*, 1952, no. 104 (as Marie à Cana, "vinum non habent"), p. 20 (reprod. in profile).

Gift from the Fund of the T. Eaton Co. Ltd. for Canadian Works of Art, 1954.

Alice DES CLAYES (1891-   )

BORN: Aberdeen, Scotland, December 22, 1891.

LIVES: Devon, England; came to Canada (Montreal) in 1914; sister to Berthe Des Clayes [q.v.].

STUDY: Bushey School of Art, under Lucy Kemp Welch, for three years; at Newlyn; and at Ambleteuse, under Dudley Hardy.

SOCIETIES: A.R.C.A., 1920.

Best known as painter of animals.

Berthe DES CLAYES (1877-   )

BORN: Aberdeen, Scotland, 1877.

LIVES: Whereabouts unknown; came to Canada (Montreal) in 1912; sister to Alice Des Clayes [q.v.].

STUDY: Herkomer School of Art, Bushey, England; Paris, Julian Academy, under Tony Robert-Fleury and J. Lefebvre, but mainly self-taught.

Landscape painter.

William A. DRAKE (1891-1946)

BORN: William Alexander Drake, Toronto, November 7, 1891.

DIED: Roche's Point, September 15, 1946.

STUDY: Toronto, Central Ontario School of Art and Design, under Cruikshank, Reid and others.

SOCIETIES: Arts and Letters Club, Toronto.

131

A BLUE DAY

Oil on canvas, 30$\frac{1}{8}$" x 35$\frac{1}{8}$".
Signed (lower left): A. Des Clayes.

NOTES: Permanent loan from C.N.E. Association, 1921-65.

EXHIBITIONS: *R.C.A.*, 1920, no. 70 (reprod.); *C.N.E.*, 1921, no. 139.

REFERENCES: O.S.A., *Annual report*, 1922, p. 6.

Gift of the Canadian National Exhibition Association, 1965.

177

EARLY SPRING IN PICARDY

Oil on canvas, 28$\frac{3}{16}$" x 37$\frac{7}{8}$".
Signed (lower left): B. Des Clayes.

NOTES: Permanent loan from C.N.E. Association, 1922-65.

EXHIBITIONS: *R.C.A.*, 1921-22, no. 46 (reprod.); *C.N.E.*, 1922, no. 210.

REFERENCES: MacTavish (1925), between p. 144 and 145 (reprod.).

Gift of the Canadian National Exhibition Association, 1965.

177   Early Spring in Picardy

659

GATE TO STABLES, THE GRANGE

Pencil on paper, 7$\frac{1}{2}$" x 9$\frac{7}{8}$".
Signed (on reverse, in ink): W. A. DRAKE.
Inscribed (on reverse, in ink): Gages leading to stables and garden./ The Grange.

NOTES: This and the following three drawings depict parts of the property surrounding The Grange, the home of D'Arcy Boulton, Jr., built in 1817, and one of the earliest brick houses in "Little York". Upon settlement of the estate of D'Arcy's widow after 1863, The Grange became the property of her daughter-in-law, Harriet Elizabeth, wife of William Henry Boulton. William Henry died in 1874, and the

659   **Gate to Stables, The Grange**

next year his widow married Goldwin Smith [q.v., p. 263]. When Harriet Elizabeth (Boulton) Smith died in 1909, she bequeathed The Grange to the Art Gallery (then the Art Museum of Toronto), after the death of her husband. Goldwin Smith died in 1910 and The Grange was officially opened to the public as a museum in 1913.

Gift of the Artist, 1918.

660

TOOL HOUSE, THE GRANGE

Pencil on paper, 7⁵/₈″ x 9⁷/₈″.
Signed and inscribed (on reverse): The tool house/The Grange/Toronto/W. A. DRAKE.

Gift of the Artist, 1918.

661

STABLE DOOR, THE GRANGE

Pencil on paper, 9⁷/₈″ x 7¹/₂″.
Signed and inscribed (on reverse, in ink): Stable door/ The Grange./ W. A. DRAKE.

Gift of the Artist, 1918.

663

THE ROOT HOUSE, THE GRANGE

Pencil on paper, 7¹/₂″ x 9³/₄″.
Signed (lower left): W. A. DRAKE.
Inscribed (on mount, lower left): Root House, the Grange.

Gift of the Artist, 1918.

662

CHERRY TREE

Oil on panel, 8³/₈″ x 11⁵/₈″.
Signed and dated (lower left): W. A. DRAKE./1911.
Signed and dated (lower right): W. A. D./ 9/11 [?].
Inscribed (on reverse): THE GRANGE/CHERRY TREE./1911.
Inscribed (on reverse): To Mʳ. GREIG/FROM FRIEND W. A. DRAKE/ 6/6/19.

Gift of the Artist, 1918.

Ann MacIntosh DUFF
(1925-   )

BORN: Toronto, 1925.

LIVES: Toronto.

STUDY: Toronto, Central Technical School, under Peter Haworth; two summers at Queen's University school of fine art, under André Biéler.

SOCIETIES: O.S.A., 1961; C.S.P.W.C., 1951; C.S.G.A., 1963.

53/19

NORTHERN CHURCH   1953

Water colour on paper, 20⁷/₁₆″ x 27¹⁵/₁₆″ [sight].
Signed (lower right): ANN MᵃᶜINTOSH DUFF.

PROV.: the artist [CSPWC, 1954].

EXHIBITIONS: *C.S.P.W.C.*, 1954, no. 29.

Gift from the John Paris Bickell Bequest Fund, 1954.

Albert DUMOUCHEL
(1916-   )

BORN: Valleyfield, P. Q., April, 5, 1916.

LIVES: Montreal.

STUDY: Montreal, engraving under James Lowe, sculpture under Médard Bourgault; Paris, lithography under Desjobert; Paris, Atelier 17, under S. W. Hayter.

TEACHING: Montreal, Institut des Arts Graphiques, Director, 1949-56; Montreal, Ecole des Beaux-Arts, head of graphics division, since 1956.

AWARDS: UNESCO fellowship for work in Europe, 1955-56; Province of Quebec scholarship, to Paris, 1957; Canada Council grants, 1961, 1967.

Painter, printmaker.

Mary A. EASTLAKE (1864-1951)

BORN: Mary Alexandra Bell, Douglas, Ontario, 1864.

DIED: Ottawa, 1951. Married Charles Eastlake, English landscape painter, whom she met while studying in Paris.

STUDY: Montreal, under Robert Harris; Art Students' League, New York, under William Chase; Paris, Colarossi.

SOCIETIES: A.R.C.A., 1893, but resigned to go and live in England; Pastel Society; Women's International Art Club.

TRAVEL: Extensively in Europe and Asia. Returned to Canada in 1939, living in Montreal for a few years, then settling in Almonte, Ontario.

Wyatt EATON (1849-1896)

BORN: Phillipsburg, Quebec, May 6, 1849.

DIED: Newport, Rhode Island, June 7, 1896.

STUDY: New York, National Academy of Design, 1867, under Samuel Colman, Daniel Huntington, and others; Paris, Ecole des Beaux-Arts, under Gérôme.

Associated with Whistler in London, 1872; influenced by Millet and the Barbizon about 1873-76.

64/74
GOUTTES DU JOUR   1963

Relief print, Imp.: $15^3/_4$" x $15^7/_8$".
Signed and dated (lower right, in pencil): Dumouchel /63.
Inscribed and numbered (lower left, in pencil): gouttes du jour 5/7.

PROV.: [Dorothy Cameron Gallery, Toronto].

EXHIBITIONS: Dorothy Cameron Gallery, *Canadian printmaking today*, 1965 (April) [exhibited, but not in catalogue].

Gift from Anonymous Fund, 1965.

65/67
LA DANSE   1965

Lithograph: Paper, $25^3/_4$" x $19^7/_8$".
Signed and dated (lower right, in pencil): Dumouchel 65.
Inscribed and numbered (lower left, in pencil): la danse 8/8.

PROV.: [Gallery Pascal, Toronto].

Anonymous Gift, 1966.

865
LITTLE BROTHER

Oil on canvas, $20^5/_{16}$" x $17^1/_4$".
Signed (upper left): M. A. EASTLAKE.

EXHIBITIONS: A.G.T., *Mrs. C. H. Eastlake*, 1927, no. 204.

Gift of W. L. Grant, 1927.

406
TIMOTHY COLE (1852-1931)   1885

Oil on canvas, $34^3/_4$" x $28^1/_2$".
Signed and dated (upper right): WYATT EATON 1885.

NOTES: Timothy Cole was born in London, 1852, and came to America in 1857, settling in Chicago. There he became a wood engraver, and a musician of considerable talent. The Chicago fire of 1871 destroyed most of his possessions including his piano and violin, and he moved to New York, there to devote his undivided attention to wood engraving. He engraved many American portraits, but is best known perhaps for

SOCIETIES: American Art Association (later Society of American Artists), founding member; Society of Canadian artists, Montreal, founding member, 1867.

TEACHING: For a time at Cooper Union, New York.

Returned to New York, 1876, where he painted a series of portraits of American poets for the *Century Magazine*, which were engraved on wood by Timothy Cole. Painted portraits in Montreal, 1892-93, but was mainly active in New York.

TRAVEL: Visited France and Italy, 1880.

Portrait painter.

his engravings after the masterpieces of the world in the great European galleries. In 1883 he was sent abroad by the *Century Magazine* for this purpose and remained there for 28 years, returning in 1910 to undertake the commission to engrave paintings in American galleries. He died in Poughkeepsie, N. Y., 1931.

An engraving by Timothy Cole, after this painting, is in this collection [acc. no. 422]. Measuring 6⁹/₁₆" x 5¹/₄", it is signed Timothy Cole, and inscribed, T·COLE·Sc·VENICE·MAR·1892 AFT PAINT·BY WYATT EATON. The engraving is included in the catalogue raisonné of Cole's work [see ref. Smith (1925), no. 260, as Timothy Cole (Man with Violin)].

The painting has also been known as *Man with Violin*.

EXHIBITIONS: A.G.T., *Loan exhibition*, 1935, no. 97.

REFERENCES: Morris, *The early painters* (n.d.), p. 31 (says painted in Florence in 1885; says "this was much exhibited under the title 'Man with Violin'"); *Canada and its provinces*, vol. 12, (1914), p. 606; Smith, *Cole* (1925), frontispiece (reprod.); MacTavish (1925), p. 31.

Gift by Subscription, 1909.

406   Timothy Cole (1852-1931)

Eskimo
Peter MATHUSIE

Carver from Povungnituk.

57/19   **Hunter**

Eskimo
MUNGITUK (1935-   )

Graphic artist from Cape Dorset, Baffin Island. His prints often portray violence and his wild dreams.

Eskimo
NIVIAKSIAK (1920-1959)

Carver from Cape Dorset, Baffin Island. Died mysteriously while out hunting [see ref. Swinton, *Eskimo sculpture* (1965), p. 200].

104

57/19

HUNTER   1957

Soapstone and bone, 16¼″ high.

PROV.: [Canadian Handicrafts Guild, Toronto].

REFERENCES: Brieger, Vickers and Winter, *Art and Man*, III (1964), p. 186, fig. 212 (reprod.); Swinton, *Eskimo sculpture* (1965), p. 55 (reprod.; dated 1957).

Gift from the Fund of T. Eaton Co. Ltd. for Canadian Works of Art, 1958.

59/25

MAN CARRIED TO THE MOON   1959

Stone cut, 20¾″ x 15¹⁵/₁₆″ [sight].
Signed (lower right) [monogram].
Inscribed (across bottom, in pencil): Man carried to the Moon Stone Block 16/50 Cape Dorset Baffin Island 1959 Mungituk.

PROV.: Department of Northern Affairs, Ottawa (through Gallery Shop, A.G.T.).

REFERENCES: *Eskimo Graphic Art* [catalogue of prints produced in 1959], no. SC-21 (reprod.); *Vie des Arts*, no. 18 (Spring, 1960), p. 36 (reprod.); Brieger, Vickers and Winter, *Art and Man*, III (1964), p. 187, fig. 213 (reprod.).

Gift from the McLean Foundation, 1960.

59/23

POLAR BEAR AND CUB IN ICE   1959

Sealskin stencil, 11″ x 19⅞″ [sight].
Signed (lower left) [monogram].
Inscribed (across bottom, in pencil): Polar Bear and Cub in Ice Skin

Stencil 30/7 Cape Dorset Baffin Island June 1959 Niviaksiak.

PROV.: Department of Northern Affairs, Ottawa (through Gallery Shop, A.G.T.).

REFERENCES: *Eskimo Graphic Art* [catalogue of prints produced in 1959], no. SS-12 (reprod.).

Gift from the McLean Foundation, 1960.

59/24

MAN HUNTING AT SEAL HOLE IN THE ICE   **1959**

Sealskin stencil, 21″ x 15″ [sight].
Signed (upper left) [monogram].
Inscribed (across bottom, in pencil): Man Hunting at a Seal Hole in the Ice Skin Stencil 30/8 Cape Dorset Baffin Island May 1959 Niviaksiak.

PROV.: Department of Northern Affairs, Ottawa (through Gallery Shop, A.G.T.).

REFERENCES: *Eskimo Graphic Art* [catalogue of prints produced in 1959], no. SS-11 (reprod.); *Canadian Art*, vol. XVII (Jan., 1960), p. 12, no. 14 (reprod.); *Texas Quarterly*, vol. VII (Spring, 1964), p. 92 (reprod.); Houston, *Eskimo prints* (1967), p. 20 (reprod. in colour).

Gift of the McLean Foundation, 1960.

Eskimo
OSHAWEETUK (1923-   )

Carver from Cape Dorset, Baffin Island. Made a carving of the Queen which was presented to her during her visit to Canada in 1959.

59/27

FOUR MUSKOXEN   **1959**

Sealskin stencil, 11⁹/₁₆″ x 23¹/₂″ [sight].
Signed (lower left) [monogram].
Inscribed (across bottom, in pencil): Four Muskoxen Skin Stencil 30/17 Cape Dorset Baffin Island 1959 Oshaweetuk.

PROV.: Department of Northern Affairs, Ottawa (through Gallery Shop, A.G.T.).

REFERENCES: *Eskimo Graphic Art* [catalogue of prints produced in 1959], no. SS-18 (reprod.); *Canadian Art*, vol. XVII (Jan., 1960), p. 13, no. 16 (reprod.); Houston, *Eskimo prints* (1967), p. 11 (reprod.).

Gift from the McLean Foundation, 1960.

Eskimo
POOTAGOK (1889-1959)

Graphic artist and carver from Cape Dorset, Baffin Island.

59/28

WOMAN WITH MUSICAL INSTRUMENT   **1959**

Stone cut, 16″ x 19¹⁵/₁₆″ [sight].
Signed (upper right) [monogram].
Inscribed (across bottom, in pencil): Woman With Musical Instrument Stone Cut 11/50 Cape Dorset Baffin Island 1959 Pootagnuk [sic].

PROV.: Department of Northern Affairs, Ottawa (through Gallery Shop, A.G.T.).

REFERENCES: *Eskimo graphic art* [catalogue of prints produced in 1959], no. SC-23 (reprod.).

Gift from the McLean Foundation, 1960.

Eskimo
TUDLIK (1888-   )

Carver from Cape Dorset, Baffin Island. Well known for his many and varied carved owls. Tudlik is now blind.

John K. ESLER (1933-   )

BORN: John Kenneth Esler, Pilot Mound, Manitoba, January 11, 1933.

LIVES: Winnipeg.

STUDY: University of Manitoba, School of Art, 1956-60.

Began printmaking seriously in 1962.

TEACHING: Instructor of Graphic Arts, College of Art, Calgary, Alberta.

Sorel ETROG (1933-   )

BORN: Jassy, Roumania, August 29, 1933.

LIVES: Toronto. Came to Canada (Toronto) in 1961.

STUDY: Roumania, 1949-50, with Lobel; Israel, 1950, Institute of painting and sculpture, Tel Aviv, under Eugene Kolb, and at the artists' village of Ein Hood, under Marcel Janco, 1952-55.

AWARDS: 1958-63, awarded scholarship to the Brooklyn Museum, New York.

Sculptor.

59/26

BIRD DREAM FOREWARNING BLIZZARDS   1959

Stone cut, 19" x 14$\frac{1}{2}$" [sight].
Signed (lower right, on margin) [monogram].
Inscribed (across bottom, in pencil): Bird Dream Forewarning Blizzards Stone Block 30/9 Cape Dorset Baffin Island 1959 Tudlik.

PROV.: Department of Northern Affairs, Ottawa (through Gallery Shop, A.G.T.).

REFERENCES: *Eskimo Graphic Art* [catalogue of prints produced in 1959], no. SC-16 (reprod.); *Canadian Art*, vol. XVII (Jan., 1960), p. 15, no. 20 (reprod. in colour): *Vie des Arts*, no. 18 (Spring, 1960), p. 37 (reprod.); *Canadian Art*, vol. XX (May-June, 1963), p. 166 (reprod.).

Gift from the McLean Foundation, 1960.

64/70

MONUMENT NO. 2   1964

Soft ground etching, Imp.: 23$\frac{7}{8}$" x 17$\frac{3}{4}$".
Signed and dated (lower right, in pencil): John K. Esler/64.
Inscribed (lower left, in pencil): Monument No. 2.
Numbered (lower centre, in pencil): 11/15.

PROV.: [Dorothy Cameron Gallery, Toronto].

EXHIBITIONS: Winnipeg, *Esler*, 1964, no. 2 (reprod.); Dorothy Cameron Gallery, *Canadian printmaking today*, 1965, reprod. in colour.

[NOTE: Impression of this print has been exhibited also, Winnipeg, *9th Winnipeg Show*, 1964.]

REFERENCES: *Canadian Art*, vol. XXII (Sept., 1965), p. 10 (reprod.).

Gift from Anonymous Fund, 1965.

59/4

SEA BIRD   1959

Painted terracotta, 11$\frac{3}{4}$".
PROV.:[Gallery Moos, Toronto].

EXHIBITIONS: Gallery Moos, *Etrog*, 1959 (Oct. 2-14) [not listed in exhibition pamphlet].

REFERENCES: Withrow, *Etrog* (1967), p. 52 (reprod.).

Gift of Mr. and Mrs. T. M. Sterling, 1959.

60/48

PREGNANT WOMAN   1960-61

Bronze, 9$\frac{3}{8}$".
Signed and numbered (underside): ETROG 1/4.

PROV.: [Gallery Moos, Toronto].

EXHIBITIONS: Gallery Moos, *Etrog*, 1961 (Feb. 25 - Mar. 12) [not listed in exhibition pamphlet].

REFERENCES: Withrow, *Etrog* (1967), pp. 19, 20 (reprod.).

Gift of Mr. and Mrs. Walter Carsen, 1961.

64/30

SUNBIRD II   **1962-64**

Bronze, 80" (incl. base).
Signed and numbered (on base): étrog 1/5.

PROV.: [Gallery Moos, Toronto].

NOTES: Original model in plaster, cast by Racine Foundry.

A bronze *Study for Sunbird II* is in the collection of the Kunstmuseum, Basel, Switzerland.

EXHIBITIONS: Gallery Moos, and others, *Etrog*, 1964-65 (Dec. 17 - Jan. 19) [not in catalogue but both plaster model and small bronze study are reproduced]; New York, Pierre Matisse Gallery, *Etrog*, 1965 (Feb. 16 - Mar. 13), no. 23, on cover (reprod. in colour), p. 2.

REFERENCES: Withrow, *Etrog* (1967), pp. 12, 44 (reprod.).

Purchase, Corporations' Subscription Endowment, 1965.

For embossed print by Etrog, see "Toronto 20", p. 453-457.

64/30   **Sunbird II**

Henry EVELEIGH (1909-   )

BORN: Shanghai, China, July 26, 1909.

LIVES: Montreal. Came to Canada in 1938.

STUDY: London, Slade School of Art, early 1930s; Paris, Ecole des Beaux-Arts.

SOCIETIES: Contemporary Art Society, Montreal.

TEACHING: Ecole des Beaux-Arts, Montreal, since 1947.

Painter, designer and educator.

2788

YOUNG GIRL   1943

Pencil on paper, 20″ x 14″ [sight].
Signed and dated (lower right): Eveleigh/43.

PROV.: [Eaton's Fine Art Galleries, Toronto].

Purchase, 1945.

2788   **Young Girl**

Marguerite FAINMEL (1910-   )

BORN: Marguerite Paquette Fainmel, Montreal, P. Q., June 4, 1910.

LIVES: Montreal.

STUDY: Ecole des Beaux-Arts, Montreal; Paris, Académie de la Grande Chaumière.

SOCIETIES: Contemporary Arts Society, Montreal; F.C.A.

2780

SHACKS   1941

Oil on board, $17^3/_8$″ x $23^1/_8$″ [sight].
Signed (upper right): M. FAINMEL.

PROV.: [Eaton's Fine Art Galleries, Toronto].

EXHIBITIONS: [?] A.G.T., *Fainmel*, 1943 (Feb.).

Purchase, 1945.

2780   **Shacks**

Barker FAIRLEY (1887-   )

BORN: Barnsley, Yorkshire, England, May 21, 1887.

LIVES: Toronto. Came to Canada in 1910.

STUDY: No formal training; began to paint in 1931, through the encouragement of Robert Finch, John Hall and others; was closely associated with members of the Group of Seven.

ACTIVITY: Professor Emeritus in German Department, University of Toronto, and an eminent authority on Goethe. Retired in 1957.

Mary Harris FILER (1920-   )

BORN: Edmonton, Alberta, December 31, 1920.

LIVES: Aldington, Kent; in England since 1957.

STUDY: Regina, Saskatchewan, Balfour Technical School, 1939-41, commercial art under Garnet Hazard; 1944-46, Art Association of Montreal, School of Art and Design, under Arthur Lismer, Goodridge Roberts, de Tonnancour and others; 1948-50 McGill University, Fine arts, and painting and drawing under John Lyman.

SOCIETIES: Contemporary Arts Society, Montreal, 1948; F.C.A.; C.S.G.A., 1949.

TEACHING: Lecturer in fine arts, McGill University, 1948-52; 1953-55, teacher in art education, Pennsylvania State University; 1955-56, taught at New York University as professor of art education.

Mural, Montreal Neurological Institute, McGill, 1954.

Augustin FILIPOVIC (1931-   )

BORN: Davor, Croatia-Yugoslavia, January 8, 1931.

LIVES: Toronto. Came to Canada in 1959.

STUDY: Zagreb, Yugoslavia, Artistic Lyceum, for five years; 1950-52 at the Academy of Fine Arts, Zagreb; Rome, Academy of Fine Arts, 1952-54.

62/11
PORTRAIT OF A. Y. JACKSON   1939

Oil on panel, $14\frac{1}{4}$" x $11\frac{1}{4}$".
Signed (upper right): BARKER FAIRLEY

PROV.: the artist.

NOTES: Painted while on a canoe trip, August, 1939. [For full details, see ref. A.G.T., *News and Notes*, April, 1963.]

For biography of sitter, see A.Y. Jackson, p. 205.

EXHIBITIONS: [?] Hart House, *Fairley*, 1956 (Mar. 11-17) [no catalogue].

REFERENCES: A.G.T., *News and Notes*, vol. 7 (April, 1963), reprod.

Purchase, 1962.

2876
GLOXINIA   1945

Water colour and ink on paper, 14" x $20\frac{1}{8}$" [sight].
Signed and dated (lower left): M. Filer '45.

PROV.: the artist [CSPWC, 1947].

EXHIBITIONS: *C.S.P.W.C.*, 1947, p. 2.

Purchase, 1947.

59/37
STUDY FOR A HEAD   1959

Plaster, 12"

PROV.: [Gallery Moos, Toronto].

EXHIBITIONS: Gallery Moos, *Filipovic*, 1960 (Mar. 22 - Apr. 8) [no catalogue].

Gift of A. M. Wilson, 1960.

51/19   **Pritchard's Fence**
Colour reproduction, p. 542

51/19

PRITCHARD'S FENCE   c. 1928

Oil on canvas, $28^3/_{16}$" x $30^1/_8$".
Signed and dated (lower right): L. L. FITZGERALD/192[8].

PROV.: the artist [Dominion Gallery, Montreal].

EXHIBITIONS: Vancouver, *Group of Seven*, 1954, no. 20 (reprod.);
A.G.O. [circulating exhibition], *Canadian paintings of the 1930s*,
1967-68, no. 7 (reprod.).

REFERENCES *Canadian Art*, vol. IX (Christmas, 1951-52), p. 59
(reprod.; collection of Dominion Gallery]; A.G.T., *Painting and
sculpture* (1959), p. 53 (reprod.).

Bequest of Isabel E. G. Lyle, 1951.

56/32

RAIN SQUALL   c. 1941

Pencil on paper, $11^7/_{16}$" x $14^1/_2$" [sight].
Inscribed (on reverse): 10 Rain Squall/Fitzgerald/probably 1941.

PROV.: [Picture Loan Society, Toronto].

EXHIBITIONS: Winnipeg, and others, *Fitzgerald memorial*, 1958, no.
17; A.G.T., *Canadian drawings*, 1960.

Gift from J. S. McLean, Canadian Fund, 1957.

56/26

FROM THE VERANDA, BOWEN ISLAND   1943

Water colour on paper, $23^5/_8$" x $17^3/_4$" [sight].
PROV.: Mrs. Felicia LeM. Fitzgerald, Winnipeg.

Gift from J. S. McLean, Canadian Fund, 1957.

48/36

HIGH TIDE   1948

Pen and ink on paper, $11^1/_2$" x $16^1/_2$".
Dated (lower left): 28.1.48.

PROV.: the artist.

EXHIBITIONS: A.G.T., *Canadian drawings*, 1960.

Gift from the Albert H. Robson Memorial Subscription Fund, 1949.

48/37

STILL LIFE WITH REFLECTOR   1948

Pen and ink on paper, 12" x 18".
Signed and dated (lower right): L. L. F. 48.
Dated (on reverse, in pencil): 24·7·48.

PROV.: the artist.

Gift from the Albert H. Robson Memorial Subscription Fund, 1949.

52/30

SNOW I   **1950**

Pencil on paper, $17^5/_8$" x $23^5/_8$" [sight].
Signed (lower left): L. L. FITZGERALD.
Inscribed and dated (on reverse): Drawn 22nd March, 1950.

PROV.: the artist.

EXHIBITIONS: A.G.T., *Canadian drawings*, 1960.

Gift from the Fund of the T. Eaton Co. Ltd. for Canadian Works of Art, 1953.

52/31

SNOW II   **1950**

Pencil on paper, 24" x 18".
Signed and dated (lower left): L. L. FITZGERALD/6·1·50.

PROV.: the artist.

EXHIBITIONS: Winnipeg, and others, *Fitgerald memorial*, 1958, no. 39 (reprod.); A.G.T., *Drawings*, 1963, p. 3.

Gift from the Fund of the T. Eaton Co. Ltd. for Canadian Works of Art, 1953.

52/52

BARLOWE'S GARAGE   **1950**

Water colour on paper, $25^5/_8$" x $18^5/_8$".
Signed and dated (lower left): L. L. FITZGERALD/20-3-50.

PROV.: the artist.

EXHIBITIONS: *C.N.E.*, 1953, no. 28; Winnipeg, and others, *Fitzgerald memorial*, 1958, no. 41.

REFERENCES: Duval (1954), pl. 42 (reprod.).

Gift from the Fund of the T. Eaton Co. Ltd. for Canadian Works of Art, 1953.

56/31

FLOODED LANDSCAPE   **1956**

Pen and ink on blue paper. $12^{13}/_{16}$" x $14^7/_8$".
Signed (lower right): L. L. F.
Dated (on margin, lower right): 4·5·56.

PROV.: [Picture Loan Society, Toronto].

NOTES: According to Mr. Douglas Duncan, Picture Loan Society, this drawing was done during the floods in the spring of 1956.
Title changed from *Landscape on Blue* to *Flooded Landscape*, 1957.

EXHIBITIONS: Winnipeg, and others, *Fitzgerald memorial*, 1958, no. 58 (reprod. in colour); A.G.T., *Canadian drawings*, 1960; Stratford, 1962, Fitzgerald, no. 24; A.G.T., *Drawings*, 1963, p. 3.

Gift from J. S. McLean, Canadian Fund, 1957.

52/52   Barlowe's Garage

Kenneth FORBES (1894-   )

BORN: Kenneth Keith Forbes, Toronto, 1894, son of John Colin Forbes.

LIVES: Toronto.

STUDY: London, St. John's Wood Art School; Newlyn Art School, Cornwall, under Stanhope Forbes; Hospital Field Art School, Arbroath, Scotland, for four years; Slade School, London, under Henry Tonks; New Art School, London.

Returned to Canada, 1924.

SOCIETIES: O.S.A., 1929, resigned 1951; A.R.C.A., 1928, R.C.A., 1933, resigned, 1959.

Figure and portrait painter.

273

THE YELLOW SCARF   1924

Oil on canvas, 24¹/₈" x 20¹/₈".
Signed and dated (lower right): K. K. Forbes/1924.

NOTES: Permanent loan from C.N.E. Association, 1926-65.

EXHIBITIONS: *C.N.E.*, 1925, no. 272; *O.S.A.*, 1925, no. 55; Ottawa, *Central Canada Exhibition*, 1926, no. 16 (reprod.); London, Tate, 1938, no. 57; Stratford, *Faces of Canada*, 1964.

REFERENCES: *Canadian Forum*, vol. V (May, 1925), p. 242; A.G.T., *Painting and sculpture* (1959), p. 70 (reprod.).

Gift of the Canadian National Exhibition Association, 1965.

273   **The Yellow Scarf**
Colour reproduction, p. 541

62/16

BOY LYING IN GRASS   1891

Oil on panel. 4" x 5¹/₂".
Signed and dated (lower right): H. F. 91.

Gift of Mrs. G. A. Reid, 1963.

Harriet FORD (1859-1939)

BORN: Harriet Mary Ford, Brockville, Ontario, 1859.

DIED: In England where she was long a resident.

STUDY: Toronto, Central Ontario School of Art and Design; St. John's Wood Art School, London; Royal Academy Schools, London; Paris, Académie Colarossi.

SOCIETIES: O.S.A., 1895, resigned, then re-elected, 1911; A.R.C.A., 1895.

62/16   **Boy Lying in Grass**

J. W. L. FORSTER (1850-1938)

BORN: John Wycliffe Lowes Forster, Norval, Ontario, December 31, 1850. Moved to Toronto, 1869.

DIED: Toronto, April 24, 1938.

STUDY: Toronto, under J. W. Bridgman; Paris, Julian Academy, 1879, under Lefebvre and Boulanger; for three years, 1880-82, in Paris, with Bouguereau and Tony Robert-Fleury; and later in Paris, 1882, under Carolus Duran.

SOCIETIES: O.S.A., 1883; A.R.C.A., 1884.

Portrait painter.

54/17   **Portrait of Senator G. A. Cox (1840-1914)**

2521

THE VISION OF NANBOZHOO

Oil on canvas, $48^{1}/_{8}$" x $63^{1}/_{4}$".
Signed (lower right): J. W. L. FORSTER.

Bequest of J. W. L. Forster, 1938.

55/20

RUSH LAKE, MÉGANTIC, P. Q.

Oil on board, $7^{1}/_{2}$" x $12^{1}/_{4}$".
Signed (lower left centre): FORSTER.

NOTES: Mégantic is located in the Eastern Townships, directly south of Quebec, and east of Sherbrooke.

Gift of George E. Kingsford, 1955.

54/17

PORTRAIT OF SENATOR G. A. COX (1840-1914)   c. 1910

Oil on canvas, $48^{1}/_{2}$" x $36^{3}/_{8}$".
Signed (lower right): J W L FORSTER.

NOTES: George Albertus Cox (1840-1914), appointed Senator of Canada in 1896, was regarded as one of the powerful interests behind the Laurier government of 1896-1911. He was one of the outstanding capitalists of Eastern Canada. [see *Macmillan Dictionary of Canadian Biography*, 1963, p. 159].

Gift of Central Canada Investments Limited, 1955.

115

Michael FORSTER (1907-   )

BORN: Calcutta, India, May 4, 1907.

LIVES: Ottawa. Came to Canada in 1928.

STUDY: London, under Bernard Meninsky and William Roberts; also in Paris and New York.

SOCIETIES: F.C.A.; C.S.G.A.

Official war artist, with the Royal Canadian Navy, 1943.

2732

STILL LIFE   **1939**

Pen and ink on paper, 11″ x 14³/₈″.
Signed and dated (upper left): F. 1939 —.

PROV.: the artist [AGT, 1943].

EXHIBITIONS: [?] *C.S.G.A.*, 1940; A.G.T., *Tacon, Faunt, Forster, and Webber*, 1943; Windsor, and others, *Canadian drawing*, 1953-54, no. 43.

Purchase, 1943.

2589

LOGS IN SNOW   **1942**

Gouache on paper, 21⁵/₈″ x 26⁵/₈″ [sight].
Signed and dated (lower right): F./1942.

PROV.: the artist [CGP, 1942].

EXHIBITIONS: *C.G.P.*, 1942, no. 91; Andover, Mass., 1942, no. 21; *D.P.C.*, 1945, no. 232.

REFERENCES: Duval (1954), pl. 56 (reprod.).

Purchase, 1942.

2589   **Logs in Snow**

Michel FORTIER (1943-   )

BORN: Montreal, December 31, 1943.

LIVES: Montreal.

STUDY: Montreal, Ecole des Beaux-Arts, under Dumouchel; Atelier libre de recherches graphiques, Montreal, under Richard Lacroix.

SOCIETIES: Montreal, Graphic Guild.

66/44

LE PÉRIL JAUNE   **1966**

Serigraph, Imp.: 16¹/₁₆″ x 16″.
Signed and dated (lower right, in ink): Michel Fortier '66.
Inscribed (right centre, in ink): le/péril/jaune.
Numbered (lower left, in ink): 25/75.

PROV.: [Gallery Pascal, Toronto].

EXHIBITIONS: Gallery Pascal, *Canadian Printmakers '67*, 1967 (May 4-30) [no catalogue].

Purchase, 1967.

Marc-Aurèle FORTIN
(1888-   )

BORN: Sainte-Rose, Quebec, March 14, 1888.

LIVES: Sainte-Rose.

STUDY: Montreal, Plateau School, under Ludger Larose; Montreal, Monument National, under Edmond Dyonnet; Chicago, school of the Art Institute of Chicago, 1909; also Boston and New York.

SOCIETIES: A.R.C.A., 1942.

TRAVEL: Europe, 1920-22, and again in 1935.

Landscape painter in water colour, and etcher.

2314

LANDSCAPE AT HOCHELAGA   1932

Water colour on paper, $12^{15}/_{16}$" x $19^{3}/_{4}$" [sight].
Signed (lower left): M A Fortin.

PROV.: the artist [CSPWC, 1935].

NOTES: Many versions, mostly in water colour, of this subject exist. This one was painted in the summer of 1932.

EXHIBITIONS: [?] N.G.C., *Annual*, 1932, no. 64; [?] *C.G.P.*, 1933, no. 99; *C.S.P.W.C*, 1935, no. 48; *C.N.E.*, 1935, no. 432; A.G.T., *Summer*, 1935, no. 83; A.G.T., *Loan exhibition*, 1935, no. 227; New York, National Arts Club, 1945 (Mar.-June) [no catalogue]; N.G.C., *Fortin*, 1964, no. 93.

REFERENCES: Barbeau (1946), p. 12; Duval (1954), pl. 67 (reprod.; dated c. 1930).

Purchase, 1935.

2314   **Landscape at Hochelaga**

1423

LIBRARY SPIRE, OTTAWA   1914

Etching, Imp.: $2^{7}/_{16}$" x $5^{1}/_{2}$". Paper: $3^{7}/_{8}$" x $6^{7}/_{8}$".
Signed and dated (lower right centre, in pencil): Ernest Fosbery/May 1914.

Gift of Sir Edmund Walker Estate, 1926.

1520

VIEW OF OTTAWA FROM THE RIVER   1914

Etching, Imp.: $5^{5}/_{16}$" x $12^{15}/_{16}$". Paper: $8^{11}/_{16}$" x $16^{1}/_{2}$".
Signed and dated (lower right centre, in pencil): Ernest Fosbery/May 19th 1914.

Gift of Sir Edmund Walker Estate, 1926.

Ernest FOSBERY (1874-1960)

BORN: Ernest George Fosbery, Ottawa, December 29, 1874.

DIED: Cowansville, P. Q., February 7, 1960.

STUDY: Ottawa Art School, under Franklin Brownell; Paris, under Fernand Corman.

SOCIETIES: A.R.C.A., 1912; R.C.A., 1929, P.R.C.A., 1943-48.

TEACHING: Headmaster, Art Students' League, Buffalo, 1907-11, and instructor, Arts Guild of Buffalo, 1910-11. Returned to Ottawa, 1911, and taught at Ottawa Art Association; from 1920, taught the R.C.A. life classes in Ottawa, and taught at Ottawa Technical High School, 1934-41.

Official war artist for the Canadian Army, 1918.

Best known as portrait painter.

PROV.: Mrs. I. J. Christie, Toronto [daughter of the artist].

NOTES: See above, acc. no. 622.

EXHIBITIONS: A.G.T., *Drawings*, 1963, p. 3, Kitchener, *Fowler*, 1967, no. 12.

Gift of Mrs. I. J. Christie, 1921.

627

BY A POND IN KNOLE PARK   1837

Pencil, charcoal and white gouache on paper, $9^1/_2$" x $13^1/_4$".
Signed and dated [at a later date] (lower left): D. FOWLER 1875.
Inscribed and dated (lower left): Knole/5th Sepr 37.

PROV.: Mrs. I. J. Christie, Toronto [daughter of the artist].

NOTES: See above, acc. no. 622.

Gift of Mrs. I. J. Christie, 1921.

608

FIGURE STANDING BY BEECH TREE, KNOLE   1837

Charcoal and pencil, heightened with white on paper, $9^5/_{16}$" x $13^3/_{16}$".
Signed and dated [at a later date] (lower left): D. FOWLER/1874.
Inscribed and dated (lower right): Knole, 5th Sep^r/37.

PROV.: Mrs. I. J. Christie, Toronto [daughter of the artist].

NOTES: See above, acc. no. 622.

EXHIBITIONS: Windsor, and others, *Canadian drawing*, 1953-54, no. 6.

Gift of Mrs. I. J. Christie, 1921.

618

OAK TREE IN KNOLE PARK   1837

Charcoal and gouache on paper, $9^3/_{16}$" x $13^1/_8$".
Inscribed and dated (lower right): Knole, 5th Sepr 37.

PROV.: Mrs. I. J. Christie, Toronto [daughter of the artist].

NOTES: See above, acc. no. 622.

Gift of Mrs. I. J. Christie, 1921

616

DEAD TREE STUDY, KNOLE   1837

Pencil, charcoal and gouache on paper, $13^1/_4$" x $9^5/_{16}$".
Inscribed and dated (lower left): Knole, 6th Sepr 37.

PROV.: Mrs I. J. Christie, Toronto [daughter of the artist].

NOTES: See above, acc. no. 622.

EXHIBITIONS: A.G.T., *Drawings*, 1963, p. 3.

Gift of Mrs. I. J. Christie, 1921.

623

STROLLING THROUGH THE PARK AT KNOLE   **1837**

Pencil, charcoal and white gouache on paper, 13$\frac{1}{2}$" x 9$\frac{1}{4}$".
Signed and dated [at a later date] (lower right centre): D. FOWLER/
1869.
Inscribed and dated (lower left): Knole/7th Sep^r/37.

PROV.: Mrs. I. J. Christie, Toronto [daughter of the artist].

NOTES: See above, acc. no. 622.

Gift of Mrs. I. J. Christie, 1921.

620

SEATED FIGURE IN THE PARK AT KNOLE   **1837**

Pencil, charcoal and white gouache on paper, 13$\frac{5}{16}$" x 9$\frac{3}{16}$".
Inscribed and dated (lower left): Knole, 8th Sepr. 37.

PROV.: Mrs. I. J. Christie, Toronto [daughter of the artist].

NOTES: See above, acc. no. 622.

Gift of Mrs. I. J. Christie, 1921.

619

DEER IN THE PARK AT KNOLE   **1837**

Charcoal and gouache on paper, 13$\frac{1}{4}$" x 9$\frac{1}{4}$".
Inscribed and dated (lower right): Knole 9th Sepr 37.

PROV.: Mrs. I. J. Christie, Toronto [daughter of the artist].

NOTES: See above, acc. no. 622.

EXHIBITIONS: A.G.T., *Drawings*, 1963, p. 3.

Gift of Mrs. I. J. Christie, 1921.

621

STUDY OF TREE AT KNOLE   **1837**

Pencil heightened with white wash on paper, 13$\frac{7}{16}$" x 9$\frac{3}{8}$".
Inscribed and dated (lower left): Knole/13th Sepr 37.

PROV.: Mrs. I. J. Christie, Toronto [daughter of the artist].

NOTES: See above, acc. no. 622.

Gift of Mrs. I. J. Christie, 1921.

607

BEECH TREE, KNOLE PARK   **1837**

Pencil, charcoal and gouache on paper, 13$\frac{5}{16}$" x 9$\frac{1}{4}$".
Inscribed and dated (lower left): Knole/14th Sepr 37.

PROV.: Mrs. I. J. Christie, Toronto [daughter of the artist].

NOTES: See above, acc. no. 622.

Gift of Mrs. I. J. Christie, 1921.

WILDERNESS **1837**

Pencil, charcoal and white gouache on paper, 9$\frac{1}{2}$" x 12$\frac{7}{8}$".
Inscribed and dated (lower left): Wilderness 14th Sepr 37.

PROV.: Mrs. I. J. Christie, Toronto [daughter of the artist].

NOTES: Drawing of the park at Knole. See above, acc. no. 622.

Gift of Mrs. I. J. Christie, 1921.

614

MILL AT DOLGELLEY **1838**

Pencil on paper, heightened with white wash, 12$\frac{1}{2}$" x 8$\frac{3}{4}$".
Inscribed and dated (lower left centre): Mill/at Dolgelley/July 1838.

PROV.: Mrs I. J. Christie, Toronto [daughter of the artist].

NOTES: Dolgelley is the county town of Mérionethshire, situated in northwest Wales.

Gift of Mrs. I. J. Christie, 1921.

626

MILL AT DOLGELLEY **1838**

Pencil, charcoal and white gouache on paper, 12$\frac{1}{4}$" x 9$\frac{1}{8}$".
Signed and dated [at a later date] (lower left): D. Fowler 1873.
Inscribed and dated (lower left centre): Mill at Dolgelley/July 1838.

PROV.: Mrs. I. J. Christie, Toronto [daughter of the artist].

NOTES: See above, acc. no. 614.

EXHIBITIONS: Kitchener, *Fowler*, 1967, no. 13.

Gift of Mrs. I. J. Christie, 1921.

614　Mill at Dolgelley

615

FRIARS AT AYLESFORD **1839**

Pencil on paper, heightened with white gouache, 8$\frac{15}{16}$" x 13".
Inscribed and dated (lower centre): Friars at Aylsford [sic] / Aug' 1839.

PROV.: Mrs. I. J. Christie, Toronto [daughter of the artist].

NOTES: Aylesford, Kent, is situated 39 miles from London, near Maidstone.

Gift of Mrs. I. J. Christie, 1921.

601

DEAD GAME **1869**

Water colour on paper, 18$\frac{1}{2}$" x 26$\frac{3}{4}$" [sight].
Signed and dated (lower left): D. FOWLER 1869.

PROV.: James Spooner, Toronto; R. Y. Ellis, Toronto; Estate of R. Y. Ellis, Toronto.

601　**Dead Game**

EXHIBITIONS: [?] *O.S.A.*, 1873, no. 160; [?] *O.S.A.*, 1875, no. 32; *R.C.A.*, 1880, either no. 216 or 221 (lent by J. Spooner, Esq.); *C.N.E.*, 1903, either no. 211 or 212 (lent by James Spooner), opp. p. 19 (reprod.); Liverpool, *Festival of Empire*, 1910, no. 39 (lent by R. Y. Ellis); A.G.T., *4th loan exhibition...deceased Canadian artists*, 1911, no. 55 (property of R. Y. Ellis); A.G.T., *6th loan exhibition*, 1920, no. 38; A.G.T., *Summer*, 1935, no. 84; A.G.T., *Loan exhibition*, 1935, no. 228; *C.N.E.*, 1939, no. 73; London, Ont., *Milestones*, 1942, no. 12; *C.S.P.W.C.*, 1951, no. 2; *C.N.E.*, 1952, no. 37.

REFERENCES: Harper (1966), p. 182.

Gift of Mrs. H. D. Warren and Subscribers, 1919.

52/9

THE MOWER　　　　　　　　　　　　　　　　　**1871**

Water colour on paper, $7^7/_{16}$″ x $12^7/_8$″.
Signed (lower left centre): 1871 D. Fowler.

PROV.: Mrs. J. H. Birkenshaw, Toronto.

EXHIBITIONS: Kitchener, *Fowler*, 1967, no. 9.

REFERENCES: Duval (1954), pl. 10 (reprod.; dated c. 1870); *Canadian Art*, vol. XI (Winter, 1954), p. 71 (reprod.).

Gift from the Fund of the T. Eaton Co. Ltd. for Canadian Works of Art, 1952.

55/6

THE WHEELBARROW　　　　　　　　　　　　　　**1871**

Water colour on paper, $9^1/_8$″ x $13^1/_{16}$″ [sight].
Signed and dated (lower right): D Fowler 1871.

EXHIBITIONS: Kingston, *Fowler*, 1964, no. 25 (reprod.); Kitchener, *Fowler*, 1967, no. 8.

REFERENCES: *artscanada*, vol. XXIV, no. 115 (Dec., 1967), p. 13 (reprod.).

Bequest of Dr. John G. Lee, 1955.

55/6　**The Wheelbarrow**

596   Cactus

Albert Jacques FRANCK
(1899-   )

BORN: Middleburg, The Netherlands, April 2, 1899.

LIVES: Toronto. Came to Canada in 1926.

STUDY: No formal art training.

SOCIETIES: O.S.A., 1958; A.R.C.A., 1961; C.S.P.W.C; C.S.G.A.

Urban landscapes.

63/17   **Behind Power Street**

596

CACTUS   1875

Water colour on paper, 18⅝" x 13⅛" [sight].
Signed and dated (lower right): D. Fowler 1875.

EXHIBITIONS: [?] *O.S.A.*, 1875, no. 60; [?] A.G.T., *4th loan exhibition ...deceased Canadian artists*, 1911, no. 29; Kitchener, *Fowler*, 1967, no. 10.

Gift of Sir Edmund Osler, 1918.

1690

DEAD DUCK   1879

Water colour on paper, 12½" x 18¹¹⁄₁₆" [sight].
Signed and dated (lower right): D Fowler 1879.

EXHIBITIONS: A.G.T., *4th loan exhibition...deceased Canadian artists*, 1911, no. 62 (property of Dr. E. St. George Baldwin); *C.N.E.*, 1952, no. 36; Kingston, *Fowler*, 1964, no. 47; Kitchener, *Fowler*, 1967, no. 7.

Bequest of Dr. E. St. George Baldwin, 1931.

58/63

SHUTER STREET   1959

Oil on canvas, mounted on masonite, 26⅜" x 32¾".
Signed and dated (lower right): FRANCK '59.

PROV.: the artist [OSA, 1959].

EXHIBITIONS: *O.S.A.*, 1959, no. 26.

Canada Council Joint Purchase Award, 1959.

63/17

BEHIND POWER STREET   1963

Oil on masonite, 23¹⁵⁄₁₆" x 29¹⁵⁄₁₆".
Signed and dated (lower right): FRANCK '63.

PROV.: [Roberts Gallery, Toronto].

EXHIBITIONS: Roberts Gallery, *Franck*, 1963 (Nov. 13-23) [no catalogue].

REFERENCES: *Canadian Art*, vol. XXI (Mar.-Apr., 1964), p. 65 (reprod.).

Gift from the McLean Foundation, 1963.

J. A. FRASER (1838-1898)

BORN: John Arthur Fraser, London, England, 1838.

DIED: New York, 1898. Came to Canada in 1856.

STUDY: London, Royal Academy Schools, under F. W. Topham and Richard Redgrave.

Worked for the Montreal photographer, Notman, in 1860, and was made a partner, in charge of the Toronto branch in 1868.

Left Canada for Chicago in 1883, and subsequently moved to Boston; visited England and Scotland in 1888 and exhibited at the Royal Academy in 1889.

SOCIETIES: O.S.A., founding member, 1872; R.C.A., charter member, 1880; Society of Canadian Artists, 1867; also American Water Color Society and New York Water Color Club.

593

THE HEART OF SCOTLAND   c. 1888

Water colour on paper, 36⅝" x 26⅞" [sight].

Signed (lower right): J A FRASER.

PROV.: Hon. George A. Cox, Toronto; H. C. Cox, Toronto.

NOTES: Awarded medals for this painting at Chicago World's Fair, 1893, and at Atlanta, 1895. [Not verified, see exhibition, Toronto, 1897].

EXHIBITIONS: Paris, *Salon*, 1891, no. 654; Chicago, *World's Columbian Exposition*, 1893, under United States, no. 1215; Atlanta, *International Exposition*, 1895, no. 194; Toronto, C. J. Townsend and Co., Auctioneers, *Water colours by John A. Fraser*, October 14, 1897, no. 46 (says "hung at Salon, 1891, in the best 'aqarelle' room, on a wall by itself, much admired by the critics. Medals, World's Fair, 1893; Atlanta, 1895."); *C.N.E.*, 1903, no. 228 (lent by Hon. Geo. A. Cox), opp. p. 21 (reprod.); *O.S.A. retrospective*, 1922, no. 57; A.G.T., *Summer*, 1935, no. 85; A.G.T., *Loan exhibition*, 1935, no. 229; *C.N.E.*, 1939, no. 75; *C.S.P.W.C.*, 1951, no. 3.

REFERENCES: Robson (1932), p. 33 (reprod. in colour).

Gift of H. C. Cox, 1918.

593   **The Heart of Scotland**

838

LONELY VILLAGE ON THE ST. LAWRENCE

Oil on canvas, 20$^1/_8$" x 26$^1/_4$".

Signed (lower left): Clarence A. Gagnon.

PROV.: the artist [AGT, 1926].

EXHIBITIONS: *R.C.A.*, 1923-24, no. 51 (as A Lonely Village on the North Shore); A.G.T., *Canadian painting*, 1926, no. 4; A.G.T., *Memorial...Gagnon, Beatty*, 1942, no. 37 (dated between 1915 and 1924, when artist was at Baie St. Paul); A.A.M., *Gagnon memorial*, 1942, no. 17; Quebec, *Gagnon*, 1942, no. 17; N.G.C., *Gagnon memorial*, 1942, no. 4; *R.C.A.*, 1954, retrospective, p. 38, no. 22; Kitchener, *Gagnon retrospective*, 1966, no. 2 (dated c. 1926).

REFERENCES: Robson, *Gagnon* (1938), p. 10.

Gift from the Reuben and Kate Leonard Canadian Fund, 1926.

896   Horse Racing in Winter, Quebec
Colour reproduction, p. 541

896

HORSE RACING IN WINTER, QUEBEC

Oil on canvas, 40$^3/_4$" x 51$^1/_2$".
Signed (lower left): Clarence. Gagnon.

PROV.: the artist [RCA, 1927-28].

EXHIBITIONS: [?] A.A.M., *Spring exhibition*, 1925, no. 116; Paris, 1927, no. 41; *R.C.A.*, 1927-28, no. 67; N.G.C., *Annual*, 1928, no. 51; St. Louis, 1930, no. 14, A.G.T., *Summer*, 1935, no. 32; A.G.T., *Loan exhibition*, 1935, no. 101; A.G.T., *Memorial...Gagnon, Beatty*, 1942, no. 43 (dated between 1924 and 1936 when artist was in Europe [?]); A.A.M., *Gagnon memorial*, 1942, no. 16; Quebec, *Gagnon*, 1942, no. 16; N.G.C., *Gagnon memorial*, 1942, no. 3; London, Ont., *Milestones*, 1942, no. 38; Kitchener, *Canadian classic*, 1959, no. 17; London, Ont., *The face of early Canada*, 1961; Bordeaux, 1962, no. 43, pl. XV (reprod.); Kitchener, *Gagnon retrospective*, 1966, no. 3 (dated c. 1927).

REFERENCES: Chauvin (1928), p. 236 (reprod.); A.G.T., *Bulletin* (May, 1928), p. 14 (reprod.); Hammond (1930), frontispiece (reprod. in colour); *American Magazine of Art*, vol. XXI (May, 1930), p. 270; A.G.T., *Special Education Bulletin*, ?[1931-32], reprod.; Robson (1932), p. 89 (reprod. in colour); *Studio*, vol. CXIV (Aug., 1937), p. 60 (reprod.); Robson, *Gagnon* (1938), pp. 10, 20-21, pl. V (reprod. in colour); A.G.T., *Canadian picture study* (1940), p. 17; *Saturday Night* (Oct. 31, 1942), p. 4 (reprod.); Colgate (1943), p. 137 (reprod.); A.G.T., *Painting and sculpture* (1959), p. 45 (reprod. in colour).

Gift from the Reuben and Kate Leonard Canadian Fund, 1927.

861

A LAURENTIAN HOMESTEAD

Oil on canvas, 20$^1/_8$" x 26$^1/_4$".
Signed (lower left): Clarence A. Gagnon.

PROV.: the artist.

861   **A Laurentian Homestead**

EXHIBITIONS: St. Louis, 1930, no. 13 (reprod.); A.G.T., and Ontario Department of Education, 1951, no. 23 (reprod.); Kitchener, *Canadian classic*, 1959, no. 18; Kitchener, *Gagnon retrospective*, 1966, no. 1 (dated c. 1927).

REFERENCES: Robson, *Gagnon* (1938), p. 10.

Gift from the Reuben and Kate Leonard Canadian Fund, 1927.

63/62

OXEN PLOUGHING, QUEBEC   1902

Dry-point, Imp.: $2^{15}/_{16}$" x $5^7/_{16}$". Paper, $4^3/_8$" x $7^1/_8$".
Signed and dated (lower right, in pencil): Clarence. A Gagnon 02.
Inscribed (lower left, in pencil): Oxen Ploughing Quebec.

EXHIBITIONS: A.G.T., *5th loan exhibition*, 1912, no. 276.

[NOTE: Impressions of this print have been exhibited also, London, *British Empire Exhibition*, 1924; *C.N.E.*, 1930; and in the Gagnon memorial exhibitions at Toronto, Montreal, Quebec, and Ottawa, 1942.]

Gift of Mr. and Mrs. Percy Waxer, 1964.

878

GRANADA   1906

Etching, Imp.: $3^7/_8$" x $4^7/_{16}$". Paper: $5^1/_{16}$" x $5^3/_4$".
Signed and dated (lower right, in pencil): Clarence A. Gagnon 06.
Inscribed (lower left, in pencil): Granada.

EXHIBITIONS: A.G.T., *5th loan exhibition*, 1912, no. 273 (lent by Frank Darling).

[NOTE: Impressions of this print have been exhibited also in the Gagnon memorial exhibitions in Toronto, Montreal, Ottawa, and Quebec, 1942.]

REFERENCES: *International Studio*, vol. LIV (Feb., 1915), p. 258 (reprod.).

Bequest of Frank Darling, 1923.

2494

RUE À CAUDEBEC   1906

Etching, Imp.: $8^1/_4$" x $5^5/_8$". Paper: $10^3/_8$" x $7^1/_4$".
Signed and dated (lower right, in pencil): Clarence A. Gagnon 06.
Inscribed (lower left, in pencil): Rue à Caudebec.

NOTES: Caudebec-en-Caux, Normandy, is situated on the Seine River, about mid-way between Le Havre and Rouen.

EXHIBITIONS: Toronto, *Canadian Art Club*, 1911, no. 24; Kitchener, *Canadian classic*, 1959, no. 21.

[NOTE: Impressions of this print have been exhibited also, A.G.T., *5th loan exhibition*, 1912; *C.N.E.*, 1930; and in the Gagnon memorial exhibitions at Toronto, Montreal, Quebec, and Ottawa, 1942.]

Gift of the Artist, 1938.

EXHIBITIONS: Toronto, *Canadian Art Club*, 1909, no. 24; Winnipeg Industrial Exhibition, *5th loan collection*, 1909, no. 51; A.G.T., *5th loan exhibition*, 1912, no. 261; Winnipeg, *R.C.A.*, 1912, no. 180.

[NOTE: Impressions of this print have been exhibited also in the Gagnon memorial exhibitions at Toronto, Montreal, Quebec, and Ottawa, 1942.]

Anonymous Gift, 1963.

62/72

CANAL DU LOING, MORET   1907

Etching, Imp.: $5^3/_4$" x $8^7/_{16}$". Paper: $7^3/_4$" x 10".
Signed and dated (lower right, in pencil): Clarence A. Gagnon 07.
Inscribed (lower left, in pencil): Canal du Loing Moret.
Numbered (lower left, in pencil): 1/50.

NOTES: Moret-sur-Loing is situated just a few miles south-east of Fontainebleau.

EXHIBITIONS: Toronto, *Canadian Art Club*, 1909, no. 25; Winnipeg Industrial Exhibition, *5th loan collection*, 1909, no. 50.

[NOTE: Impressions of this print have been exhibited also, *C.N.E.*, 1930; in Gagnon memorial exhibitions at Toronto, Montreal, Quebec, and Ottawa, 1942.]

REFERENCES: *International Studio*, vol. LIV (Feb., 1915), p. 259 (reprod.); Colgate (1943), p. 210.

Anonymous Gift, 1963.

62/73

PORTE DE BOURGOGNE, MORET   1907

Etching, Imp.: $8^3/_{16}$" x $5^7/_{16}$". Paper: $9^3/_4$" x $7^3/_4$".
Signed and dated (lower right, in pencil): Clarence A. Gagnon 07.
Inscribed (lower left, in pencil): Porte de Bourgogne Moret.
Numbered (lower left, in pencil): 1/50 FC.M.

NOTES: Moret-sur-Loing is situated just a few miles south-east of Fontainebleau.

EXHIBITIONS: Toronto, *Canadian Art Club*, 1909, no. 23; Winnipeg Industrial Exhibition, *5th loan collection*, 1909, no. 46.

[NOTE: Impressions of this print have been exhibited also in the Gagnon memorial exhibitions at Toronto, Montreal, Quebec, and Ottawa, 1942.]

Anonymous Gift, 1963.

62/75

ST. VALERY   1907

Etching, Imp.: $5^1/_2$" x $8^1/_4$". Paper: $7^1/_4$" x $10^1/_2$".
Signed and dated (lower right, in pencil): Clarence A. Gagnon 07.
Inscribed (lower left, in pencil): St. Valery.

NOTES: St. Valery-en-Caux, Normandy, is situated approximately fifteen miles west of Dieppe.

Anonymous Gift, 1963.

62/71

L'ORAGE **1907**

Etching, Imp.: $5^3/_4$" x $6^5/_8$". Paper: $7^9/_{16}$" x 9".
Signed and dated (lower right, in pencil): Clarence A. Gagnon 07.

NOTES: Impressions of this print have been exhibited in Gagnon memorial exhibitions at Toronto, Montreal, Ottawa, and Quebec, 1942.

Anonymous Gift, 1963.

62/74

CARRENAGE D'UN TERRENEUVAS, ST. MALO **1907**

Etching, Imp.: $5^3/_4$" x $8^1/_2$". Paper: $7^{11}/_{16}$" x $10^1/_8$".
Signed and dated (lower right, in pencil): Clarence A. Gagnon 07.
Numbered (lower left, in pencil): 1/50 FC.M.

NOTE: Impressions of this print have been exhibited in Gagnon memorial exhibitions at Toronto, Montreal, Ottawa, and Quebec, 1942.

Anonymous Gift, 1963.

2492

VIEUX MOULIN EN PICARDIE **1908**

Etching, Imp.: $9^1/_2$" x $7^5/_8$". Paper: $12^7/_8$" x 10".
Signed and dated (lower right, in pencil): Clarence A. Gagnon 08.
Inscribed (lower left, in pencil): Vieux Moulin en Picardie.

NOTES: Picardy, an old province of France, of which the capital was Amiens.

EXHIBITIONS: A.G.T., *5th loan exhibition*, 1912, no. 270; Winnipeg, *R.C.A.*, 1912, no. 181; London, *British Empire Exhibition*, 1925, Canadian section of fine arts, p. 8; London, Whitechapel Art Gallery, 1925, no. 137; A.G.T., *Canadian prints*, 1949.

[NOTE: Impressions of this print have been exhibited also, A.G.T., *7th loan exhibition*, 1920; *C.N.E.*, 1930; in Gagnon memorial exhibitions at Toronto, Montreal, Quebec, and Ottawa, 1942; Rio de Janeiro, 1944.]

REFERENCES: Duval (1952), reprod. in introduction.

Gift of the Artist, 1938.

2493

CANAL SAN AGOSTINO, VENICE **1908**

Etching, Imp.: $8^1/_4$" x $5^3/_4$". Paper: $9^{13}/_{16}$" x 8".
Signed and dated (lower right, in pencil): Clarence A. Gagnon 08.
Inscribed (lower left, in pencil): Canal San Agostino, Venise [sic].

Gerald GLADSTONE
(1929-   )

BORN: Toronto, January 7, 1929.

LIVES: Toronto

STUDY: Largely self-taught.

AWARDS: Canada Council grants, 1961-62, to England; and 1962-63, to New York.

Best known as sculptor; also does paintings and drawings.

58/57
GROWTH   1958

Welded steel, 58" high.

PROV.: [Greenwich Gallery, Toronto].

EXHIBITIONS: Toronto, Greenwich Gallery, [Group exhibition], 1959 (Jan.) [no catalogue]; A.G.T., *Four Canadians*, 1959, no. 2.

Gift from the McLean Foundation, 1959.

62/65
FEMALE GALAXY IN RECLINE   1961

Welded steel, 116" x 50" x 21".

PROV.: [Isaacs Gallery, Toronto]; Mr. and Mrs. S. J. Zacks, Toronto.

EXHIBITIONS: Isaacs Gallery, *Gladstone*, 1961 (Mar. 23 - Apr. 13) [no catalogue].

Gift of Mr. and Mrs. S. J. Zacks, 1963.

62/65   **Female Galaxy in Recline**

63/8
DRAWING NO. 71   1961

Brush and ink on paper, $10^{15}/_{16}$" x $14^7/_8$".
Signed (lower right centre): gladstone.

PROV.: [Dorothy Cameron Gallery, Toronto].

NOTES: According to the artist, this drawing was exhibited in London, 1961 [not verified].

EXHIBITIONS: Dorothy Cameron Gallery, *Gladstone*, 1963 (Feb. 9-26) [no catalogue].

Purchase, 1963.

63/7
DRAWING NO. 22   1962

Pencil on paper, $19^{11}/_{16}$" x $15^3/_4$" [sight].
Signed, dated and inscribed (lower right): gladstone 1962 London.

PROV.: [Dorothy Cameron Gallery, Toronto].

NOTES: According to the artist, this drawing was exhibited in London, 1961. [not verified].

EXHIBITIONS: Dorothy Cameron Gallery, *Gladstone*, 1963 (Feb. 9-26) [no catalogue].

Purchase, 1963.

64/6

GALAXY PAINTING I (LONDON SERIES)　　　　　　**1962**

Oil on canvas, 59" x 59".
Signed and dated (upper left): Gladstone 1962.

PROV.: the artist.

Gift from the Corporations' Subscription Fund, 1964.

64/6　　**Galaxy Painting I
(London Series)**

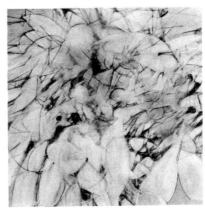

64/8　　**Galaxy Painting III (London
Series)**

64/7

GALAXY PAINTING II (LONDON SERIES)　　　　　　**1962**

Oil on canvas, 59" x 59".
Signed and dated (upper left): Gladstone/1962.

PROV.: the artist.

Gift from the Corporations' Subscription Fund, 1964.

64/8

GALAXY PAINTING III (LONDON SERIES)　　　　　　**1962**

Oil on canvas, 59" x 59".
Signed and dated (lower right): gladstone/1962.

PROV.: the artist.

Gift from Corporations' Subscription Fund, 1964.

Ted GODWIN (1933-   )

BORN: Calgary, Alberta, August 13, 1933.

LIVES: Regina, Saskatchewan, since 1958.

STUDY: Calgary, Provincial Institute of Technology and Art, 1951-55, with Illingworth H. Kerr; University of Saskatchewan Emma Lake workshops under Barnett Newman, John Ferren, Jules Olitski, and Lawrence Alloway.

TEACHING: University of Saskatchewan, Regina Campus, Assistant Professor of Art.

AWARDS: Canada Council grant 1962-63, to Greece.

64/79

"G" CORNERS   **1964**

Polymer on canvas, 53$^7/_8$" x 51".
Signed, dated and inscribed (on reverse): "G" CORNERS T. GODWIN FALL/64   CO-POLYMER ON CANVAS.

PROV.: the artist.

EXHIBITIONS: Charlottetown, *Directors' Choice*, 1967-68, no. 18 (as Glorious Corners).

Gift from the Georgia J. Weldon Estate and Canada Council Matching Grant, 1965.

64/79   **"G" Corners**

Charles GOLDHAMER (1903-   )

BORN: Philadelphia, Pennsylvania, August 21, 1903.

LIVES: Toronto. Came to Canada as a child.

STUDY: Toronto, Ontario College of Art, under J. E. H. MacDonald, Lismer, Reid, Manly, Beatty, and Varley.

SOCIETIES: O.S.A., 1933; C.S.P.W.C., 1936, Pres. 1941-43; C.P.E.; C.S.G.A.; Arts and Letters Club, Toronto.

TEACHING: Instructor, Ontario College of Art, 1926-28; since 1928 on staff of Central Technical School, Toronto.

Official war artist with R.C.A.F., 1943-46.

Figure and landscape painter, lithographer.

2552

INCOMING TIDE   **1939**

Water colour on paper, 11$^1/_{16}$" x 15$^1/_8$".
Signed (lower right): Charles Goldhamer.

PROV.: the artist [CSPWC, 1940].

EXHIBITIONS: *C.S.P.W.C.*, 1940; Quebec, *Exposition...O.S.A.*, 1944, no. 55 (as Morning Tide).

Purchase, 1940.

For lithographs by Goldhamer, see "Lithographs of Ontario" p. 257-258.

Sam GOODMAN (1919-1967)

BORN: George Samuel Goodman, Toronto, February 15, 1919.

DIED: New York, April 29, 1967.

Lived, worked and exhibited mostly in the United States where he was described as an avant garde artist of social protest.

Hortense M. GORDON (1887-1961)

BORN: Hortense Mattice, Hamilton, Ontario, November 24, 1887.

DIED: Hamilton, November 6, 1961. Married John Sloan Gordon, also a Hamilton artist.

STUDY: Mostly self-taught, though studied some in Paris, London and Vienna, and later under Hans Hofmann, in Provincetown, Mass.

SOCIETIES: A.R.C.A., 1930; C.S.G.A.; Painters Eleven, 1953.

TEACHING: From 1916, art instructor and later (1934) head of the art department, Hamilton Institute of Technology.

64/4   **Vertical Assemblage**

2765
ROOF TOPS   1944

Water colour and ink on paper, 18" x 14$^{13}/_{16}$".

PROV.: the artist [CSPWC, 1944].

EXHIBITIONS: *C.S.P.W.C.*, 1944, p. 3.

Purchase, 1944.

2866
LIGHT HOUSEKEEPING

Water colour on paper, 25$^3/_{16}$" x 19$^3/_{16}$" [sight].
Signed (upper left): HORTENSE M. GORDON.

PROV.: the artist [RCA, 1946].

EXHIBITIONS: *R.C.A.*, 1946, no. 49, p. 10 (reprod.); Hamilton, *Gordon memorial*, 1963, no. 32.

Purchase, 1946.

64/5
MUSIC IN SOLUTION

Gouache on cardboard, 39$^1/_2$" x 26$^1/_4$".
Signed (lower right): HORTENSE M GORDON.

PROV.: Mrs. A. B. Colerick, Chatham, Ontario.

NOTES: Written, on reverse, in ink: Painters Eleven, Montreal Museum of Fine Arts, Stable Gallery; and in pencil, 1958. [not verified].

Gift of the Heirs of the Hortense Mattice Gordon Estate, 1964.

64/4
VERTICAL ASSEMBLAGE   1949

Oil on canvas, 32" x 22".
Signed and dated (lower left): HORTENSE M. GORDON - 49 -.
Signed again (centre, upper left): HORTENSE M. G.
Inscribed (on reverse): 'VERTICAL ASSEMBLAGE'/HORTENSE M. GORDON - A.R.C.A.

PROV.: Mrs. A. B. Colerick, Chatham, Ontario.

NOTES: Label on reverse reads: O.S.A., 1949 - 77th annual exhibition. Written on stretcher: No. 29 AT MOOS GALLERY.

EXHIBITIONS: [?] *O.S.A.*, 1949, no. 30 (as Abstraction No. 1); [?] A.G.T., *Contemporary Canadian arts*, 1950, no. 46 (as Vertical Arrangement); [?] Toronto, Moos Gallery, *Gordon*, 1961 (Feb. 2-19) [no catalogue].

Gift of the Heirs of the Hortense Mattice Gordon Estate, 1964.

2463

LAKE, ALGONQUIN PARK

Oil on board, 12" x 15".

PROV.: the artist.

Gift from Friends of Canadian Art Fund, 1938.

2464

ALGOMA LAKE

Oil on panel, 10½" x 14".

PROV.: the artist.

EXHIBITIONS: London, Ont., *Group of Seven*, 1946 [exhibited, but not in catalogue].

Gift from Friends of Canadian Art Fund, 1938.

2468

BIRCH TREE

Oil on board, 10½" x 14".

PROV.: the artist.

Gift from Friends of Canadian Art Fund, 1938.

58/22

THE GAS WORKS   **1911-12**

Oil on canvas, 23 1/16" x 22 3/16".
Signed (lower right): LAWREN/HARRIS.

PROV.: the artist; [Laing Galleries, Toronto].

EXHIBITIONS: Laing Galleries, *Harris*, 1958 (Nov. 15-29) [no catalogue].

Gift from the McLean Foundation, 1959.

58/22   **The Gas Works**

2590

OLD HOUSES, TORONTO, WINTER   **1919**

Oil on canvas, 32½" x 38⅝".
Signed and dated (upper right): LAWREN/HARRIS/ 1919.

NOTES: Permanent loan from C.N.E. Association, 1942-65.
This painting was received from the artist in 1942, in exchange for *Snowfall*, purchased by the C.N.E. Association in 1921.

EXHIBITIONS: London, Ont., *Group of Seven*, 1946 [exhibited, but not in catalogue]; *C.N.E.*, 1950, no. 76; Edmonton, *Group of Seven*, 1955 [no catalogue; see Edmonton Museum of Arts, *Bulletin* (Jan., 1955), p. 2]; Victoria, *Group of Seven*, 1955, no. 21.

Gift of the Canadian National Exhibition Association, 1965.

2467

RED HOUSE AND YELLOW SLEIGH 1919

Oil on board, 10$^1/_2$" x 13$^1/_4$".

PROV.: the artist.

NOTES: Sketch for the painting, 36$^1/_4$" x 50", in the collection of The Vancouver Art Gallery.
Sketched in Toronto in 1919, on Spadina Avenue below College.

REFERENCES: Kilbourn (1966), p. 70 (reprod. in colour).

Gift from Friends of Canadian Art Fund, 1938.

2467 **Red House and Yellow Sleigh**
Colour reproduction, p. 538

48/9

ALGOMA COUNTRY c. 1919-20

Oil on canvas, 40$^1/_2$" x 50$^3/_{16}$".
Signed (lower right): LAWREN/HARRIS.

PROV.: the artist [AGT, 1948].

EXHIBITIONS: A.G.T., *Harris*, 1948, no. 26 [actually loaned by the artist to Emmanuel College]; *C.N.E.*, 1952, no. 129; Vancouver, *Group of Seven*, 1954, no. 23 (reprod.); Chautauqua, N. Y., *Group of Seven*, 1963.

Gift from the Fund of the T. Eaton Co. Ltd. for Canadian Works of Art, 1948.

2466

WHITE HOUSES c. 1920

Oil on board, 10$^1/_2$" x 13".
Signed (lower left): LAWREN/HARRIS.

PROV.: the artist.

NOTES: Sketch for large canvas, dated 1920, in the artist's collection, 1948; present whereabouts unknown.

EXHIBITIONS: London, Ont., *Group of Seven*, 1946 [exhibited, but not in catalogue]; A.G.T., *Harris*, 1948, no. 103.

Gift from Friends of Canadian Art Fund, 1938.

1320-A

DR. SALEM BLAND

1925

Oil on canvas, 40³/₄" x 36".
Signed and dated (lower right): LAWREN/HARRIS/1925.
Inscribed (on stretcher): PORTRAIT OF/DR. SALEM BLAND.

NOTES: Salem Goldworth Bland (1859-1950) was ordained Minister of the Methodist Church, 1884, and became a Minister of the United Church of Canada in 1925. He was a special writer on the *Toronto Daily Star*, and the author of several books. [see *Macmillan Dictionary of Canadian Biography*, 1963, p. 63].

EXHIBITIONS: *C.N.E.*, 1925, no. 284; A.G.T., *Group of Seven*, 1926, no. 26; Philadelphia, 1926, no. 1549; A.G.T., *Loan exhibition of portraits*, 1927, no. 163; N.G.C., *Annual*, 1927, no. 87; A.G.T., *Summer*, 1935, no. 33; A.G.T., *Loan exhibition*, 1935, no. 106; N.G.C., *Retrospective...Group of Seven*, 1936, no. 68 (reprod.); London, Tate, 1938, no. 82; London, Ont., *Milestones*, 1942, no. 59; Albany, 1946, no. 58 (reprod.); London, Ont., *Group of Seven*, 1946, no. 9; A.G.T., *Harris*, 1948, no. 37; *C.N.E.*, 1952, no. 7; N.G.C., and Vancouver, *Harris*, 1963, no. 14; N.G.C., *300 years of Canadian art*, 1967, no. 225, p. 139 (reprod.).

REFERENCES: A.G.T., *Bulletin* (Dec., 1929), p. 12 (reprod.); Brooker, *Yearbook* (1936), pl. 39 (reprod.); *Canadian Art*, vol. VI (Christmas, 1948), p. 50 (reprod.); A.G.T., *Painting and sculpture* (1959), p. 70 (reprod.); Vancouver Art Gallery, *Bulletin*, vol. XXX (Oct., 1963), inside cover (reprod.); on cover (reprod. detail); *Canadian Art*, vol. XXI (July/Aug., 1964), p. 194 (reprod.); Kilbourn (1966), p. 80 (reprod. in colour), p. 3 (detail).

Gift of the Toronto Daily Star, 1929.

1320-A **Dr. Salem Bland**

48/8　**Lake and Mountains**

48/8

LAKE AND MOUNTAINS　　　　　　　　　**1927-28**

Oil on canvas, 51$\frac{1}{2}$" x 63$\frac{1}{4}$".

PROV.: the artist [AGT, 1948].

NOTES: This painting has been called *Mountain Forms* in error. There are many versions of Rocky Mountain paintings by Harris, some of which are entitled Mountain Form, followed by an identifying number, as in a series.

EXHIBITIONS: *C.N.E.*, 1928, no. 351 (reprod.); [?] N.G.C., *Annual*, 1931, no. 103; New York, Roerich Museum, *Paintings by contemporary Canadian artists*, 1932, no. 14; N.G.C., *Retrospective... Group of Seven*, 1936, no. 76; San Francisco, 1939, p. 28, no. 8; A.G.T., *Harris*, 1948, p. 32, no. 40, pl. 11 (reprod.); M.M.F.A., *Lismer and Harris*, 1950 (June 14 - July 19) [no catalogue]; Vancouver, *Group of Seven*, 1954, no. 22 (reprod.).

REFERENCES: *R.A.I.C. Journal*, vol. V (Oct., 1928), p. 366 (reprod.); *Canadian Review of Music and Art*, vol. I (Oct., 1942), p. 10 (reprod.); A.G.T., *Accessions 1948-49*, reprod., *Saturday Night*, vol. 64 (Oct. 9, 1948), p. 2 (reprod.); N.G.C., and Vancouver Art Gallery, *Lawren Harris Retrospective*, 1963, p. 25 [not exhibited].

Gift from the Fund of the T. Eaton Co. Ltd. for Canadian Works of Art, 1948.

2459

ESKIMO TENT, PANGNIRTUNG, BAFFIN ISLAND　　**c. 1930**

Oil on board, 12" x 15".
Inscribed (on reverse): Eskimo Tent – Pangnirtung/Baffin Island –.

PROV.: the artist.

EXHIBITIONS: A.G.T., *Arctic paintings and sketches by A. Y. Jackson and Lawren Harris*, 1931, no. 404; London, Ont., *Group of Seven*, 1946 [exhibited, but not in catalogue].

Gift from Friends of Canadian Art Fund, 1938.

58/23

ABSTRACT SKETCH　　　　　　　　　　**c. 1940**

Oil on cardboard, 14$\frac{7}{8}$" x 12$\frac{1}{8}$".
Signed (lower right): LAWREN/HARRIS.
Inscribed (on reverse): abstract sketch/Lawren/Harris.

PROV.: [Laing Galleries, Toronto].

EXHIBITIONS: Laing Galleries, *Harris*, 1958 (Nov. 15-29) [no catalogue]; A.G.T., *Art and Engineering*, 1965, no. 9A (reprod.).

Gift from the McLean Foundation, 1959.

2555   **Ploughed Lands**

2744

3 R.D. BOMBING PRACTICE   **1943**

Gouache on paper, $15^{13}/_{16}$" x $22^{3}/_{4}$".
Inscribed (on boat, foreground): R.C.A.F. M438.

PROV.: the artist.

NOTES: Painted during a visit to the R.C.A.F. on the British Columbia
coast in the summer of 1943.

Purchase, 1943.

2745

OFFICERS MESS, ALLIFORD BAY   **1943**

Gouache on paper, $15^{7}/_{16}$" x $22^{13}/_{16}$".
Signed (lower right): B. COGILL./HAWORTH.

PROV.: the artist.

NOTES: Painted during a visit to the R.C.A.F. on the British Columbia
coast in the summer of 1943.

Purchase, 1943.

2746

FAIRMILES, ESQUIMALT   **1943**

Gouache on paper, 16" x $22^{7}/_{8}$".
Signed (lower right, in pencil): .B. COGILL./.HAWORTH.
Inscribed (on ships' bows, left to right): Q-067, Q-070, Q-071.

PROV.: the artist.

Purchase, 1943.

164

60/53

SANDERLINGS   **1960**

Water colour on paper, 14⅝" x 21⅞" [sight].
Signed (lower right): B. Cogill/Haworth.

PROV.: [Roberts Gallery, Toronto].

EXHIBITIONS: Roberts Gallery, *B. Cogill Haworth*, 1961 (Apr. 2/ -
May 9) [no catalogue].

Gift from the McLean Foundation, 1961.

60/54

GANNETS NO. 3   **1960**

Pencil and chalk on paper, 14$\frac{5}{16}$" x 10$\frac{9}{16}$" [sight].
Signed (lower right): B. Cogill./Haworth.
PROV.: [Roberts Gallery, Toronto].

EXHIBITIONS: Roberts Gallery, *B. Cogill Haworth*, 1961 (Apr. 2/ -
May 9) [no catalogue].

Canada Council Joint Drawings Purchase Fund, 1961.

Peter HAWORTH (1892-   )

BORN: Oswaldtwistle, Lancashire, England,
February 28, 1892.

LIVES: Toronto. Came to Canada in 1922.

STUDY: Manchester School of Art; Royal
College of Art, London, graduating 1922,
under Sir William Rothenstein, and Anning
Bell.

SOCIETIES: O.S.A., 1932, P.O.S.A. 1954-57;
A.R.C.A., 1946, R.C.A., 1954; C.S.P.W.C.,
1931, Pres. 1934-37; C.G.P., 1938; F.C.A.,
1942; Arts and Letters Club, Toronto.

TEACHING: Instructor, Central Technical
School, Toronto, since 1923, and Director
1929-55.

Painted during World War II in British Columbia and East coast ports.

Water colour painter, and designer in stained
glass.

53/20

NORTHERN LAKE

Water colour on paper, 19½" x 24⅝" [sight].
Signed (lower right): PETER - HAWORTH.

PROV.: the artist [CSPWC, 1954].

EXHIBITIONS: *C.S.P.W.C.*, 1954, no. 43.

Gift from the John Paris Bickell Bequest Fund, 1954.

2599

ONTARIO HOUSE   **1941**

Water colour on paper, 19$\frac{5}{16}$" x 24$\frac{11}{16}$" [sight].
Signed (lower right centre): PETER. HAWORTH.

PROV.: the artist [CSPWC, 1942].

NOTES: Label on reverse reads: ONTARIO FARM HOUSE, PEEL.

EXHIBITIONS: *C.S.P.W.C.*, 1942; *D.P.C.*, 1945, no. 178.

REFERENCES: *Saturday Night*, vol. 57 (July 11, 1942), p. 4 (reprod.);
Canadian Forum, vol. 22 (Feb., 1943), p. 325 (reprod.).

Purchase, 1942.

G. S. HAYWARD (1845-1926)

BORN: Gerald Sinclair Hayward, Port Hope, Ontario, January 22, 1845.

DIED: New York, March 31, 1926; buried at Gore's Landing, Rice Lake, Ontario.

STUDY: Encouraged in Toronto by Marmaduke Matthews, he went to England in 1870 and studied there.

Became a miniature painter of some note, and painted many prominent leaders of society in England. There he exhibited at the Royal Academy from 1879 to 1883. After a season in Boston, Hayward was living in New York, from about 1883. In 1889 an exhibition of 90 miniatures of prominent persons from Boston and New York society was shown in Mr. Samuel P. Avery's gallery.

Miniature painter.

640

PORTRAIT OF L. R. O'BRIEN, R. C. A. (1832-1899)   **1900**

Water colour on ivory, oval: $2^{7}/_{8}$" x $2^{5}/_{16}$" [sight].
Signed and dated (lower right): Gerald S Hayward 1900.

NOTES: Framed under glass in silver-gilt frame.

For biography of sitter, see O'Brien, p. 339.

Gift of Mrs. L. R. O'Brien, 1922.

640   **Portrait of L. R. O'Brien, R.C.A. (1832-1899)**

Henri HEBERT (1884-1950)

BORN: Montreal, April 3, 1884; son of sculptor, Philippe Hébert (1850-1917).

DIED: Montreal, May 11, 1950.

STUDY: School of the Art Association of Montreal under William Brymner, and Edmond Dyonnet; Paris, Ecole des Beaux-Arts, with Gabriel-Jules Thomas and Antoine Injalbert.

SOCIETIES: A.R.C.A., 1912; R.C.A., 1920; Pen and Pencil Club, Montreal, 1915.

TEACHING: Monument National, Montreal, and at McGill University.

Well known for his monument to Evangeline, at Grand Pré, and others.

Sculptor.

1337

HEAD OF ALPHONSE JONGERS   **1926**

Bronze, $12^{3}/_{4}$" high [$20^{1}/_{4}$" incl. base].
Signed, dated and inscribed (on back of neck): à l'ami Jongers/bien cordialement/Henri Hébert 1926.

PROV.: the artist.

NOTES: Alphonse Jongers (1872-1945), born in Mézières, France, studied in Paris, where he first became associated with Cullen and Suzor-Côté. In 1896, he came to Canada for the first time, comissioned to paint the portrait of the Marquis of Aberdeen, Governor-General at that time. He lived in New York from about 1900 to 1924, when he returned to Montreal, there to remain the rest of his life. He is best known as a portrait painter.

Two other castings of this piece, widely exhibited, are in the collections of the Musée du Québec, and the National Gallery of Canada, the latter catalogued and illustrated in N. G. C., *Catalogue of the Canadian School* (1960), p. 347, acc. no. 3521.

168

1337   **Head of Alphonse Jongers**

Robert HEDRICK (1930-   )

BORN: Windsor, Ontario, May 1, 1930.

LIVES: Toronto.

STUDY: H. B. Beal Technical School, London, Ont.; 1953, Instituto Allende, San Miguel, Mexico, with Rico Lebrun and James Pinto.

TEACHING; Toronto's New School of painting and sculpture.

AWARDS: Canada Council grant, 1961-62, to Spain; 1967.

Sculptor, painter.

Plaster cast from which these heads were cast belonged in 1929 to Ernest Cormier, architect.

EXHIBITIONS: *R.C.A.*, 1926-27, no. 160 (reprod.); A.G.T., *Exhibition of Canadian sculpture*, 1928, no. 59, p. 12 (reprod.).

REFERENCES: Chauvin (1928), pp. 51, 60 (reprod); A.G.T., *Bulletin* (Apr., 1929), p. 8 (reprod.); Brooker, *Yearbook of the arts in Canada 1928-29* (1929), pp. 77, 95; Colgate (1943), p. 126; *Canadian Art*, vol. X (Summer, 1953), p. 163 (reprod.); A.G.T., *Painting and sculpture* (1959), p. 67 (reprod.); Hubbard (1960), pl. 71 (reprod.).

Purchase, 1929.

61/30

BETWEEN SEASONS   1961

Oil on canvas, 80³/₁₆″ x 71⁵/₁₆″.
Signed and dated (lower right): hedrick 61.
Inscribed (on reverse): TITLE — BETWEEN SEASONS.

PROV.: [Isaacs Gallery, Toronto].

EXHIBITIONS: Isaacs Gallery, *Hedrick*, 1961 (Oct. 5-25) [no catalogue, but painting may be seen in background of photograph of artist reproduced on Isaacs Gallery poster, announcing exhibition].

Gift from the McLean Foundation, 1961.

61/30   **Between Seasons**

2540   **Portrait Study**

50/8

MY CADDY 1941

Oil on canvas, 24$\frac{1}{8}$" x 20$\frac{1}{8}$".
Signed (lower right): P. H.

PROV.: Mrs. A. R. G. Heward, Montreal.

EXHIBITIONS: *C.G.P.*, 1942, no. 52; New York, Grand Central Art Galleries, *Canadiana*, 1942, no. 265; N.G.C., *Heward memorial*, 1948, no. 17; A.G.T., and Ontario Department of Education, 1951, no. 5, on cover (reprod.); *C.N.E.*, 1952, no. 9.

REFERENCES: A.G.T., *Painting and sculpture* (1959), p. 75 (reprod.).

Gift of the Heward family, Montreal, 1950.

2800

STILL LIFE, AUTUMN 1944

Oil on canvas, 22" x 25".
Signed (upper right): P. HEWARD.
Inscribed and dated (on stretcher): P. HEWARD 1944.

PROV.: the artist [CGP, 1944].

EXHIBITIONS: *C.G.P.*, 1944; N.G.C., *Heward memorial*, 1948, no. 95.

Purchase, 1945.

172

Randolph S. HEWTON
(1888-1960)

BORN: Randolph Stanley Hewton, Megantic, P. Q., June 12, 1888.

DIED: Trenton, Ontario, March 17, 1960.

STUDY: School of Art Association of Montreal, under William Brymner, 1903-07; Paris, Julian Academy, with Jean-Paul Laurens, 1908-10, and with Caro Delvaille, 1910-13;

SOCIETIES: A.R.C.A., 1921, R.C.A., 1934; C.G.P., founding member, 1933; Pen and Pencil Club, Montreal, 1922.

TEACHING: Principal School of Art, Art Association of Montreal, 1921-24.

From 1936 lived at Glen Miller, Ontario, where he was president of Miller Brothers Co. Ltd., manufacturers of paper boxes etc.

Landscape and portrait painter.

2727
DAUGHTER OF AN INDIAN CHIEF 1937

Oil on canvas, 24$^1/_8$" x 20$^3/_{16}$".
Signed (lower right): R. S. HEWTON.

PROV.: the artist [AGT, 1943].

EXHIBITIONS: A.G.T., *Hewton and Alfsen*, 1943 (Apr.).

Purchase, 1943.

Russell J. HIDER (1899-   )

BORN: Toronto, April 10, 1899.

LIVES: Toronto.

STUDY: Toronto, Ontario College of Art, c. 1918-22.

Spent six years in New York; three years in Los Angeles.

In early '20's painted and exhibited with a group of artists in the Red Barn Studio, Toronto.

Commercial artist.

2490
MAN WITH HOE IN FARM LANDSCAPE c. 1920

Water colour and ink on paper, 5$^1/_{16}$" x 6$^1/_8$".
Signed (lower left): RUSSELL HIDER.

Bequest of Ambia L. Going, 1938.

James HOCH (1827-1878)

BORN: St. Kitts, B.W.I., November 7, 1827.

DIED: Toronto, May 1, 1878. Came to Canada in 1870.

STUDY: England.

SOCIETIES: O.S.A., foundation member, 1872.

TEACHING: Art Instructor, Bishop Strachan School, Toronto, and Trinity University, Toronto.

2330
FORKS OF THE CREDIT c. 1870-75

Water colour on paper, 14$^1/_2$" x 21$^1/_2$".
Signed (lower left): J. Hoch.

EXHIBITIONS: [?] *O.S.A.*, 1875, no. 15; *D.P.C.*, 1945, no. 53 (dated c. 1870-75).

Bequest of Ernest Hoch, 1935.

PROV.: the artist [CSGA, 1928].

EXHIBITIONS: *C.S.G.A.*, 1928, no. 366; New York, *World's Fair*, 1939, section CSGA, no. 60; A.G.T., *Canadian prints*, 1949.

Purchase, 1928.

1683

HOUSES, LA MALBAIE

Oil on panel, 10¹/₄″ x 12⁷/₈″.
Signed (lower right): E H.

NOTES: Permanent loan from C.N.E. Association, 1930-65.

EXHIBITIONS: *C.N.E.*, 1930, no. 403; London, Ont., *Group of Seven*, 1946, no. 40; A.G.T., and Ontario Department of Education, 1951, no. 33.

Gift of the Canadian National Exhibition Association, 1965.

51/4

HAZELTON, B. C.   1926

Oil on panel, 8³/₈″ x 10³/₄″.
Signed (lower right): E. Holgate.
Inscribed and dated (on reverse): HAZELTON — B. C. —/ SEPT. 4 - 1926/E. Holgate.

PROV.: the artist.

Gift from the Fund of the T. Eaton Co. Ltd. for Canadian Works of Art, 1951.

1326

NUDE   1930

Oil on canvas, 25¹/₂″ x 29″.
Signed (lower right): E Holgate.

PROV.: the artist [AGT, 1930].

EXHIBITIONS: A.G.T., *Group of Seven*, 1930, no. 64; N.G.C., *Retrospective...Group of Seven*, 1936, no. 92; Quebec, *Exposition... Fortin, Hébert, Hébert, Holgate*, 1944, no. 80.

Gift from Friends of Canadian Art Fund, 1930.

2155

INTERIOR   c. 1933

Oil on canvas, 30″ x 25″.
Signed (lower right): E Holgate.

PROV.: the artist [CGP, 1933].

EXHIBITIONS: *C.G.P.*, 1933, no. 30; A.G.T., *Summer*, 1935, no. 35; A.G.T., *Loan exhibition*, 1935, no. 111; N.G.C., *Retrospective... Group of Seven*, 1936, no. 91 (reprod.); London, Tate, 1938, no. 100; A.G.T., *Holgate, Jackson, Lismer, and Newton*, 1940; Yale, 1944;

London, Ont., *Group of Seven*, 1946, no. 39; Mexico, 1960, no. 135; St. Catharines, *The Figure Form*, 1963 (Dec. 6-29) [no catalogue]; A.G.O. [circulating exhibition], *Canadian paintings of the 1930s*, 1967-68, no. 10.

REFERENCES: Buchanan (1945), pl. 83 (reprod.); *Saturday Night*, vol. 63 (Sept. 13, 1947), p. 2 (reprod.); A.G.T., *Paintings and sculpture* (1959), p. 76 (reprod.).

Purchase, 1933.

2155   **Interior**

2719

FREE FRENCH SUBMARINE "SURCOUF" AND H.M.S. "YORK"   **1941**

Oil on masonite, 18" x 21".
Signed and dated (lower left): E. Holgate '41.

PROV.: the artist [OSA, 1943].

NOTES: Painted at Halifax.

EXHIBITIONS: *O.S.A.*, 1943, no. 105; Quebec, *Exposition...Fortin, Hébert, Hébert, Holgate*, 1944, no. 79.

Purchase, 1943.

56/34 **Laurentian Cemetery**

56/34

LAURENTIAN CEMETERY 1948

Oil on panel, 8½" x 10½".
Signed (lower right): E H.
Inscribed (on reverse, in ink): E. Holgate/1948./15 Morin Heights 1.

PROV.: [Dominion Gallery, Montreal].

Purchase, 1957.

56/35

APRIL THAW 1950

Oil on panel, 8½" x 10⅝".
Signed (lower right): E. Holgate.
Dated (lower centre): AP 11 — 50.
Inscribed (on reverse, in ink): Edwin H Holgate/April 11 — 1950.

PROV.: [Dominion Gallery, Montreal].

Purchase, 1957.

Robert HOLMES (1861-1930)

BORN: Cannington, Ont., June 25, 1861.

DIED: Toronto, May 14, 1930.

STUDY: Ontario School of Art, graduating, 1884; in England with Gerald Moira at the Royal College of Art, London; also University of New York.

SOCIETIES: A.R.C.A., 1909, R.C.A., 1920; O.S.A., 1909, P.O.S.A., 1919-24; C.S.P.W.C., founding member, 1926; C.S.G.A., Pres. 1909-11; Toronto Art Students League, Pres. 1891-1904; Arts and Letters Club, Toronto, 1908.

TEACHING: Drawing master, at Upper Canada College, 1891-1920; instructor, Ontario College of Art, 1912-30.

Floral painter.

NOTE: Holmes' signature often appears in the form of a monogram, with the initials R and H respectively above and below a Sugar Maple Key.

133

WILD PHLOX
Phlox divaricata L. (Polemoniaceae)

Water colour on paper, mounted on card, 21" x 14⅜" [sight].
Signed (lower left): R. Holmes.

NOTES: Permanent loan from C.N.E. Association, 1921-65.

EXHIBITIONS: *O.S.A.*, 1921, no. 61; *C.N.E.*, 1921, no. 178; A.G.T., *Loan exhibition*, 1935, no. 237; *O.S.A.*, 1947, no. 162; A.G.T., *Holmes*, 1964, no. 57, on cover (reprod. in colour).

REFERENCES: O.S.A., *Annual report* (1922), p. 6; Robson (1932), p. 119 (reprod. in colour).

Gift of the Canadian National Exhibition Association; 1965.

NOTE: The following (72) water colours were purchased by subscription from the Estate of the artist. Chronological sequence of dated works has been sacrificed to maintain the sequence of accession numbers.

2009

BLACK LOCUST
Robina Pseudo-acacia L. (Leguminosae)

Gouache on brown paper, mounted on card, 17½" x 11" [sight].
Signed (lower right): R. Holmes.

EXHIBITIONS: A.G.T., *Holmes*, 1964, no. 38, pl. IV (reprod.).

Gift by Subscription, 1931.

133   Wild Phlox

2010

HELLEBORINE
Epipactie helleborine (L.) Crantz (Orchidaceae)

Gouache on grey paper, mounted on card, 13⅝" x 9¾" [sight].
Signed (lower left): R. Holmes.

EXHIBITIONS: [?] *C.N.E.*, 1928, no. 549; A.G.T., *Holmes*, 1964, no. 18.

Gift by Subscription, 1931.

2011

CANADA COLUMBINE
Aquilegia canadensis L. (Ranunculaceae)

Water colour on paper, mounted on card, 14" x 10".
Signed (lower left): R. Holmes.

EXHIBITIONS: [?] *O.S.A.*, 1912, no. 73; A.G.T., *Holmes*, 1964, no. 26.

Gift by Subscription, 1931.

2012

CORAL ROOT
Corallorrhiza striata Lindl. (Orchidaceae)

Water colour on paper, mounted on card, 17½" x 11" [sight].
Signed (lower right): R. Holmes.

EXHIBITIONS: [?] *O.S.A.*, 1912, no. 72; [?] *R.C.A.*, 1912, no. 267;
A.G.T., *Holmes*, 1964, no. 21.

Gift by Subscription, 1931.

2013

JACK-IN-THE-PULPIT I
Arisaema atrorubens (Ait.) Bl. (Araceae)

Water colour and gouache on paper, mounted on card, 14" x 10".
Signed (lower right): R. Holmes.

EXHIBITIONS: [?] *O.S.A.*, 1924, no. 62; [?] *C.N.E.*, 1928, no. 524;
A.G.T., *Holmes*, 1964, no. 6.

Gift by Subscription, 1931.

2014

CANADA ANEMONE
Anemone canadensis L. (Ranunculaceae)

Water colour on paper, mounted on card, 17½" x 11".
Signed (lower right): R. Holmes.

EXHIBITIONS: [?] *O.S.A.*, 1922, no. 65; Ste. Anne de Bellevue, Que.,
MacDonald College, *Semi-centenary exhibition*, 1955, no. 23;
A.G.T., *Holmes*, 1964, p. 5 (says "apparently part of a larger composi-
tion"), no. 27, pl. I (reprod.).

Gift by Subscription, 1931.

2016 **Trilliums**
Colour reproduction, p. 537

2017 **Marsh Calla**

2015

GREAT LOBELIA
Lobelia siphilitica L. (Lobeliaceae)

Water colour on paper, mounted on card, $17\frac{1}{4}$" x $10\frac{3}{4}$" [sight].
Signed (lower left): R. Holmes.

EXHIBITIONS: A.G.T., *Holmes*, 1964, no. 69.

Gift by Subscription, 1931.

2016

TRILLIUMS
Trillium grandiflorum (Michx.) Salisb. (White) (Liliaceae)
Trillium erectum L. (Red) (Liliaceae)

Water colour on paper, mounted on card, 14" x 10".

EXHIBITIONS: [?] *O.S.A.*, 1909, no. 66; London, Tate, 1938, no. 104; *D.P.C.*, 1945, no. 103; A.G.T., *Holmes*, 1964, no. 11, pl. V (reprod.).

Gift by Subscription, 1931.

2017
MARSH CALLA
Calla palustris L. (Araceae)

Gouache on paper, mounted on card, 14" x 10".

EXHIBITIONS: [?] *C.N.E.*, 1928, no. 519; London, Tate, 1938, no. 105; A.G.T., *Holmes*, 1964, no. 5, pl. VII (reprod.).

REFERENCES: *Canadian Art*, vol. XXI (Jul. - Aug., 1964), p. 256 (reprod.).

Gift by Subscription, 1931.

2018

TRAILING ARBUTUS
Epigaea repens L. (Ericaceae)

Water colour on paper, mounted on card, 14" x 10".
Signed (lower right): R. Holmes.

EXHIBITIONS: A.G.T., *Holmes*, 1964, no. 54.

Gift by Subscription, 1931.

2019

CONE FLOWER   1902
Rudbeckia hirta L. (Compositae)

Water colour on paper, mounted on card, 14" x 10".
Signed (lower right): R. Holmes.
Inscribed (on mount): Blackeyed Susan/Cone Flower/Rudbeckia Hirta/Beaverton — Aug. 13 - 1902.

EXHIBITIONS: A.G.T., *Holmes*, 1964, no. 71.

Gift by Subscription, 1931.

2020

LARGE CORAL ROOT   **1909**
Corallorhiza maculata Raf. (Orchidaceae)

Gouache on brown paper, 17¹/₂″ x 11″ [sight].
Signed (lower right): [Monogram].
Inscribed (on reverse): Toronto, July 27, 1909/Corallorrhiza multi-
flora.

EXHIBITIONS: [?] *C.N.E.*, 1928, no. 541; A.G.T., *Holmes*, 1964, no. 20.

Gift by Subscription, 1931.

2021

TURTLEHEAD I   **1903**
Chelone glabra L. (Scrophulariaceae)

Gouache on grey paper, 14″ x 10″.
Signed (lower left): [Monogram].
Inscribed (on reverse): Turtlehead/Chelone Glabra/Cannington/
Aug. 1, 1903 light yellow — green/and blue green.

EXHIBITIONS: [?] *C.N.E.*, 1928, no. 529; A.G.T., *Holmes*. 1964, no. 61,
pl. III (reprod.).

Gift by Subscription, 1931.

2022

PIPSISSEWA
Chimaphila umbellata (L.) Nutt. (Ericaceae)

Water colour on paper, mounted on card, 17¹/₂″ x 11″.
Signed (lower left): R. Holmes.

EXHIBITIONS: A.G.T., *Holmes*, 1964, no. 50.

Gift by Subscription, 1931.

2023

WILD SUNFLOWER
Helianthus strumosus L. (Compositae)

Water colour on paper, 17¹/₂″ x 11″.
Signed (lower right centre): R. Holmes.

EXHIBITIONS: [?] *O.S.A.*, 1915, no. 61; [?] *C.N.E.*, 1928, no. 521;
A.G.T., *Holmes*, 1964, no. 72.

Gift by Subscription, 1931.

2024

SHOWY ORCHIS I
Orchis spectabilis L. (Orchidaceae)

Water colour on paper, mounted on card, 17¹/₂″ x 11″.

EXHIBITIONS: [?] *O.S.A.*, 1910, no. 61; [?] *C.N.E.*, 1928, no. 547;
A.G.T., *Holmes*, 1964, no. 14.

Gift by Subscription, 1931.

2025

GOLDEN JEWEL WEED
Impatiens pallida Nutt. (Balsaminaceae)

Water colour on paper, 20½" x 14".
Signed (lower left): R. Holmes.

EXHIBITIONS: [?] *C.N.E.*, 1928, no. 534; Rio de Janeiro, 1944, no. 95;
A.G.T., *Holmes*, 1964, no. 43.

Gift by Subscription, 1931.

2026

RATTLESNAKE PLANTAIN
Goodyera tesselata (Lodd.) Eat.

Water colour on paper, mounted on card, 19½" x 13½".
Signed (lower right): R. Holmes.

EXHIBITIONS: [?] *O.S.A.*, 1930, no. 77; A.G.T., *Holmes*, 1964, no. 19.

Gift by Subscription, 1931.

2027

LABRADOR TEA
Ledum groenlandicum Oeder. (Ericaceae)

Gouache on brown paper, mounted on card, 17½" x 11".

EXHIBITIONS: A.G.T., *Holmes*, 1964, no. 52.

Gift by Subscription, 1931.

2028

WATERLEAF AND WILD GARLIC
Hydrophyllum canadense L. (Hydrophyllaceae)
Allium canadense L. (Liliaceae)

Water colour on paper, mounted on card, 20" x 13½".
Signed (lower centre): R. Holmes.

EXHIBITIONS: *O.S.A.*, 1930, no. 78; A.G.T., *Holmes*, 1964, no. 58.

Gift by Subscription, 1931.

2029

FIREWEED (GREAT WILLOW HERB)
Epilobium angustifolium L. (Onagraceae)

Water colour and gouache on paper, mounted on card, 17½" x 11".
Signed (lower right): R. Holmes.

EXHIBITIONS: [?] *C.N.E.*, 1928, no. 513; Ste. Anne de Bellevue, Que.,
MacDonald College, *Semi-centenary exhibition*, 1955, no. 22;
A.G.T., *Holmes*, 1964, no. 46.

Gift by Subscription, 1931.

2030

PURPLE LOOSETRIFE AND TURTLEHEAD
Lythrum salicaria L. (Lythraceae)
Chelone glabra L. (Scrophulariaceae)

Water colour on paper, mounted on card, $19^1/_2$" x $13^1/_2$".
Signed (lower left): [Monogram].

EXHIBITIONS: *O.S.A.*, 1924, no. 61, p. 14 (reprod.); [?] *C.N.E.*, 1928,
528; Rio de Janeiro, 1944, no. 97; A.G.T., *Holmes*, 1964, no. 45.

Gift by Subscription, 1931.

2031

SHOWY ORCHIS II
Orchis spectabilis L. (Orchidaceae)

Water colour and gouache on paper, mounted on card, $19^1/_2$" x $13^3/_8$"
[sight].
Signed (lower left): R. Holmes.

EXHIBITIONS: [?] *O.S.A.*, 1910, no. 61; [?] *C.N.E.*, 1928, no. 547;
A.G.T., *Holmes*, 1964, no. 15.

Gift by Subscription, 1931.

2032

RAGGED ORCHIS
Habenaria lacera (Michx.) R. Br. (Orchidaceae)

Gouache on buff paper, mounted on card, $19^3/_8$" x $13^1/_2$" [sight].

EXHIBITIONS: A.G.T., *Holmes*, 1964, no. 16.

Gift by Subscription, 1931.

2033

EVENING PRIMROSE
Oenothera biennis L. (Onagraceae)

Water colour on paper, mounted on card, $14^1/_2$" x 8".
Signed (lower left): R. Holmes.

EXHIBITIONS: [?] *O.S.A.*, 1923, no. 71; [?] *C.N.E.*, 1928, no. 539;
A.G.T., *Holmes*, 1964, no. 48.

Gift by Subscription, 1931.

2034

BLOODROOT
Sanguinaria canadensis L. (Papaveraceae)

Water colour on paper, mounted on card, $28^3/_8$" x $20^1/_2$" [sight].
Signed (lower left): R. Holmes.

EXHIBITIONS: [?] *O.S.A.*, 1926, no. 132; *C.N.E.*, 1952, no. 40;
A.G.T., *Holmes*, 1964, no. 31.

Gift by Subscription, 1931.

2035

GERARDIA (DOWNY FALSE FOXGLOVE)
Gerardia flava L. (Scrophulariaceae)

Water colour on paper, mounted on card, $25^3/_4$" x $19^1/_8$" [sight].
Signed (lower left): [Monogram].

EXHIBITIONS: *C.N.E.*, 1952, no. 39; A.G.T., *Holmes*, 1964, no. 63.

Gift by Subscription, 1931.

2036

STEMLESS LADY'S SLIPPER
Cypripedium acaule Ait. (Orchidaceae)

Water colour on paper, mounted on card, 25" x $18^1/_2$".
Signed (lower left): R. Holmes.

EXHIBITIONS: [?] *R.C.A.*, 1925, no. 103; [?] *O.S.A.*, 1918, no. 82; A.G.T., *Holmes*, 1964, p. 4, no. 12.

Gift by Subscription, 1931.

2037

PITCHER PLANT
Sarracenia purpurea L. (Sarraceniaceae)

Water colour on paper, mounted on card, $37^5/_8$" x $25^3/_{16}$".
Signed (lower left): R. Holmes.

EXHIBITIONS: *C.N.E.*, 1919, no. 86; A.G.T., *Holmes*, 1964, p. 4, no. 32.

Gift by Subscription, 1931.

2038

CARDINAL FLOWER I
Lobelia cardinalis L. (Lobeliaceae)

2038   Cardinal Flower I

Water colour on paper, mounted on card, $39^1/_8$" x $25^{13}/_{16}$" [sight].
Signed (lower left): [Monogram].

EXHIBITIONS: *O.S.A.*, 1920, no. 56; London, *British Empire Exhibition*, 1924, Catalogue of the Palace of Art, p. 99, no. FF. 116, and Canadian section of fine arts, no. 100; *C.N.E.*, 1928, no. 525 (reprod.); Rio de Janeiro, 1944, no. 96; A.G.T., *Holmes*, 1964, no. 67.

REFERENCES: *Saturday Night* (June 26, 1926), reprod.; *R.A.I.C. Journal*, vol. V (Oct., 1928), p. 375 (reprod.); A.G.T., *Bulletin and annual report*, (March, 1932), p. 12 (reprod.); *Canadian Review of Music and Art*, vol. 3, nos. 7-8 (Aug. - Sept., 1944), p. 32 (reprod.).

Gift by Subscription, 1931.

2039

TULIP TREE I
Liriodendron tulipifera L. (Magnoliaceae)

Water colour on paper, mounted on card, $38^3/_{16}$" x $25^3/_4$".
Signed (lower right): [Monogram].

184

NOTES: The paper is impressed, upper right, R. Holmes.

EXHIBITIONS: A.G.T., *Holmes*, 1964, no. 29.

Gift by Subscription, 1931.

2040

IN THE WOODS

Water colour on paper, mounted on card, 38¹/₂″ x 26″.
Signed (lower left): [Monogram].

EXHIBITIONS: A.G.T., *Holmes*, 1964, p. 4, no. 1.

Gift by Subscription, 1931.

2041

WITCH-HAZEL
Hamamelis virginiana L. (Hamamelidaceae)

Gouache on paper, mounted on card, 13¹/₂″ x 19¹/₂″.
Signed (lower right): [Monogram].

EXHIBITIONS: [?] *O.S.A.*, 1928, no. 139; A.G.T., *Holmes*, 1964, no. 35.

REFERENCES: Harper (1966), p. 267, fig. 240 (reprod.).

Gift by Subscription, 1931.

2041   **Witch-hazel**

2042

WOOD LILY
Lilium Philadelphicum L. (Liliaceae)

Water colour on paper, mounted on card, 14″ x 10″.
Signed (lower left): R. Holmes.

EXHIBITIONS: [?] *C.N.E.*, 1928, no. 536; A.G.T., *Holmes*, 1964, no. 10.

Gift by Subscription, 1931.

2043

ONE-FLOWERED WINTERGREEN
Moneses uniflora (L.) Gray. (Ericaceae)

Water colour and gouache on paper, mounted on card, 14″ x 10″.
Signed (lower left): R. Holmes.

EXHIBITIONS: A.G.T., *Holmes*, 1964, no. 51.

Gift by Subscription, 1931.

2044

WILD ROSE
Rosa blanda Ait. (Rosaceae)

Water colour on paper, mounted on card, 14″ x 10″.
Signed (lower left centre): R. Holmes.

EXHIBITIONS: *O.S.A., little pictures*, 1928, no. 175; [?] *C.N.E.*, 1928, no. 523; A.G.T., *Holmes*, 1964, no. 37.

Gift by Subscription, 1931.

2045

ELECAMPANE
Inula helenium L. (Compositae)

Gouache on grey paper, mounted on card, 13⅝″ x 9¾″.
Signed (lower left): R. Holmes.

EXHIBITIONS: [?] *C.N.E.*, 1928, no. 526; A.G.T., *Holmes*, 1964, no. 70.

Gift by Subscription, 1931.

2046

ROUND-LEAVED SUNDEW
Drosera Rotundifolia L. (Droseraceae)

Gouache on paper, mounted on card, 14″ x 10″.
Signed (lower left): R. Holmes.

EXHIBITIONS: [?] *O.S.A.*, 1912, no. 70; A.G.T., *Holmes*, 1964, no. 34.

Gift by Subscription, 1931.

2047

WILD GINGER
Asarum canadense L. (Aristolochiaceae)

Water colour on paper, mounted on card, 14″ x 10″.
Signed (lower left): R. Holmes.

EXHIBITIONS: [?] *C.N.E.*, 1928, no. 527; A.G.T., *Holmes*, 1964, no. 23.

Gift by Subscription, 1931.

2048

MILKWEED
Asclepias syriaca L. (Asclepiadaceae)

Gouache on brown paper, mounted on card, $13^1/_2$" x $9^5/_8$" [sight].
Signed (lower right centre): R. Holmes.

EXHIBITIONS: A.G.T., *Holmes*, 1964, no. 56.

Gift by Subscription, 1931.

2049

ROSE POGONIA
Pogonia ophioglossoides (L.) Ker. (Orchidaceae)

Water colour on paper, mounted on card, 13" x 8".

EXHIBITIONS: [?] *C.N.E.*, 1928, no. 550; A.G.T., *Holmes*, 1964, no. 17.

Gift by Subscription, 1931.

2050

FRINGED POLYGALA
Polygala paucifolia Willd. (Polygalaceae)

Water colour on paper, mounted on card, 13" x 8".

EXHIBITIONS: [?] *C.N.E.*, 1928, no. 520; A.G.T., *Holmes*, 1964, no. 40.

Gift by Subscription, 1931.

2051

VETCH
Vicia cracca L. (Leguminosae)

Gouache on grey paper, mounted on card, 13" x 8".
Signed (lower left): [Monogram].

EXHIBITIONS: [?] *C.N.E.*, 1928, no. 540; A.G.T., *Holmes*, 1964, no. 39.

Gift by Subscription, 1931.

2052

PUSSY WILLOW
Salix sp. (Salicaceae)

Gouache on paper, mounted on card, 13" x 8".

NOTES: Impressed into paper, lower centre: R. H.

EXHIBITIONS: A.G.T., *Holmes*, 1964, no. 22.

Gift by Subscription, 1931.

2053

WATER PERSICARIA   **1901**
Polygonum amphibium L. (Polygonaceae)

Gouache on paper, mounted on card, 8" x 5".
Inscribed (across bottom): High View/Ottawa River/Aug. 22-1901.

EXHIBITIONS: A.G.T., *Holmes*, 1964, no. 24.

Gift by Subscription, 1931.

2054

BITTERSWEET
Solanum dulcamara L. (Solanaceae)

Water colour on paper, mounted on card, 10" x 6".
Signed (lower right): R. Holmes.

EXHIBITIONS: A.G.T., *Holmes*, 1964, no. 59.

Gift by Subscription, 1931.

2055

TURTLEHEAD II
Chelone glabra L. (Scrophulariaceae)

Gouache on brown paper, mounted on card, 10" x 6".

EXHIBITIONS: A.G.T., *Holmes*, 1964, no. 62.

Gift by Subscription, 1931.

2056

JACK-IN-THE-PULPIT II
Arisaema atrorubens (Ait.) B. (Araceae)

Water colour on paper, mounted on card, 10" x 7".
Signed (lower left centre): R. Holmes.

EXHIBITIONS: A.G.T., *Holmes*, 1964, no. 7.

Gift by Subscription, 1931.

2057

STEMLESS LADY'S SLIPPER II
Cypripedium acaule Ait. (Orchidaceae)

Water colour on paper, mounted on card, 11" x 8" [oval].
Signed (left centre): [Monogram].

EXHIBITIONS: A.G.T., *Holmes*, 1964, p. 5, no. 13.

Gift by Subscription, 1931.

2058

FLOWERING CACTUS
Cactaceae

Water colour and gouache on paper, mounted on card, 10″ x 7″.
Signed (left centre): R. Holmes.

EXHIBITIONS: A.G.T., *Holmes*, 1964, no. 44.

Gift by Subscription, 1931.

2059

BALSAM CONES
Abies balsamea (L.) Mill. (Pinaceae)

Gouache on paper, mounted on card, $13^5/_8$″ x $9^5/_8$″ [sight].
Signed (lower left): [Monogram].

EXHIBITIONS: A.G.T., *Holmes*, 1964, no. 4.

Gift by Subscription, 1931.

2060

WHITE SPRUCE
Picea glauca (Moench) Voss (Pinaceae)

Gouache on paper, mounted on card, 14″ x 10″.
Signed (lower right): [Monogram].

EXHIBITIONS: [?] *C.N.E.*, 1928, no. 516; A.G.T., *Holmes*, 1964, no. 2.

Gift by Subscription, 1931.

2061

MOTH MULLEIN
Verbascum blattaria L. (Scrophulariaceae)

Gouache on paper, mounted on card, $14^1/_2$″ x 8″.
Signed (lower left): R. Holmes.

EXHIBITIONS: [?] *C.N.E.*, 1928, no. 517; A.G.T., *Holmes*, 1964, no. 60.

Gift by Subscription, 1931.

2062

EVENING PRIMROSE
Oenothera biennis L. (Onagraceae)

Water colour on paper, mounted on card, $19^1/_2$″ x $13^1/_2$″ [sight].
Signed (lower right): R. Holmes.

EXHIBITIONS: [?] *O.S.A.*, 1923, no. 71; [?] *C.N.E.*, 1928, no. 539;
A.G.T., *Holmes*, 1964, no. 47.

Gift by Subscription, 1931.

2075

SYCAMORE MAPLE
Acer pseudo-platanus L. (Aceraceae)

Gouache on grey paper, mounted on card, $13\frac{1}{2}$" x $9\frac{1}{2}$".

EXHIBITIONS: A.G.T., *Holmes*, 1964, no. 41.

Gift by Subscription, 1931.

2076

SUGAR MAPLE WITH KEYS
Acer saccharum marsh (Aceraceae)

Gouache on grey paper, mounted on card, $13\frac{1}{2}$" x $9\frac{1}{2}$".

EXHIBITIONS: A.G.T., *Holmes*, 1964, no. 42, pl. VI (reprod.).

Gift by Subscription, 1931.

2077

SPRUCE BRANCH WITH CONES (NORWAY SPRUCE)
Picea abies (L.) Karst. (Pinaceae)

Gouache on grey paper, mounted on card, $13\frac{1}{2}$" x $9\frac{1}{2}$".

EXHIBITIONS: A.G.T., *Holmes*, 1964, no. 3.

Gift by Subscription, 1931.

2078

CARDINALS II
Lobelia cardinalis L. (Lobeliaceae)

Gouache on paper, mounted on card, $13\frac{3}{8}$" x $9\frac{3}{8}$" [sight].
Signed (lower left): R. Holmes.

EXHIBITIONS: A.G.T., *Holmes*, 1964, no. 68.

Gift by Subscription, 1931.

2079

PUMPKIN BLOSSOM I
Cucurbito pepo L. (Cucurbitaceae)

Water colour on paper, mounted on card, $14\frac{3}{16}$" x $10\frac{1}{8}$".
Signed (lower left): R. Holmes.

EXHIBITIONS: A.G.T., *Holmes*, 1964, no. 66.

Gift by Subscription, 1931.

2080

PUMPKIN BLOSSOM II
Cucurbito pepo L. (Cucurbitaceae)

Water colour on paper, mounted on card, $14\frac{1}{2}$" x 10".
Signed (lower right): R. H.

EXHIBITIONS: A.G.T., *Holmes*, 1964, no. 65.

Gift by Subscription, 1931.

2081

PITCHER PLANT
Sarracenia purpurea L. (Sarraceniaceae)

Water colour on paper, mounted on card, $13^1/_2$" x $9^1/_2$".
Signed (lower centre): R. Holmes.
Inscribed (on reverse of mount): Balsam Fir/Abies Balsamea 1. (Mill.)
[sic].

EXHIBITIONS: A.G.T., *Holmes*, 1964, no. 33.

Gift by Subscription, 1931.

2082

BUTTERWORT AND LICHENS
Pinguicula vulgaris L. (Cucurbitaceae)

Water colour on paper, mounted on card, $13^3/_8$" x $9^3/_8$" [sight].
Signed (lower left): [Monogram].

EXHIBITIONS: A.G.T., *Holmes*, 1964, no. 64.

Gift by Subscription, 1931.

2083

PICKEREL WEED AND DRAGON-FLY
Pontederia cordata L. (Pontederiaceae)

Water colour and gouache on paper, mounted on card, $9^1/_2$" x 7".
Signed (lower left): R. Holmes.

EXHIBITIONS: A.G.T., *Holmes*, 1964, no. 8.

Gift by Subscription, 1931.

2084

MILKWEED
Ascelpias syriaca L. (Asclepiadeceae)

Water colour and ink on paper, mounted on card, $13^1/_2$" x $9^1/_2$".
Signed (lower left): [Monogram].

EXHIBITIONS: A.G.T., *Holmes*, 1964, no. 55.

REFERENCES: Wood, *Rambles of a Canadian Naturalist* (1916), opp.
p. 144 (reprod. in colour, as "Monarch Butterfly — King Billy").

Gift by Subscription, 1931.

63/55

BRACTED BINDWEED   **1903**

Water colour on paper, $12^7/_8$" x 8".
Signed and dated (lower centre): R. Holmes./1903.

193

Yvonne McKague HOUSSER
(1898-   )

BORN: Toronto, August 4, 1898.

LIVES: Willowdale, Ontario. Widow of Frederick Broughton Housser, author of *A Canadian art movement* (1926) [see bibliography].

STUDY: Ontario College of Art, 1914-18; Paris, Grande Chaumière, Colarossi, Ranson academies, 1921-22, and 1924, under Lucien Simon, and Maurice Denis; Vienna, 1930; New Mexico.

SOCIETIES: A.R.C.A., 1942, R.C.A., 1951; O.S.A., 1928; C.G.P., charter member, 1933, Pres. 1955-56; F.C.A., 1942.

TEACHING: Ontario College of Art, from early 1920's until 1949.

Landscape, figure and abstract paintings.

2553

AUTUMN, RED LAKE   1940

Oil on masonite, 13" x 15⅞".
Signed (lower right centre): YVONNE McKAGUE/HOUSSER.

PROV.: the artist [OSA, 1940].

EXHIBITIONS: *O.S.A. small pictures*, 1940, p. 31, no. 272.

Purchase, 1940.

2553   **Autumn, Red Lake**

57/22

HILL TOWN, MEXICO   1957

Oil on masonite, 23¹³⁄₁₆" x 24⅛".
Signed (lower left): Y. M. H.

PROV.: the artist [RCA, 1957].

EXHIBITIONS: *R.C.A.*, 1957-58, no. 36 (reprod.); M.M.F.A., Gallery XII, *Goldberg and Housser*, 1958 (Jan. 17 - Feb. 2) [no catalogue].

Gift from the McLean Foundation, 1958.

D. Mackay HOUSTOUN
(1916-   )

BORN: Donald Mackay Houstoun, Stevensville, Ontario, November 27, 1916.

LIVES: Toronto.

STUDY: Toronto, Western Technical School, under L. A. C. Panton, H. C. Clarke, and C. Griffin.

SOCIETIES: A.R.C.A., 1960, R.C.A., 1965; O.S.A., 1946, P.O.S.A. 1961-64; C.S.P.W.C., 1958, Pres. 1960-62.

Landscape painter, commercial illustrator.

61/40

AUTUMN FIELD   1961

Water colour collage, 20³⁄₁₆" x 28½".
Signed and dated (upper right): Houstoun/'61.

PROV.: the artist [CSPWC, 1961].

EXHIBITIONS: *C.S.P.W.C.*, 1961, no. 51, opp. foreword (reprod.).

Gift from the McLean Foundation, 1962.

61/40 **Autumn Field**

A. H. HOWARD (1854-1916)

BORN: Alfred Harold Howard, Liverpool, England, July 12, 1854.

DIED: Toronto, February 26, 1916. Came to Canada (Toronto) in 1876.

STUDY: Had no formal art training; was apprenticed as a lithographer in the firm of Maclure, Macdonald, and MacGregor, in Liverpool.

SOCIETIES: R.C.A., 1883; O.S.A., 1906; Toronto Art Students' League, 1886; Arts and Letters Club, Toronto.

Designer, illuminator.

591

GARDEN SKETCH   **1915**

Water colour on paper, $6^{15}/_{16}$" x $4^3/_8$".
Signed (lower left) [monogram].
Dated (lower left): June 23/ 1915.
Inscribed (on reverse, in pencil): I tried to get/impression without/ much draw [ ]/but not any style.

Gift of F. Stanley Harrod, 1918.

Barbara HOWARD (1926-   )

BORN: Long Branch, Ontario, March 10, 1926.

LIVES: Toronto.

STUDY: Ontario College of Art, graduating, 1951.

TRAVEL: Europe for two years, travelling and studying.

59/29

BLUE PINE   **1959**

Conte and pastel on paper, $23^7/_8$" x $18^1/_8$" [sight].
Signed (lower left): BARBARA HOWARD.

PROV.: [Picture Loan Society, Toronto].

EXHIBITIONS: Picture Loan Society, *Howard*, 1960 (Mar. 5-18) [no catalogue].

Gift from the McLean Foundation, 1960.

197

H. S. HOWLAND, Jr. (1855-   )

BORN: Henry Stark Howland, Kleinberg, Ontario, 1855.

DIED: [Unknown].

STUDY: ? [In A.G.T. exhibition catalogue, 1912, Howland is listed as an "amateur".]

SOCIETIES: Royal Society of Painter-Etchers, London; Toronto Etching Society.

Etcher.

E. J. HUGHES (1913-   )

BORN: Edward John Hughes, February 17, 1913, North Vancouver, B. C.

LIVES: Shawnigan Lake, B. C.

STUDY: Vancouver School of Art, from 1929-35, under F. H. Varley, C. H. Scott, J. W. G. Macdonald, and others.

SOCIETIES: C.G.P., 1948; A.R.C.A., 1966.

TRAVEL: Cross-country trip, painting Canadian cities, 1956.

AWARDS: Emily Carr Memorial scholarship, 1947, to travel and sketch along the B. C. coast; Canada Council grants, 1958, 1963, travelling and sketching on coast and in interior of B. C., and 1967.

1942-46, official war artist with the Canadian army, painting in England and the Aleutian Islands.

1435

THE GRANGE   **1887**

Etching, Imp.: 5" x 8". Paper: 10³/₈" x 16¹/₂".
Inscribed and dated (lower left): H. S. HOWLAND Jr./TORONTO 1887.

NOTES: Impression in collection of National Gallery of Canada is signed Henry S. Howland Jr.

EXHIBITIONS: A.G.T., *5th loan exhibition*, 1912, no. 308.

Gift of Sir Edmund Walker Estate, 1926.

49/55

LOGS, LADYSMITH HARBOUR   **1949**

Oil on canvas, 30" x 40".
Signed and dated (lower left): E. J. HUGHES 1949.

PROV.: the artist.

NOTES: Ladysmith is located on Vancouver Island just south of Nanaimo, on the Strait of Georgia.

EXHIBITIONS: A.G.T., *Contemporary Canadian arts*, 1950, no. 69, p. 6. (reprod.); *C.N.E.*, 1952, no. 130; Stratford, Ont., 1963; Vancouver, *Hughes*, 1967, no. 13 (reprod.).

REFERENCES: *Canadian Homes*, vol. 27 (May, 1950), p. 89 (reprod.); Canadian Pulp and Paper Association, *With palette and brush*, (1954), reprod. in colour.

Gift from the Albert H. Robson Memorial Subscription Fund, 1950.

49/55   **Logs, Ladysmith Harbour**

Gerald HUMEN (1935-　　)

BORN: The Ukraine, March 15, 1935.

LIVES: Toronto.

STUDY: Toronto, Central Technical School; Ontario College of Art, until 1957.

66/20

DRAWING NO. 20　　　　　　　　　**1966**

Ink on paper, 12⅝" x 22⅞".
Signed and dated (lower right): Humen/66.

PROV.: the artist.

Purchase, 1967.

66/20　**Drawing no. 20**

2524

POTTERY MARKET, TAXCO　　　　　　　**1938**

Water colour on paper, 19½" x 24¾" [sight].
Signed and dated (lower right): Jack Humphrey, 1938.

PROV.: the artist [CSPWC, 1939].

EXHIBITIONS: *C.S.P.W.C.*, 1939; New York, *World's Fair*, 1939, section CSPWC, SSC, no. 49; [?] Brooklyn, N. Y., *International water colour exhibition, 11th biennial*, 1941, no. 201; New York, National Arts Club, 1945 (Mar. - June) [no catalogue]; Fredericton, *Humphrey*, 1966-67, no. 14.

Purchase, 1939.

Jack HUMPHREY (1901-1967)

BORN: Jack Weldon Humphrey, St. John, N. B., January 12, 1901

DIED: St. John, N. B., March, 1967.

STUDY: Boston Museum of Fine Arts school, 1920-23, under Phillip Hale; New York, National Academy of Design, 1924-29, under Charles Hawthorn; New York, Art Students' League; Paris, Grande Chaumière, and under André Lhote, 1929-30; Munich, at the Hans Hofmann school.

SOCIETIES: C.S.P.W.C.; C.G.P.; C.S.G.A.; Contemporary Arts Society, Montreal.

TRAVEL: Europe, 1929-30; Mexico, 1938; France, 1952-54.

AWARDS: Canadian government overseas fellowship, 1952-54, to Paris and Brittany; Canada Council grants, 1958, 1960.

Landscape and figure painter, mostly in water colour.

2524　**Pottery Market, Taxco**

2549

CHARLOTTE   **1939**

Oil on canvas, 24" x 19⁷/₈".
Signed (lower right): Jack Humphrey.

PROV.: the artist [AGT, 1940].

EXHIBITIONS: A.G.T., *Warrener, Roberts, Goldberg, and Humphrey,*
1940; Andover, Mass., 1942, no. 33, p. 49 (reprod.); Yale, 1944;
D.P.C., 1945, no. 221, p. 47 (reprod.); Paris, UNESCO, 1946, no. 15;
A.G.T., *50 years of painting in Canada,* 1949, no. 81, p. 14 (reprod.);
A.G.T., and Ontario Department of Education, 1951, no. 9; Stratford,
Faces of Canada, 1964; Fredericton, *Humphrey,* 1966-67, p. 12, no. 17.

REFERENCES: McRae (1944), p. 46 (reprod.); *Canadian Art,* vol. V
(Spring, 1948), p. 169 (reprod.); A.G.T., *Painting and sculpture*
(1959), p. 81 (reprod.).

Gift from the Albert H. Robson Memorial Subscription Fund, 1940.

2549   **Charlotte**
Colour reproduction, p. 545

2548

BLONDE HEAD   **1940**

Oil on masonite, 20" x 16".
Signed (upper left): Jack Humphrey.
Inscribed (on reverse, in pencil): Painted March 1940/Varnished
Sept. 1940 Dammar.

PROV.: the artist [AGT, 1940].

EXHIBITIONS: A.G.T., *Warrener, Roberts, Goldberg, and Humphrey,*
1940; A.G.T., and Ontario Department of Education, 1951, no. 8;
A.G.O. [circulating exhibition], *Canadian paintings of the 1930s,*
1967-68, no. 11.

REFERENCES: *Maritime Art,* vol. I (Dec., 1940), opp. p. 14 (reprod.);
Beaverbrook Art Gallery, Fredericton, *Humphrey,* 1966-67, p. 12
[not exhibited].

Purchase, 1940.

2566

FIESTA PEOPLE, TAXCO   **1940**

Monotype, 13″ x 19$^7/_{16}$″ [sight].
Signed (lower right, in pencil): Jack Humphrey.

PROV.: the artist [CSGA, 1941].

EXHIBITIONS: *C.S.G.A.*, 1941, no. 57.

Purchase, 1941.

2714

FIELDS OF BELLE ISLE   **1942**

Water colour on paper 15$^1/_{16}$″ x 22″ [sight].
Signed and dated (lower right): Jack Humphrey 1942.

PROV.: the artist [CSPWC, 1943].

EXHIBITIONS: *C.S.P.W.C.*, 1943.

Purchase, 1943.

48/27

UP KING FROM MARKET SLIP   **1948**

Water colour on paper, 14$^1/_8$″ x 19$^1/_2$″ [sight].
Signed (lower left): J Humphrey.

PROV.: the artist [CSPWC, 1949].

NOTES: View from artist's studio, St. John, N.B.

EXHIBITIONS: *C.S.P.W.C.*, 1949, p. 3.

Gift from the Albert H. Robson Memorial Subscription Fund, 1949.

**HUNT, Dora de Pédery, see
PEDERY-HUNT, Dora de**

**William Stewart HUNTER
(1823-1894)**

BORN: 1823.

DIED: Belleville, Ontario, 1894.

Published *Hunter's Ottawa Scenery, in the vicinity of Ottawa City, Canada,* by Wm. S. Hunter, Jr., Ottawa City, Canada West, 1855.

58/47

MRS. PARSONS

Oil on canvas, 18$^1/_4$″ x 12$^{11}/_{16}$″.

PROV.: [The Chelsea Shop, Toronto].

NOTES: Label on reverse: Painted by/William Stewart Hunter/born — 1823/married 1846/died — 1894 — at Bellville [sic], Ontario.

Gift from Corporations' Subscription Fund, 1959.

58/47   **Mrs. Parsons**

Jacques HURTUBISE
(1939-   )

BORN: Montreal, 1939.

LIVES: Montreal.

STUDY: Montreal, Ecole des Beaux-Arts.

AWARDS: Max Beckmann scholarship for study in New York, 1960-61; Canada Council, 1965; Grand Prix de Peinture, Concours artistiques de la Province de Quebec, 1965.

Artist-in-residence, Hopkins Center, Dartmouth College, Hanover, N. H., 1967.

Frederick W. HUTCHISON
(1871-1953)

BORN: Frederick William Hutchison, Montreal, P. Q., 1871.

DIED: Hudson Heights, P. Q., May 1, 1953.

STUDY: Art Association of Montreal, under William Brymner; New York, Chase School; Paris, Julian Academy, under Jean-Paul Laurens.

Moved to New York in 1910, where he lived for some years.

SOCIETIES: R.C.A., 1941; National Academy of Design, New York; Salmagundi Club, New York; Pen and Pencil Club, Montreal, 1901.

Landscape painter.

66/41

PHILOMÈNE   **1966**

Serigraph, Imp.: 18$\frac{1}{8}$" [diagonal].
Signed and dated (lower right, in pencil): Hurtubise 1966.
Inscribed and numbered (lower left, in pencil): Philomene 22/100.

PROV.: [Gallery Pascal, Toronto].

EXHIBITIONS: Gallery Pascal, *Canadian Printmakers '67*, 1967 (May 4-30) [no catalogue].

Purchase, 1967.

845

OCTOBER SNOW, BAIE ST. PAUL   **c. 1914**

Oil on canvas, 30$\frac{1}{4}$" x 36".
Signed (lower left): F. W. Hutchison.

EXHIBITIONS: A.G.T., *Summer*, 1935, no. 56 (as American artist); *C.N.E.*, 1939, no. 110.

REFERENCES: A.G.T., *Bulletin* (May, 1927), p. 8 (reprod.); Robson (1932), p. 109 (reprod. in colour).

Gift of Mr. and Mrs. Frank P. Wood, 1926.

202

Laurence HYDE (1914-   )

BORN: London, England, June 6, 1914.

LIVES: Ottawa, Ontario. Came to Canada (Toronto), 1926.

STUDY: Toronto, Central Technical School.

SOCIETIES: C.S.G.A.

Art Director, National Film Board.

Illustrator, designer.

2323

ILLUSTRATION FOR "DISCOVERY"   **1935**

Wood engraving, Imp.: 4³/₁₆" x 3⁵/₁₆". Paper: 6¹/₈" x 5¹/₄".
Signed (lower right, in pencil): Laurence Hyde.
Inscribed (lower left, in pencil): For "Discovery".

PROV.: the artist [CSGA, 1935].

NOTES: Intended as an illustration for a book that was never actually published.

EXHIBITIONS: *C.S.G.A.*, 1935, no. 79b or 79c.

Gift from Friends of Canadian Art Fund, 1935.

INUKPUK, see
ESKIMO —Johnnie INUKPUK

Robert IRVINE (active, first quarter, 19th century), attributed to

Amateur artist, from Orkney Islands, Scotland, who was visiting in York [Toronto] between 1812 and 1816, the guest of his cousin, the Hon. George Crookshank, at his residence, north-east corner of Front and Peter Streets. According to descendants, Irvine went to visit relatives in St. John, N. B., 1817, and later to the West Indies. He was in the service of the North West Company, as Master of the "Caledonia", one of the company's ships when the war of 1812 broke out, and he and his ship were commandeered by the Provincial Marine.

52/32   **View of York**
Colour reproduction, p. 527

52/32

VIEW OF YORK   **1820**

Oil on canvas, 26⁵/₈" x 35⁵/₈".

NOTES: The attribution of the painting to Robert Irvine is made by the donors.

Robertson's Landmarks, 1898 [see ref.] names the artist simply Mr. Irvine, and sometimes "Irving".

J. Russell Harper has suggested that the artist may be John Irvine, who exhibited in London 1787-1843.

Label on reverse: Property of Alfred Walker, Esq. [one of Mrs. Heward's descendants; see credit line].

REFERENCES: *Robertson's Landmarks of Toronto*, vol. II (1896), p. 680 (sketches history of the lighthouse here depicted), opp. p. 680 (reprod. pen and ink drawing after the painting); *Robertson's Landmarks of Toronto*, vol. III (1898), p. 92 (described as "one of the most interesting of the early views of the town of York...an oil painting, made by Mr. Irving [sic], a Scotch artist, who, prior to 1821, was a visitor in York..."; dated 1820; described as a "painting from a point on the Island near the lighthouse, which gives an absolutely correct... view, with the locations of all the houses on Front Street from a hundred yards west of the Old Fort and Garrison to the second Parliament buildings..."), between p. 94 and 95 (reprod. pen and ink sketch illustrating in detail the buildings in the background of the painting); A.G.T., *Painting and sculpture* (1959), p. 50 (reprod.); *Landmarks of Canada* (1917), p. 184, under 1144.

Gift of the descendants of the late Mrs. Stephen Heward, a daughter of the Hon. George Crookshank and cousin of the artist who painted the picture, 1953.

P. K. IRWIN (1916-   )

BORN: Patricia Kathleen Page, in Dorset, England, November 23, 1916.

LIVES: Victoria, B. C. Came to Canada in 1919. Wife of W. Arthur Irwin, former Canadian ambassador to Australia, Brazil, Mexico.

STUDY: Privately in Rio de Janeiro, where she first began to draw and paint in 1957; New York, etching, for a few months in 1962.

Before P. K. Irwin took up painting, she devoted much of her time to writing stories and poems. A second published volume of her poems, entitled *The Metal and the Flower*, was awarded the Governor General's medal for poetry in 1954.

Poet, painter.

60/23

A KIND OF OSMOSIS   1960

Crayon, 17³/₄" x 27¹/₈" [sight].
Signed and dated (lower left): Irwin 60.

PROV.: [Picture Loan Society, Toronto].

EXHIBITIONS: Picture Loan Society, *Colour crayon drawings, P. K. Irwin*, 1960 (Apr. 23 - May 6) [no catalogue]; Victoria, *Irwin*, 1965-66, no. 8.

Canada Council Joint Drawings Purchase Fund, 1961.

60/23   **A Kind of Osmosis**

Gershon ISKOWITZ (1921-   )

BORN: Kielce, Poland, November 24, 1921.

LIVES: Toronto.

STUDY: Munich Academy of Fine Arts, after World War II; Munich, privately under Oskar Kokoschka.

Imprisoned by the Nazis in 1939, and spent six years in concentration camps.

65/73

SUMMER SOUND   1965

Oil on canvas, 68" x 55".
Signed and dated (lower right): ISKOWITZ 65.

PROV.: [Gallery Moos, Toronto].

EXHIBITIONS: Gallery Moos, *Iskowitz*, 1966 (Feb. 17 - Mar. 2).

Purchase, 1966.

65/73   **Summer Sound**
Colour reproduction, p. 556

204

A. Y. JACKSON (1882-   )

BORN: Alexander Young Jackson, Montreal, P. Q., October 3, 1882.

LIVES: Kleinberg, Ontario.

STUDY: Montreal, Monument National, under Edmond Dyonnet, and William Brymner; Chicago, Art Institute of Chicago, evening classes, while employed in a firm of advertising designers, 1906-07; Paris, Julian Academy, under Jean-Paul Laurens, for six months, 1907.

SOCIETIES: A.R.C.A., 1914, R.C.A., 1919, resigned, 1932, re-instated, 1953; O S.A., 1915; Group of Seven, original member, 1919-33; C.G.P., 1933, Pres. 1946-47, and 1953-54; Arts Club, Montreal, 1913; Arts and Letters Club, Toronto, 1913.

TRAVEL: 1905, to Europe — Paris and Rotterdam; 1907-9, study in Paris, and travel in France, Italy and Holland; 1911-13, France, painting in Brittany, Paris, Etaples, also England and Italy. Settled in Toronto, 1913, where he remained until 1955.

AWARDS: C.M.G., 1946.

Served in the army from 1915, and painted for the Canadian War Memorials, 1917-19.

Landscape painter.

62/56

ST. TITE DES CAPS

Pencil on paper, $7^3/_4$" x $10^1/_2$" [sight].
Signed (lower left): a y Jackson.
Inscribed (lower right): St. Tite des Caps.

PROV.: [Galerie Dresdnere, Toronto].

NOTES: St. Tite des Caps is situated just inland from the north shore of the St. Lawrence, northeast of Ste. Anne de Beaupré. Pencil notes all over the drawing; intended as a guide for an oil sketch to be made from the drawing.

EXHIBITIONS: Galerie Dresdnere, *Jackson drawings 1908-30*, 1963 (Mar.) [no catalogue]; A.G.T., *Drawings*, 1963, p. 6.

Gift from the McLean Foundation, 1963.

2573

EARLY SPRING, HEMMINGFORD   1905

Water colour on paper, $10^7/_8$" x $15^1/_{16}$" [sight].
Signed and dated (lower right): A. Y. JACKSON/1905.

NOTES: Hemmingford is situated about 30 miles south of Montreal.

Gift of A. Y. Jackson, 1941.

52/33

VEERE, HOLLAND   1909

Oil on cardboard, $7^3/_8$" x $9^1/_2$".
Signed (lower right): A. Y. JACKSON.
Inscribed (on reverse, in ink): 1909/VEERE/HOLLAND/A. Y. JACKSON.

EXHIBITIONS: A.G.T., and others, *Jackson*, 1953-54, no. 200; Hamilton, *Jackson retrospective*, 1960, no. 80.

Gift of A. Y. Jackson, 1953.

57/23

SAND DUNES, CUCQ   1911-12

Oil on panel, $8^3/_8$" x $10^5/_8$".
Signed (lower right): A. Y. JACKSON.

PROV.: D. S. Barrie, Galt.

NOTES: Sketched at Cucq in Picardy.

Gift from the McLean Foundation, 1958.

2826

ASSISI FROM THE PLAIN   1912

Oil on canvas, $25^1/_2$" x $31^3/_4$".
Signed (lower right): A. Y. JACKSON.
PROV.: the artist.

EXHIBITIONS: A.A.M., *30th spring exhibition*, 1913, no. 202; *O.S.A.*, 1913, no. 45; [?] *O.S.A.*, 1917, no. 62; [?] *C.N.E.*, 1917, no. 164; M.M.F.A., Gallery XII, *Lismer and Jackson*, 1952 (Nov. 15-26) [no catalogue]; A.G.T., and others, *Jackson*, 1953-54, no. 7; Hamilton, *Jackson retrospective*, 1960, no. 76.

REFERENCES: Arts and Letters Club of Toronto, *Yearbook*, (1913), pp. 187, 235; Housser (1926), pp. 71, 73; Jackson (1958), p. 19.

Purchase, 1946.

2827

CEDAR SWAMP, EMILEVILLE 1913

Oil on canvas, $25^5/_8$" x $31^{11}/_{16}$".
Signed (lower left): A Y Jackson.

PROV.: the artist.

NOTES: Emileville is situated about 30 miles east of Montreal.

EXHIBITIONS: [?] *R.C.A.*, 1916, no. 121; [?] *O.S.A.*, 1917, no. 60; [?] *C.N.E.*, 1917, no. 165; A.G.T., and others, *Jackson*, 1953-54, no. 9; Hamilton, *Jackson retrospective*, 1960, no. 77; Chautauqua, N. Y., *Group of Seven...*, 1963.

REFERENCES: Jackson (1958), p. 20 (says painted in the spring of 1913).

Purchase, 1946.

2704

MAPLE AND BIRCHES 1915

Oil on canvas, $32^1/_2$" x $29^3/_8$".
Signed (lower right): JACKSON.
Inscribed and dated (on stretcher): MAPLE and BIRCH JANUARY/ 1915.

PROV.: Dr. T. R. Wilson, Montreal; Mrs. T. R. Wilson, Montreal.

EXHIBITIONS: [?] *C.N.E.*, 1915, no. 187; *D.P.C.*, 1945, no. 129.

Purchase, 1942.

2544

SPRINGTIME IN PICARDY 1918

Oil on canvas, $25^5/_8$" x $30^1/_2$".
Signed and dated (lower right): A. Y. JACKSON./1918.

PROV.: the artist.

EXHIBITIONS: A.G.T., *Holgate, Jackson, Lismer and Newton*, 1940 (April); London, Ont., *Milestones*, 1942, no. 53; London, Ont., *Group of Seven*, 1946, no. 15; A.G.T., and others, *Jackson*, 1953-54, no. 27; Hamilton, *Jackson retrospective*, 1960, no. 78.

REFERENCES: Jackson (1958), p. 39-40 (says painted at Lens), p. 41; *Canadian Art*, vol. XVII (July, 1960), p. 237; *Canadian paintings in the twentieth century* (1961), pl. 2 (reprod. in colour).

Gift from the Albert H. Robson Memorial Subscription Fund, 1940.

2544   **Springtime in Picardy**
Colour reproduction, p. 538

135

EARLY SPRING, QUEBEC   **c. 1921**

Oil on canvas, 21″ x 26″.
Signed (lower left centre): A Y JACKSON.

NOTES: Permanent loan from C.N.E. Association, 1921-65.

Originally entitled *Cacouna*, a village on the south shore of the St.
Lawrence, near Rivière du Loup.

EXHIBITIONS: A.G.T., *Group of Seven*, 1921, no. 22; *C.N.E.*, 1921,
no. 184; *D.P.C.*, 1945, no. 145, p. 36 (reprod.); M.M.F.A., Gallery
XII, *Lismer and Jackson*, 1952 (Nov. 15-26) [no catalogue]; Edmonton, *Group of Seven*, 1955 [no catalogue; see Edmonton Museum
 of Arts, *Bulletin*, Jan., 1955]; Victoria, B. C., *Group of Seven*, 1955,
no. 4; Dallas, 1958; London, Ont., *The Face of early Canada*, 1961;
London, Ont., *Master Canadian painters and sculptors*, 1963-64,
no. 26; N.G.C., [travelling exhibition], *Canadian painting 1850-1950*,
1967-68, no. 53, p. 26 (reprod. in colour).

REFERENCES: O.S.A., *Annual report*, 1922, p. 6; Robson (1932),
p. 209 (reprod. in colour); Robson, *Jackson* (1938), pp. 11, 18,
pl. IV (reprod. in colour); *New World Illustrated* (Apr. 1940), p. 26
(reprod. in colour); Shoolman, and Slatkin (1942), p. 694, pl. 714
(reprod.); A.G.T., *Programme 1943-44*, on cover (reprod. in colour);
Saturday Night, vol. 60 (Jan. 13, 1945), p. 5 (reprod.); *Canadian Art*,
vol. II (Mar., 1945), p. 100 (reprod.); *Studio*, vol. CXXIX (Apr., 1945),
p. 102 (reprod. in colour); A.G.T., *50th anniversary* (1950), p. 30
(reprod.); *R.A.I.C. Journal*, vol. 27 (Jan., 1950), p. 24 (reprod.);
A.G.T., *Painting and sculpture* (1959), p. 41 (reprod. in colour);
Brieger, Vickers, and Winter, *Art and Man*, III (1964), p. 168, fig. 187
(reprod.); *artscanada*, vol. XXIV (Jan., 1967), p. 10.

Gift of the Canadian National Exhibition Association, 1965.

52/5

MORNING, CACOUNA   **1921**

Oil on panel, 8³/₈" x 10¹/₂".
Signed, twice (lower right): A Y JACKSON.
Inscribed (on reverse): "MORNING – CACOUNA".
Dated (on reverse): 1921 [and again] MAR 1921.

PROV.: [Dominion Gallery, Montreal].

*Gift from the Fund of the T. Eaton Co. Ltd. for Canadian Works of
Art, 1952.*

51/47

NEAR LAKE SUPERIOR   **c. 1924-25**

Oil on panel, 8³/₈" x 10¹/₂".
Signed (on reverse): A. Y. Jackson.
Inscribed (on reverse, upper right): Near Lake Superior.

EXHIBITIONS: [?] *O.S.A. small pictures*, 1923, no. 83; Port Arthur,
Group of Seven and Lake Superior, 1964, no. 24.

Gift of Stanford E. Dack, 1952.

846

BARNS   **c. 1926**

Oil on canvas, 32¹/₈" x 40³/₁₆".
Signed (lower left centre): A Y JACKSON.

PROV.: the artist.

NOTES: Sketch for the painting, oil on panel, 8¹/₂" x 10¹/₂" is in the
McMichael Conservation Collection, Kleinberg; illustrated in catalogue of the McMichael Collection, 1967.

EXHIBITIONS: *R.C.A.*, 1926-27, no. 70 (reprod.); N.G.C., *Annual*,
1927, no. 111; Paris, 1927, no. 85 (reprod.); *R.C.A.*, 1927-28,
no. 98; Buffalo, 1928, no. 25; St. Louis, 1930, no. 33 (reprod.);
A.G.T., *Summer*, 1935, no. 36; A.G.T., *Loan exhibition*, 1935, no. 112;
N.G.C., *Retrospective...Group of Seven*, 1936, no. 102; London,
Ont., *Milestones*, 1942, no. 54; London, Ont., *Group of Seven*, 1946,
no. 14; Hamilton, *Inaugural*, 1953-54, no. 25, pl. 15 (reprod.);
Vancouver, *Group of Seven*, 1954, no. 35 (reprod.); Hamilton,
Jackson retrospective, 1960, no. 79, on cover (reprod.); N.G.C.,
300 years of Canadian art, 1967, no. 227, p. 139 (reprod.).

REFERENCES: *R.A.I.C. Journal*, vol. 4 (Jan., 1927), p. 25 (reprod.);
American Magazine of Art, vol. XXI (May, 1930), pp. 267, 269 (reprod.);
Barbeau, *Quebec, where ancient France lingers* (1936), p. 15
(reprod.); Barbeau, *Québec, où survit l'ancienne France* (1937), p. 17
(reprod.); *Studio*, vol. CXIV (Aug., 1937), p. 69 (reprod.); Robson,
Jackson (1938), p. 11; *Studio*, vol. CXXV, (Apr. - May 1943), p. 124
(reprod.); Buchanan (1945), pl. 52 (reprod.); Jackson (1958), p. 67;
Hubbard (1963), p. 99, pl. 169 (reprod.); Carr, *Hundreds and Thousands* (1966), p. 13.

Gift from the Reuben and Kate Leonard Canadian Fund, 1926.

846   **Barns**

50/18

ST. HILARION, P. Q.   **c. 1927**

Oil on panel, 8³/₈″ x 10¹/₂″.
Signed (lower left centre): A Y JACKSON.

PROV.: [Garfield Fine Art Gallery, Toronto].

NOTES: St. Hilarion is situated inland from the north shore of the St. Lawrence, southwest of Murray Bay.

EXHIBITIONS: [?] *O.S.A. small pictures*, 1927, no. 90; Hamilton, *Jackson retrospective*, 1960, no. 81.

Gift from the Fund of the T. Eaton Co. Ltd. for Canadian Works of Art, 1951.

50/18   **St. Hilarion, P.Q.**

1284

AURORA   **1927**

Oil on canvas, 21¹/₄″ x 26¹/₄″.

NOTES: Permanent loan from C.N.E. Association, 1928-65.

Also known as *Northern Lights*.

Depicts the "northern lights" over hills near Port Burwell, Labrador.

A drawing of the same subject, entitled *Labrador*, was used to illustrate, plate 17, *The Far North, a book of drawings*, by A. Y. Jackson, [1927], which describes in text and illustrations a voyage to the Arctic aboard the "Beothic" in 1927.

EXHIBITIONS: *C.N.E.*, 1928, no. 447; A.G.T., *Exhibition of Canadian sculpture...recent accessions*, 1928, no. 7; Windsor, *Group of Seven*, 1948, no. 13; A.G.T., and others, *Jackson*, 1953-54, no. 46.

REFERENCES: *American Magazine of Art*, vol. 30 (Sept., 1937), p. 568 (reprod.); Robson, *Jackson* (1938), p. 11; MacDonald, *The Group of Seven*, (1944), p. 33 (reprod.); *Saturday Night*, vol. 60 (Mar. 3, 1945), p. 5 (reprod.); *Saturday Night*, vol. 63 (Mar. 20, 1948), p. 3 (reprod.); *Maclean's Magazine*, vol. 62 (Sept. 1, 1949), p. 17 (reprod. in colour); Jackson (1958), p. 99.

Gift of the Canadian National Exhibition Association, 1965.

PROV.: the artist.

REFERENCES: Jackson (1958), p. 122-23.

Purchase, 1940.

2829

PRECAMBRIAN HILLS   **1939**

Oil on canvas, 28¹/₈″ x 36″.
Signed and dated (lower right): A Y JACKSON/1939.

PROV.: the artist.

EXHIBITIONS: *C.N.E.*, 1939, no. 113, p. 32 (reprod.); A.G.T., *Holgate, Jackson, Lismer, and Newton*, 1940 (Apr.); Paris, UNESCO, 1946, no. 16; Windsor, *Group of Seven*, 1948, no. 12; *C.N.E.*, 1952, no. 69; A.G.O. [circulating exhibition], *Canadian paintings of the 1930s*, 1967-68, no. 12.

REFERENCES: *Canadian Review of Music and Art*, vol. I (Nov., 1942), p. 13 (reprod.); Buchanan (1945), pl. 50 (reprod.).

Purchase, 1946.

2829 **Precambrian Hills**

2830

GEM LAKE   **1941**

Oil on canvas, 25¹/₈″ x 32³/₁₆″.
Signed (lower left): A. Y. JACKSON.

PROV.: the artist.

EXHIBITIONS: *O.S.A.*, 1942, no. 98; M.M.F.A., Gallery XII, *Lismer and Jackson*, 1952 (Nov. 15-26) [no catalogue]; A.G.T., and others, *Jackson*, 1953-54, no. 70; Mexico, 1960, no. 123.

Purchase, 1946.

212

MONUMENT CHANNEL, GEORGIAN BAY   **1953**

Oil on panel, $10^7/_{16}$" x $13^1/_2$".
Signed (lower right): A Y Jackson.
Inscribed (on reverse): Monument Channel/Georgian Bay/Painted July 1953.

NOTES: Oil sketch on reverse.

EXHIBITIONS: A.G.T., and others, *Jackson*, 1953-54, no. 234.

Gift of Dr. A. Y. Jackson, 1953.

Otto R. JACOBI (1812-1901)

BORN: Otto Reinhold Jacobi, Königsberg, East Prussia, February 27, 1812.

DIED: Taiva, Dakota, February 20, 1901. Came to Canada in 1860, expressly to paint a presentation canvas of Shawinigan Falls for the Prince of Wales.

Lived in Montreal from 1860, and after travel in the United States and Canada, settled in Toronto in 1891.

STUDY: Königsberg Academy, under Christian Ernst Rauschke; Berlin Academy; Dusseldorf Academy, 1833-37, under Johann Wilhelm Schirmer.

Worked at Dusseldorf, and subsequently, as painter to the Duchess of Nassau, at Wiesbaden, where he remained for 20 years.

SOCIETIES: R.C.A., charter member, 1880, P.R.C.A., 1890-93; O.S.A.; Society of Canadian Artists, Montreal, 1867; Pen and Pencil Club, Montreal, 1890.

Landscape and portrait painter.

52/8

LANDSCAPE   **1847**

Water colour on paper, $8^1/_2$" x $10^3/_4$".
Signed and dated (lower right): O R jacobi – 1847 –.

PROV.: Mrs. John Henry Birkenshaw, Toronto.

NOTES: Title changed from *Scene* to *Landscape*, 1965.

REFERENCES: Duval (1954), pl. 16 (reprod.).

Gift of the Fund of the T. Eaton Co. for Canadian Works of Art, 1952.

52/8   **Landscape**

49/51

LANDSCAPE WITH FIGURES   **1858**

Oil on canvas, $25^7/_8$" x $35^{15}/_{16}$".
Signed and dated (lower left): O R jacobi 1858.

Gift of Mrs. F. T. Large, 1949.

1693

EVENING 1882

Water colour on paper, 12" x 16".
Signed and dated (lower right): O R jacobi. 1882.

EXHIBITIONS: [?] A.G.T., *4th loan exhibition*, 1911, no. 94 (as Sunset; property of Dr. E. St. George Baldwin).

Bequest of Dr. E. St. George Baldwin, 1931.

Don JEAN-LOUIS (1937-   )

BORN: Donald Jean-Louis, Ottawa, Ontario, May 17, 1937.

LIVES: Toronto.

STUDY: Self-taught.

64/22

INTERIOR, TWO WALLS, LANDSCAPE 1964

Tempera on masonite, 48" x 48".

PROV.: [Isaacs Gallery, Toronto].

EXHIBITIONS: Winnipeg, *9th Winnipeg show*, 1964, no. 52 (reprod.).

REFERENCES: *Canadian Art*, vol. XXIII (Jan., 1966), p. 60 (reprod.).

Gift from the McLean Foundation, 1965.

64/22   **Interior, Two Walls, Landscape**

C. W. JEFFERYS (1869-1951)

BORN: Charles William Jefferys, Rochester, Kent, England, August 25, 1869.

DIED: Toronto, October 8, 1951.
In the 1870s the family emigrated to America, spending some time in Philadelphia, then Hamilton, until they settled in Toronto, about 1880.

STUDY: Toronto, under G. A. Reid, and C. M. Manly; also at Toronto Art Students' League. Had previously been apprenticed to a firm of lithographers, and subsequently worked for

1688

THE FOUNDING OF HALIFAX, 1749

Water colour on paper, 20" x 28" [sight].
Signed (lower left): C. W. JEFFERYS.

PROV.: the artist.

NOTES: The painting was reproduced on the Canadian four cent stamp, 1949, a commemorative issue marking the 200th anniversary of the founding of Halifax.

A drawing of the same subject is in the Imperial Oil Collection, and has been used to illustrate two books by Jefferys: *Dramatic episodes in Canada's story* (1930), p. 45, and *Canada's Past in Pictures* (1934), p. 72.

The Globe; 1892-99 worked in New York as an illustrator for the New York *Herald.*

SOCIETIES: A.R.C.A., 1912, R.C.A., 1925; O.S.A., 1902, P.O.S.A., 1913-19; Toronto Art Students' League, 1886-1904; Graphic Arts Club [later C.S.G.A.], Toronto, 1903, first Pres. 1903-04; C.S.P.W.C., founding member, 1925, Pres. 1928-31; Arts and Letters Club, Toronto, Pres. 1924-26; Mahlstick Club.

TRAVEL: Extensively in Canada.

Author of *The Picture Gallery of Canadian History,* c. 1942-1950.

Worked for the Canadian War Memorials, 1916-18.

Painter, illustrator, muralist, engraver, designer, historian.

1689   **La Vérendrye Brothers**

EXHIBITIONS: *R.C.A.,* 1926-27, no. 71, opp. p. 5 (reprod.); A.G.T., *International exhibition...and historical paintings and drawings by C. W. Jefferys,* 1927, no. 222; *R.C.A.,* 1927-28, no. 102; N.G.C., *Annual,* 1928, no. 82; *C.N.E.,* 1928, no. 761b; N.G.C., *Canadian paintings,* 1935, no. 78, p. 17 (reprod.); A.G.T., *Summer,* 1935, no. 89; A.G.T., *Works by senior painters in Canada,* 1937, no. 49, p. 24 (reprod.); London, Tate, 1938, no. 116, pl. 3 (reprod.); A.G.T., *Jefferys,* 1942, no. 219; Halifax, *200 years of art in Halifax,* 1949, no. 204; *O.S.A.,* 1952, Jefferys memorial, no. 15.

REFERENCES: *R.A.I.C. Journal,* vol. IV (Jan., 1927), p. 19 (reprod.); McEwen, and Moore, *A picture history of Canada* (1938), pl. 19 (reprod. in colour); *Picture Gallery of Canadian History,* vol. I (1942), p. 219 (reprod.); *Educational Record of the Province of Quebec,* vol. LXXX (July/Sept., 1954), pp. 144, 149; MacNutt, *Making of the Maritime Provinces* 1713-1784 (1955), on cover (reprod.).

Purchase, 1930.

1689

LA VÉRENDRYE BROTHERS

Water colour on paper, 21" x 28".
Signed (lower right): C. W. JEFFERYS.

NOTES: Louis Joseph de La Vérendrye (1717-1761), and his brother François, Chevalier de la Vérendrye (1715-1794), Canadian explorers, discovered the foothills of the Rocky Mountains on an expedition in 1742-43 [see *Macmillan Dictionary of Canadian Biography,* 1963, pp. 397-98.].

EXHIBITIONS: A.G.T., *International exhibition...and historical paintings and drawings by C. W. Jefferys,* 1927, no. 221; *R.C.A.,* 1927-28, no. 101; N.G.C., *Annual,* 1928, no. 81; *C.N.E.,* 1928, no. 761a; Calgary, *Loan exhibition, R.C.A.,* 1929, no. 80; A.G.T., *Summer,* 1935, no. 90; London, Ont., *Milestones,* 1942, no. 36; A.G.T., *Jefferys,* 1942; *C.S.P.W.C.,* 1951, no. 12; *O.S.A.,* 1952, Jefferys memorial, no. 14.

REFERENCES: *Canadian Magazine,* vol. 68 (July, 1927), p. 9 (reprod.); A.G.T., *Bulletin and Annual report* (Mar., 1931), p. 12 (reprod.); C.S.P.W.C., *42nd annual exhibition* (1967), p. 9 (reprod. [not exhibited]).

Gift of R. Y. Eaton, 1933.

859

EMIGRANTS IN THE WOODS, 1830

Pen and ink on cardboard, 14" x 11 $\frac{1}{16}$".
Signed (lower left): C. W. JEFFERYS.
Inscribed (across top, in pencil): The Journey through the Woods — Chapter V.

PROV.: the artist [AGT, 1927].

EXHIBITIONS: A.G.T., *International exhibition...and historical paintings and drawings by C. W. Jefferys,* 1927, no. 276; *O.S.A.,* 1952,

New York."); Colgate, *Jefferys* (1944), pp. 16, 17 (reprod.); Buchanan (1945), pl. 24 (reprod.); *Saturday Night*, vol. 63 (Mar. 20, 1948), p. 2 (reprod.); Harper (1966), p. 267.

Gift of the Canadian National Exhibition Association, 1965.

1984

OFFICER AT NIAGARA   **1918**

Lithograph, Imp.: $13^3/_{16}$" x $9^1/_2$". Paper: 19" x $12^5/_8$".
Signed (lower left, in pencil): C. W. Jefferys.
Inscribed and dated (lower right): C. W. JEFFERYS/NIAGARA/1918.

Gift of the Artist, 1926.

1968

CANADIAN SOLDIERS LEAVING CAMP IN FULL KIT   **1919**

Lithograph, Imp.: $22^5/_8$" x 19". Paper: 28" x 21".
Inscribed and dated (lower right): C. W. JEFFERYS. '19.

Gift of the Artist, 1926.

1969

CANADIAN SOLDIERS AT BAYONET PRACTICE   **1919**

Lithograph, Imp.: $17^1/_2$" x $24^3/_{16}$". Paper: 21" x $28^1/_8$".
Signed (lower right, in pencil): Charles W. Jefferys.
Inscribed and dated (lower left): C. W. JEFFERYS '19.

Gift of the artist, 1926.

179

WOODLAND INTERIOR   **1921**

Water colour on paper, $20^1/_4$" x $14^5/_{16}$" [sight].
Signed and dated (lower left): C. W. JEFFERYS 21.

NOTES: Permanent loan from C.N.E. Association, 1922-65.

EXHIBITIONS: *R.C.A.*, 1921-22, no. 76; *C.N.E.*, 1922, no. 254; London, *British Empire Exhibition*, 1925, Canadian section of fine arts, p. 12; London, Whitechapel Art Gallery, 1925, no. 126; Manchester, 1926, no. 33; Paris, 1927, no. 93; A.G.T., *Summer*, 1935, no. 88; A.G.T., *Loan exhibition*, 1935, no. 239; *O.S.A.*, 1947, no. 163.

REFERENCES: Colgate, *Jefferys* (n.d.), opp. p. 26 (reprod. in colour); Robson (1932), p. 123 (reprod. in colour).

Gift of the Canadian National Exhibition Association, 1965.

51/86

NEAR BOBCAYGEON   **1924**

Oil on panel, $10^1/_2$" x $13^1/_2$".
Signed (lower left): C. W. JEFFERYS.

Anne KAHANE (1924-

BORN: Vienna, Austria, March 1, 1924

LIVES: Montreal.

STUDY: Cooper Union, New York, 19

SOCIETIES: A.R.C.A., 1960; S.S.C.

TEACHING: Montreal, Sir George \
University, since 1966.

AWARDS: International competition,
1953, for "Unknown Political Prisone
cours artistique, Quebec, 1956; Canada
grant, 1961.

Began as a painter and commerci
since 1949 has worked mainly as a
primarily in wood.

58/2   **Woman with Apron**

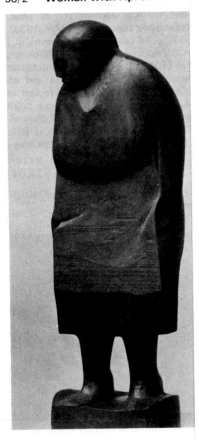

Louis JOBIN (1844-1928)

BORN: St. Raymond, P. Q., 1844.

DIED: Ste. Anne de Beaupré, March, 1928.

STUDY: Quebec, under François-Xavier
Berlinguet, about 1855; was apprenticed to his
uncle, a woodcarver, carving figureheads,
nameboards, and other ship decoration.

Spent some time in New York, carving cigar-
store Indians; lived in Montreal, 1870-75;
retired to Ste. Anne de Beaupré, where he
worked at religious carvings for pilgrims and
churches.

Wood carver.

779   **Angel with Lyre**

Inscribed and dated (on reverse): Near Bobcaygeon/Easter 1924.

PROV.: [Roberts Gallery, Toronto].

*Gift of the Fund of the T. Eaton Co. Ltd. for Canadian Works of Art,
1952.*

58/56

LANDSCAPE WITH FENCE   1924

Water colour on paper, 11¼" x 20" [sight].
Signed and dated (lower right): C. W. JEFFERYS '24.

PROV.: Ivor Lewis, Toronto; [his sister] Mrs. C. H. Watson, Toronto.

Gift from the McLean Foundation, 1959.

779

ANGEL WITH LYRE

Wood [originally painted], 51½".
Signed (lower right): L JOBIN

PROV.: the artist.

EXHIBITIONS: A.G.T., *Group of Seven, and painting, sculpture and
wood carving of French Canada*, 1926, no. 237 or 238; A.G.T., *5th
biennial ..architecture and allied arts*, [and] *exhibition of traditional
arts of French Canada*, 1935, no. 525.

REFERENCES: *Art Digest*, vol. 9 (Jan. 15, 1935), p. 11; Barbeau,
Quebec, where ancient France lingers (1936), p. 85 (reprod.);
Barbeau, *Québec, où survit l'ancienne France* (1937), p. 92 (reprod.);
Canadian Review of Music and Art, vol. 4 (Dec. Jan., 1946), pp. 22,
29 (reprod.); *Saturday Night*, vol. 70 (July 24, 1954), p. 5 (reprod.);
Jackson, *A painter's country* (1958), p. 66.

Gift of E.R. Greig, 1925.

Roy KIYOOKA (1926-   )

BORN: Roy Kenzie Kiyooka, Moose Jaw, Saskatchewan, January 18, 1926.

LIVES: Montreal.

STUDY: Calgary, Provincial Institute of Technology and Art, 1946-49, under J. W. G. Macdonald and I. H. Kerr; Mexico, Instituto Allende, 1958, under James Pinto; also University of Saskatchewan Emma Lake workshops under Will Barnet, Barnett Newman and Clement Greenberg, 1958-60.

SOCIETIES: A.R.C.A., 1965.

TEACHING: Regina College School of Art, 1957-59; Vancouver School of Art, 1960-65; since 1965, Sir George Williams University, Montreal.

AWARDS: Canada Council grant, 1964.

Painter, poet, printmaker, muralist.

Fred W. JOPLING (1859/60-1945)

BORN: Frederic Waistell England, April 23, 1859 or

DIED: Toronto, April, 1945 (Toronto) 1873.

STUDY: Toronto, Ontario S 78, under O'Brien and Fra Students' League, under 1880-83; Toronto, lithogr Howard, and W. D. Blatchl

Worked in Toronto with lithographers. Began etcl 1916-17; did etching of historical interest in the Ni

Artist, illustrator, painter.

Dorothy KNOWLES (1927-   )

BORN: Unity, Saskatchewan, April 7, 1927.

LIVES: Saskatoon; married to artist Bill Perehudoff.

STUDY: University of Saskatchewan; Goldsmith School of Art, London, England, 1951; Paris, 1952; and University of Saskatchewan Emma Lake workshops under Noland, Olitski, and others.

64/17

BAROMETER NO. 2   1964

Polymer on canvas, 97" x 69".
Signed and dated (lower right): R. Kiyooka - 64.
Inscribed (across stretcher): "BAROMETER NO. 2" Roy Kiyooka - 64.

PROV.: [David Mirvish Gallery, Toronto].

EXHIBITIONS: David Mirvish Gallery, *Kiyooka*, 1964 (Nov.) [no catalogue]; New York, Grippi and Waddell, *Kiyooka*, 1964 (Nov. 21 - Dec. 26) [no catalogue]; A.G.T., *Art and Engineering*, 1965, no. 10A (reprod.); São Paulo, *VIII Bienal*, 1965, p. 165, no. 10 (reprod.); and special edition, *Canada at São Paulo*, 1965, no. 10 (reprod.); N.G.C., *6th biennial*, 1965, no. 50.

REFERENCES: *Canadian Art*, vol. XXII (May, 1965), p. 60 (reprod.).

Gift from the McLean Foundation, 1964.

64/17   **Barometer no. 2**

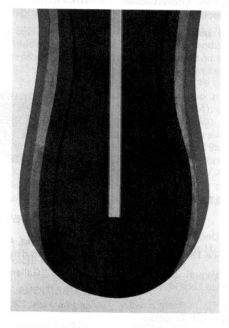

64/80

REEDY LAKE   1962

Oil on masonite, 41³/₄" x 48".
Signed and dated (lower right): KNOWLES 62.

PROV.: the artist.

EXHIBITIONS: Charlottetown, *Directors' Choice*, 1967-68, no. 26.

Gift from the Georgia J. Weldon Estate and Canada Council Matching Grant, 1965.

64/80   **Reedy Lake**

Elizabeth McGillivray
KNOWLES (1866-1928)

BORN: Elizabeth Annie Beach, Ottawa, Ontario, January 8, 1866.

DIED: Riverton, New Hampshire, October 5, 1928.

STUDY: Toronto, Ontario School of Art, c. 1885-90, under Farquhar McGillivray Knowles, later her husband; initially encouraged by her uncle, F. M. Bell-Smith.

SOCIETIES: O.S.A., 1906, resigned, 1909; A.R.C.A., 1908; National Association of Women Painters and Sculptors, New York; Pennsylvania Society of Miniature Painters, Philadelphia; American Water Colour Society.

Lived in London and Paris, 1890-95, while her husband studied further.

Landscape painter; miniaturist depicting domestic animals, especially fowl.

59/17   An Exciting Moment

59/17

AN EXCITING MOMENT

Oil on canvas, 12″ x 15⅞″.
Signed (lower left): Elizabeth A. McGillivray Knowles.

PROV.: R. S. McLaughlin, Oshawa; Mrs. J. B. Pangman, Charlottesville and Magog; Mrs. M. Eileen McEachern, Stonecroft, Todmorden, Ontario.

EXHIBITIONS: *R.C.A.*, 1924, no. 116; *R.C.A.*, 1925, no. 131; *C.N.E.*, 1925, no. 303; Toronto, Robert Simpson Company, *Knowles memorial loan exhibition*, 1929, no. 110 (lent by R. S. McLaughlin).

REFERENCES: *Paintings by Farquhar McGillivray Knowles and Elizabeth A. McGillivray Knowles* (n.d.), reprod.

Bequest of Mrs. M. Eileen McEachern, 1960.

19

CASE OF SIX MINIATURES   1910-12

Poplars
Water colour on ivory, 2⅜″ x 1¾″ [sight].
Signed and dated (lower left): Elizabeth A. McG. Knowles/1912.

Dutch Landscape
Water colour on ivory, 1¾″ x 2⅜″ [sight].
Signed (lower left): Elizabeth A. McG. Knowles.

Landscape with flowering tree and fowl
Water colour on ivory, 2⅜″ x 1¾‴ [sight].
Signed and dated (lower left): Elizabeth A. McG. Knowles. 1912.

Landscape in green and gold
Water colour on ivory, ¾″ x ¾″ [sight].
Signed and dated (lower left): Elizabeth A. McG. Knowles 1910.

Orchard
Water colour on paper, 3¼″ x 4¾″ [sight].
Signed and dated (lower left): Elizabeth A. McGillivray Knowles. 1910.

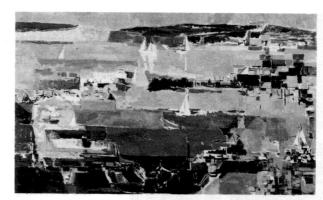

56/30   **Island Passage**

Ted KRAMOLC (1922-   )

BORN: Theodore Maria Kramolc, Ljubljana, Yugoslavia, March 27, 1922.

LIVES: Rexdale, Ontario. Came to Canada in 1948.

STUDY: Yugoslavia; Austria; Toronto, Ontario College of Art, 1949-51, with post-graduate studies in graphics.

SOCIETIES: C.P.E.

Painter, graphic designer.

Cornelius KRIEGHOFF (1815-1872)

BORN: Amsterdam, The Netherlands, 1815.

DIED: Chicago, 1872.

Emigrated to New York about 1836; served with the American army in the Seminole War; discharged in 1840. Married a French-Canadian girl and moved to Canada in the early 1840's.

STUDY: Believed to have studied in Rotterdam and Düsseldorf.

Lived briefly in Toronto and Longueuil, then settled in Montreal where he lived from 1847 to 1853; thereafter in Quebec, until he moved to Chicago in 1868 to live with his daughter.

TRAVEL: Through Europe as an itinerant artist and musician; is said to have travelled in England and on the continent, 1854-55, and perhaps again in 1862. Only returned to Quebec from Chicago once, in 1871, at which time he painted three of his largest and best canvases.

61/58

YELLOW AND BLACK   1960

Monotype, $20^{15}/_{16}$" x $31^{1}/_{4}$" [sight].
Signed (lower right, in pencil): Ted Kramolc.
Dated and numbered (lower left, in pencil): 1./I. 1960.

PROV.: [Picture Loan Society, Toronto].

EXHIBITIONS: Picture Loan Society, *Kramolc*, 1961 (Apr. 22 - May 5) [no catalogue].

Gift from the McLean Foundation, 1962.

55/4

HABITANT WITH BLUE TOQUE AND PIPE

Oil on canvas, $12^{1}/_{8}$" x $9^{5}/_{16}$" oval.

NOTES: According to Marius Barbeau's monograph on Krieghoff, 1934, p. 122, this subject was painted by Krieghoff during his period in Quebec, that is, between 1854 and 1868.

Bequest of Dr. John G. Lee, 1955.

50/71

THE BASKET SELLER   c. 1850

Oil on cardboard, $9^{3}/_{4}$" x $7^{7}/_{16}$".
Signed (lower right): C. Krieghoff.

PROV.: Henry Fletcher Jackson, Longueuil, P. Q., and Berlin, Ontario (c. 1850-1894); Miss Geneva Jackson, Berlin (1894-1951); John Hayward, Hamilton (1951).

NOTES: Label on reverse of frame reads: (CORNELIUS KRIEGHOFE [sic])/Purchased from the artist at/Longueuil about 1850 by/Henry F[   ] Jackson.

Gift from the Fund of the T. Eaton Co. Ltd. for Canadian Works of Art, 1951.

55/4 **Habitant with Blue Toque and Pipe**

2532

MIDDAY REST 1854

Oil on canvas, 14⅛" x 21⅛".
Signed and dated (lower right): C. Krieghoff/1854.

PROV.: Mr. Howard [?]; Mrs. Mary Mowat, Toronto (1877-1939).

NOTES: According to Marius Barbeau [see ref.], this was Krieghoff's "greatest single favourite" theme; "Lorette hunters, dressed in Hudson's Bay blanket coats, camping at the foot of a large square rock surrounded by bright autumn foliage, and enjoying their 'Midday Rest'". Krieghoff painted more than thirty versions of the subject between 1854 and 1866.
Sticker on reverse: #42. [?].

EXHIBITIONS: A.G.T., *4th loan exhibition*, 1911, no. 140 (as Indians on Shore of St. Lawrence; property of Mrs. Mary Mowat); Fredericton, *Krieghoff*, 1961, no. 71.

REFERENCES: Barbeau, *Krieghoff* (1934), pp. 18, 19, 65-66, 80, 135 (gives provenance).

Bequest of Mrs. H. M. Mowat, 1939.

886

THE DEAD STAG c. 1854

Oil on canvas, 8⅞" x 10⅝".
Signed (lower left): C. Krieghoff.

PROV.: Thomas Jenkins, Toronto.

EXHIBITIONS: A.G.T., *Inaugural*, 1926, no. 205 (lent by Thomas Jenkins); London, Ont., *Milestones*, 1942, no. 6.

REFERENCES: A.G.T., *Bulletin* (May, 1928), p. 18 (reprod.); Robson (1932), p. 25 (reprod. in colour); Barbeau, *Krieghoff* (1934), p. 128 (dated c. 1854); Robson, *Krieghoff* (1937), p. 18, pl. V (reprod. in colour); McRae (1944), p. 57 (reprod.).

Gift from the Reuben and Kate Leonard Canadian Fund, 1927.

2531

HABITANTS SLEIGHING c. 1855

Oil on canvas, 12⅛" x 18".
Signed (lower left): C. [Kr]ieghoff [partially obliterated].

PROV.: Mr. Howard [?]; Mrs Mary Mowat, Toronto (1877-1939).

NOTES: There are many versions of the subject: one closely resembling ours is in the collection of the National Gallery of Canada, acc. no. 4350; catalogued and illustrated in N.G.C., *Catalogue of the Canadian school*, 1960, p. 163.

EXHIBITIONS: A.G.T., *4th loan exhibition*, 1911, no. 141 (property of Mrs. H. M. Mowat); *C.N.E.*, 1948, no. 1.

REFERENCES: Barbeau, *Krieghoff* (1934), p. 112 (dated in "Quebec period"; gives provenance).

Bequest of Mrs. H. M. Mowat, 1939.

E. L. LAUR (1867-c. 1940)

BORN: Edgar Lee Laur, Elgin County, Ontario, 1867.

DIED: Woodbridge, Ontario, about 1940.

STUDY: Toronto, Ontario School of Art, under Cruikshank and Challener.

In early life was a school teacher, and later a telegrapher on the Michigan Central Railroad.

SOCIETIES: Art Students' League, Toronto; Mahlstick Club, Toronto; C.P.E., 1919.

Etcher.

287

NOCTURNE

1922

Aquatint, Imp.: $9^5/_8$" x $11^3/_8$". Paper: $13^7/_{16}$" x $15^1/_4$".
Signed and dated (lower right, in pencil): E L Laur/22.
Numbered (lower left, in pencil): 1/49.

NOTES: Permanent loan from C.N.E. Association, 1925-66.

EXHIBITIONS: *C.N.E.*, 1925, no. 690.

Gift of the Canadian National Exhibition Association, 1966.

Ernest LAWSON (1873-1939)

BORN: Halifax, N. S., March 22, 1873.

DIED: Coral Gables, Florida, December 18, 1939.

STUDY: Kansas City, 1888, with Ella Holman and others; Mexico City, working as a draughtsman, 1890; New York, Art Students' League, 1891; Cos Cob, Conn., under John Twachtman and J. Alden Weir; Paris, Académie Julian, 1893, under Jean-Paul Laurens.

SOCIETIES: Canadian Art Club, 1912; National Academy of Design; National Institute of Arts and Letters.

Exhibited with *The Eight* in 1908.

1895, returned to United States from Europe; 1896, settled briefly in Toronto; from 1898 lived in New York; 1916-36 travelled all over the U. S., Canada, and taught in several centres.

Landscape painter, portraitist.

1356

THE ROAD TO THE MOUNTAINS

c. 1926

Oil on canvas, $24^1/_8$" x $29^7/_8$".
Signed (lower left): E. LAWSON.

PROV.: the artist [AGT, 1930].

EXHIBITIONS: A.G.T., *Kroll, and Lawson*, 1930, no. 30; A.G.T., *Loan exhibition*, 1935, no. 119; Stratford, *Canada on canvas*, 1963; London, Ont., *Canadian Impressionists*, 1965, no. 23; N.G.C., *Lawson*, 1967, no. 63 (says painted about 1926 in Colorado), p. 40 (reprod.).

REFERENCES: Price, *Lawson* (1930), pl. 39 (reprod. as Road to the Mountain, Colorado).

Purchase, 1930.

1356   **The Road to the Mountains**

240

LEBLOND dit LATOUR,
Jacques, attributed to, see
UNKNOWN, Cap Tourmente,
beginning of 18th century

Jean-Paul LEMIEUX
(1904-   )

BORN: Quebec, P. Q., November 18, 1904.

LIVES: Quebec (Sillery).

STUDY: Montreal, 1926, in studio of Suzor-Côté; Montreal, École des Beaux-Arts, 1926-29, under Charles Maillard, and Edwin Holgate, and others; Paris, Colarossi, and Grande Chaumière.

SOCIETIES: A.R.C.A., 1951; R.C.A., 1966.

TEACHING: Montreal, 1934-35 at Ecole des Beaux-Arts, and 1935-36 at Ecole du Meuble, Montreal; Ecole des Beaux-Arts de Quebec, since 1937.

TRAVEL: Europe, 1929, spending most of time in Paris.

AWARDS: Canadian government scholarship, 1954-55, for work in France.

Landscape and figure painter.

2574 **Lazare**
Colour reproduction, p. 545

2574

LAZARE   1941

Oil on masonite, 39³/₄″ x 32⁷/₈″.
Signed and dated (lower left): JEAN PAUL LEMIEUX/1941.

PROV.: the artist [AGT, 1941].

EXHIBITIONS: A.G.T., *Goldhamer, Haworth, Lemieux, and Wood*, 1941; Paris, UNESCO, 1946, no. 17; A.G.T., *Religious art*, 1963, no. 12, pl. IV (reprod.); London, Ont., *Surrealism in Canadian painting*, 1964, no. 50; London, and Kitchener, *Lemieux*, 1966, no. 3 (reprod.); N.G.C., *300 years of Canadian art*, 1967, no. 259, p. 156 (reprod.). M.M.F.A., *Lemieux*, 1967, no. 13, p. 27 (reprod.).

REFERENCES: A.G.T., *Accessions 1941*, reprod.; *Saturday Night*, vol. 60 (Mar. 3, 1945), p. 5 (reprod.); Barbeau (1946), p. 35 (reprod.); *The Arts in Canada* (1957), p. 101; A.G.T., *Painting and sculpture* (1959), p. 80 (reprod.); *Canadian painting in the twentieth century* (1961), pl. 7 (reprod. in colour); Hubbard (1963), p. 115; *Canadian Art*, vol. XX (Nov. - Dec., 1963), p. 331 (reprod.); Kilbourn (1966), p. 333, fig. 303 (reprod.).

Purchase, 1941.

58/58

LES CLÔTURES   1958

Oil on canvas, 22¹/₄″ x 51⁵/₈″.
Signed and dated (lower right): JEAN PAUL LEMIEUX 58

PROV.: [Roberts Gallery, Toronto].

EXHIBITIONS: Vancouver, U. B. C. Fine Arts Gallery, *Lemieux*, 1958 (June 27 - July 18) [no catalogue]; Mexico, 1960, no. 142; Paris, Musée Galliera, *Lemieux, and others*, 1963-64; London, and Kitchener, *Lemieux*, 1966, no. 4 (reprod.).

Gift from the McLean Foundation, 1959.

58/58 **Les clôtures**

64/81 **Structure**

Arthur LISMER (1885-1969)

BORN: Sheffield, England, June 27, 1885.

DIED: Montreal, March 23, 1969. Came to Canada (Toronto) in 1911.

STUDY: Sheffield, Sheffield School of Art, c. 1897-1904; Antwerp, Académie Royale des Beaux-Arts, c. 1904-06.

Worked at Grip firm, 1911-12.

SOCIETIES: A.R.C.A., 1919; R.C.A., 1946; O.S.A., 1913; Group of Seven, original member, 1919; C.G.P., founding member, 1933, Pres. 1954-55, and 1956-57; Arts and Letters Club, Toronto.

TEACHING: Halifax, Victoria School of Art and Design, principal, 1916-19; Toronto, Ontario College of Art, 1919-27; Toronto, Art Gallery of Toronto, educational supervisor, 1927-38; New York, Columbia University, 1938; Ottawa, National Gallery of Canada, 1939; Montreal, Montreal Museum of Fine Arts, Principal of School of Art and Design, since 1940.

1936-37, leave of absence from Art Gallery of Toronto, to spend a year in South Africa, establishing educational programs, and to visit centres in Australia, and New Zealand,

50/47

ALGONQUIN PARK 1913

Oil on panel, $9^1/_8$" x $12^1/_{16}$".
Signed and dated (lower right): A Lismer '13.

NOTES: Unfinished sketch on reverse.

Label taken from back of panel, now in accession file: Painted in Algonquin P./ · Spruce 1913 · /(with T. T.).

Gift of Arthur Lismer, 1951.

50/49

SMOKE LAKE, ALGONQUIN PARK 1913 or 1914

Oil on panel, $9^3/_{16}$" x $12^1/_4$".
Signed (lower left): A. Lismer.
Dated and inscribed (on reverse, in pencil): Smoke L./Algonquin Pk/A Lismer/Spring 1914.

NOTES: Label on reverse: Painted. Smoke Lake/Algonquin Park. 1913/ (With T. Thomson. May 1913).

Gift of Arthur Lismer, 1951.

52/13

LAKE IN AUTUMN 1914

Oil on panel, 9" x $12^3/_{16}$".
Signed and dated (lower left): A. Lismer. 14.

244

in the interests of Child Art and Teacher Training.

AWARDS: Canada Council Medal in 1962 for his contribution to Canadian art.

Worked for the Canadian War Memorials in Halifax, 1917-18.

Landscape painter, educationist.

Inscribed (on reverse): PRESENTED TO MY HUSBAND AND ME/ BY/DOCTOR JAMES M. MACCALLUM — /JUNE 3 - 1914 — / ISABEL MACKAY ROSS.
(and): HONOURABLE W. D. AND MRS. ROSS — /PRESENTED BY MRS. W. D. ROSS.

Gift of Mrs. W. D. Ross, 1952.

50/50

MacCALLUM's ISLAND, GEORGIAN BAY   **1915**

Oil on cardboard, 9$\frac{1}{8}$" x 12$\frac{1}{16}$".
Dated (on reverse): 1915.

NOTES: Label on reverse: At MacCallum's Island/Georgian Bay. 1915.

Gift of Arthur Lismer, 1951.

50/51

MY GARDEN, JOHN STREET, THORNHILL   **1916**

Oil on canvas board, 11$\frac{15}{16}$" x 15$\frac{3}{8}$".

NOTES: Label on reverse: This is my garden at the/back of my house at JOHN ST/THORNHILL — where we lived from Sept. 1915 — 15. Sept 1916/.../Feb. - Mar 1916.

REFERENCES: Kilbourn (1966), p. 39 (reprod. in colour).

Gift from the Fund of the T. Eaton Co. Ltd. for Canadian Works of Art, 1951.

50/51   **My Garden, John Street, Thornhill**

1952

BIG GUNS AT NIGHT   **1917-18**

Lithograph, Imp.: 15$\frac{1}{2}$" x 12$\frac{1}{2}$". Paper: 24" x 17$\frac{7}{8}$".
Signed (lower right, in pencil): A Lismer.

1967

SOLDIERS DISEMBARKING   **1917-18**

Lithograph, Imp.: $15^1/_2$" x $13^{11}/_{16}$". Paper: $23^1/_4$" x $18^3/_8$".
Signed (lower right, in pencil): A Lismer.

Gift of the Artist, 1926.

50/48

MY WIFE, SACKVILLE RIVER, NOVA SCOTIA   **1918**

Oil on panel, $8^{15}/_{16}$" x $12^1/_{16}$".
Signed and dated (lower left): A Lismer/1918.

NOTES: Label on reverse: Painted along the/Sackville R. – N. S./
N. S. – 1917 or 1918/'My Wife'.

Gift of Arthur Lismer, 1951.

2547

ROCK, PINE AND SUNLIGHT (SKETCH)   **c. 1920**

Oil on panel, $11^3/_4$" x 16".
Signed (lower left): A. Lismer.

NOTES: Sketch for painting by the same title in this collection; see
below, acc. no. 1334.

EXHIBITIONS: London, Ont., *Milestones*, 1942, no. 65; A.G.T.,
N.G.C., *Lismer*, 1950, no. 102.

Gift of Arthur Lismer, 1940.

1334

ROCK, PINE AND SUNLIGHT   **1920**

Oil on canvas, 36" x 44".
Signed and dated (lower right): A Lismer/20.

PROV.: the artist [AGT, 1928].

NOTES: Painted at Go Home Bay, Ontario.

Sketch for the painting is in this collection; see above, acc. no. 2547.

EXHIBITIONS: London, *British Empire Exhibition*, 1924, Catalogue
of the Palace of Arts, p. 96, no. EE. 63, and Illustrated souvenir, p. 113
(reprod.), and Canadian section of fine arts, no. 129; A.G.T., *Group
of Seven*, 1928, no. 53; A.G.T., *Summer*, 1935, no. 38; N.G.C., *Retrospective...Group of Seven*, 1936, no. 127; London, Ont., *Milestones*,
1942, no. 64; New York, National Arts Club, 1945 (Mar. - June)
[no catalogue]; London, Ont., *Group of Seven*, 1946, no. 21; Albany,
1946, no. 56; A.G.T., and Toledo, Ohio, *Two Cities Collect*, 1948,
no. 20 (reprod.); Boston, 1949, no. 47; Richmond, Va., 1949, no. 46;
A.G.T., N.G.C., *Lismer*, 1950, no. 7, pl. 4 (reprod.); Mexico, 1960,
no. 128; N.G.C., *300 years of Canadian art*, 1967, no. 210, p. 133
(reprod.).

REFERENCES: A.G.T., *Bulletin* (Mar., 1930), p. 12 (reprod.); MacDonald, *Group of Seven* (1944), p. 20 (reprod.); Buchanan (1945), pl. 56 (reprod.); *Canadian Art*, vol. IV (Mar., 1947), p. 51 (reprod.); A.G.T., *Programme 1948-49*, p. 12 (reprod.); A.G.T., *50th anniversary* (1950), p. 31 (reprod.); McInnes (1950), between pp. 84, 85 (reprod.); *R.A.I.C. Journal*, vol. 27 (Jan., 1950), p. 25 (reprod.); *Canadian Art*, vol. VII (Spring, 1950), p. 89; McLeish, *September Gale* (1955), p. 31 (says painted at Go Home Bay), opp. p. 53 (reprod.), pp. 72, 182, 203; A.G.T., *Painting and sculpture* (1959), p. 53 (reprod.).

Purchase, 1929.

1334   Rock, Pine and Sunlight

50/46

GO HOME BAY   1921

Oil on panel, 11$^{15}/_{16}$ x 16$^{1}/_{16}$".
Signed and dated (lower right): A Lismer/21.
Inscribed (on reverse): Rocks & Water/ — /Arthur Lismer/ 26 Severn St./Toronto.

NOTES: Label on reverse: This was painted/at Go-home Bay — on the/same spot — at the same time,/'Rock, pine & sunlight' in/the Art G. of T. permanent collection.

EXHIBITIONS: [?] A.G.T., *Group of Seven*, 1921, no. 37 (as Rock and Water).

Gift of Arthur Lismer, 1951.

49/58

SOMBRE HILL, ALGOMA   1922

Oil on canvas, 40" x 45".
Signed (lower centre): A Lismer.

PROV.: the artist.

This sketch has been alternately entitled, *Old Mill, Ile d'Orleans*, and *Old Mill, Baie St. Paul*.

EXHIBITIONS: [?] A.G.T., *Group of Seven*, 1926, no. 73 (as The Mill, Quebec); *C.N.E.*, 1926, no. 284 (as Old Mill, Baie St. Paul, P. Q.); [?] N.G.C., *Retrospective...Group of Seven*, 1936, no. 137 (as Old Mill, French Canada).

Gift from the Fund of the T. Eaton Co. Ltd. for Canadian Works of Art, 1951.

50/54

OPPOSITE MY STUDIO   **1926 or 1927**

Oil on panel, 11$^{15}/_{16}$" x 15$^{7}/_{8}$".
Signed (lower centre): A. Lismer.
Inscribed (on reverse): Opposite my studio/at Bedford Park Ave/Toronto/1926 — or 1927/Arthur Lismer.

PROV.: the artist.

Gift from the Fund of the T. Eaton Co. Ltd. for Canadian Works of Art, 1951.

2484

PINE WRECKAGE, GEORGIAN BAY   **c. 1929**

Oil on board, 12$^{7}/_{8}$" x 16$^{1}/_{8}$".
Signed (lower right): A Lismer.
Inscribed (on reverse): Pine Wreckage/A Lismer.

NOTES: Sketch for canvas by the same title in the collection of Mr. and Mrs. Charles S. Band, Toronto. The painting, oil on canvas, 32$^{1}/_{4}$" x 40", has been reproduced often: *The collection of Mr. and Mrs. Charles S. Band*, 1963, p. 17, no. 31; *Canadian Art*, vol. 18 (May, 1961), p. 160; and A.G.T., N.G.C., *Lismer*, 1950, no. 27, pl. 10, where it is dated c. 1929.

EXHIBITIONS: *O.S.A. little pictures*, 1929, no. 165; *C.N.E.*, 1930, no. 435; A.G.T., N.G.C., *Lismer*, 1950, no. 114; A.G.T., and Ontario Department of Education, 1951, no. 31.

Bequest of Ambia L. Going, 1938.

2851

SUNLIGHT IN A WOOD (SKETCH)   **1929**

Crayon on paper, 11" x 14$^{7}/_{8}$".
Signed and dated (lower right): A — Lismer/29.

NOTES: Sketch for painting by the same title in this collection; see below, acc. no. 2847.

EXHIBITIONS: A.G.T., N.G.C., *Lismer*, 1950, no. 303.

Gift of the Artist, 1946.

252

2847   **Sunlight in a Wood**

2847

SUNLIGHT IN A WOOD   **1930**

Oil on canvas, 36" x 40".
Signed and dated (lower left): A Lismer 30.

PROV.: the artist.

NOTES: A crayon sketch for this painting is in this collection; see above, acc. no. 2851.

EXHIBITIONS: A.G.T., *Group of Seven*, 1930, no. 92; *R.C.A.*, 1931, no. 166; *C.N.E.*, 1931, no. 432; New York, Roerich Museum, 1932, no. 37; N.G.C., *Retrospective...Group of Seven*, 1936, no. 133; San Francisco, 1939, p. 28, no. 15; A.G.T., *Holgate, Jackson, Lismer, and Newton*, 1940 (Apr.); London, Ont., *Group of Seven*, 1946, no. 22; A.G.T., N.G.C., *Lismer*, 1950, no. 33; Chautauqua, N. Y., *Group of Seven*, 1963; A.G.O. [circulating exhibition], *Canadian paintings of the 1930s*, 1967-68, no. 13.

REFERENCES: A.G.T., *Programme 1947-48*, p. 2 (reprod.).

Bequest of John M. Lyle, 1946.

2316

ROCK AND PINE SHADOWS   **1933**

Brush and ink on card, 11" x 15".
Signed and dated (lower left): A Lismer/33.

PROV.: [Galleries of J. Merritt Malloney, Toronto].

EXHIBITIONS: Malloney, *Lismer*, 1935 (May 4-25), one of nos. 66-80.

REFERENCES: Duval (1952), pl. 22 (reprod.); Duval, *Group of Seven drawings* (1965), pl. 20 (reprod.).

Gift from Friends of Canadian Art Fund, 1935.

2317
GEORGIAN BAY   **1933**

Brush and ink on paper, $10^9/_{16}$" x $13^9/_{16}$" [sight].
Signed and dated (lower right): A. Lismer/33.

PROV.: [Galleries of J. Merritt Malloney, Toronto].

EXHIBITIONS: Malloney, *Lismer*, 1935 (May 4-25), one of nos. 66-80; New York, *World's Fair*, 1939, section CSGA, no. 80; A.G.T., N.G.C., *Lismer*, 1950, no. 304.

REFERENCES: *Maclean's Magazine* (May 7, 1960), p. 26 (reprod.); Kilbourn (1966), p. 26 (reprod.).

Gift from Friends of Canadian Art Fund, 1935.

2318

PINES, GEORGIAN BAY   **1933**

Brush and ink on paper, 11" x 15".
Signed and dated (lower centre): A Lismer. 33.

2839

DOCK VISTA   **1945**

Oil on canvas board, 11$^7/_8$" x 15$^3/_4$".
Signed and dated (lower centre): A LISMER 45.
Inscribed (on reverse): DOCK VISTA/Arthur Lismer.

PROV.: [Eaton's Fine Art Galleries, Toronto].

EXHIBITIONS: Eaton's Fine Art Galleries, *Lismer*, 1946 (Feb.) [no catalogue].

Purchase, 1946.

2841

KILLICK PARADE   **1945**

Brush and ink on paper, 11$^3/_4$" x 18".
Signed, dated and inscribed (lower right): A Lismer 1945 — /Neils Harbour. C. B. I.

PROV.: [Eaton's Fine Art Galleries, Toronto].

EXHIBITIONS: Eaton's Fine Art Galleries, *Lismer*, 1946 (Feb.) [no catalogue]; A.G.T., N.G.C., *Lismer*, 1950, no. 307.

REFERENCES: *New Liberty* (May, 1951), p. 33 (reprod.).

Purchase, 1946.

2841   **Killick Parade**

48/29

GEORGIAN BAY BACKWATER   **1948**

Oil on panel, 12" x 16".
Signed and dated (lower left): AUG 2/A Lismer.

PROV.: the artist.

256

EXHIBITIONS: [?] N.G.C., *Retrospective...Group of Seven*, 1936, no. 141 (lent by the artist).

Gift from the Fund of the T. Eaton Co. Ltd. for Canadian Works of Art, 1949.

48/30

LILY POND, GEORGIAN BAY   **1948**

Oil on aluminum, 12" x 15$^3/_4$".
Signed (lower left): A L.

PROV.: the artist.

EXHIBITIONS: [?] A.G.T., *Purchase Fund Sale*, 1948, p. 2; A.G.T., N.G.C., *Lismer*, 1950, no. 128, pl. 15 (reprod.).

Gift from the Fund of the T. Eaton Co. Ltd. for Canadian Works of Art, 1949.

LITHOGRAPHS OF ONTARIO.
by Charles Goldhamer, A.O.C.A., and Tom Stone, O.S.A.

The following (15) lithographs come from a portfolio, one of two hundred copies produced by the artists' hands, in Toronto, about 1932.

Each page originally measured 14" x 10$^1/_2$", and was contained in a portfolio measuring 15$^3/_4$" x 12$^1/_2$". The portfolio *Per se* is missing, as are the two introductory pages, one with an introduction by Arthur Lismer. There is a copy (no. 21) of the complete portfolio in the Toronto Public Library.

The measurements given below are those of the impression only. All the lithographs are signed, in pencil, lower right, to the exclusion of one, acc. no. 2087 by Goldhamer. All are inscribed, in pencil, lower left, as given in the title.

Charles GOLDHAMER
(1903-   )
For biography see p. 140

2085

ONTARIO VILLAGE, 8$^3/_{16}$" x 7$^3/_4$".

2086

SOUTH RIVER, 11$^1/_4$" x 9".

2087

GEORGIAN BAY, 8$^1/_2$" x 11$^7/_{16}$".

2088

FISHING SHEDS, NORTH SHORE, GEORGIAN BAY, 8$^1/_2$ x 11".
Reproduced, in reverse, in Charles Goldhamer, *How to get started Drawing for Pleasure*, 194—., p. 15.

Frances LORING (1887-1968)

BORN: Frances Norma Loring, Wardner, Idaho, October 14, 1887.

DIED: Toronto, February 5, 1968. Came to Canada (Toronto) in 1913.

STUDY: Geneva, Ecole des Beaux-Arts, c. 1900-03; Munich under Carl Güttner, c. 1903-04; Paris, Académie Colarossi, c. 1904-06; Chicago, Art Institute of Chicago, 1907; Boston, School of Museum of Fine Arts, 1908-09; New York, Art Students' League, 1910.

SOCIETIES: A.R.C.A., 1920, R.C.A., 1947; O.S.A., 1920, resigned, 1933, reinstated, 1948; S.S.C., charter member, 1928, Pres. 1950; Women's Art Association of Canada, Pres. 1939; F.C.A.

AWARDS: L.L.D. (Toronto), 1955.

Sculptor, monumentalist.

1686   The Derelicts

1686

THE DERELICTS   **1929**

Bronze, 23" high.

NOTES: Permanent loan from C.N.E. Association, 1930-36.

Cast also in the collection of the National Gallery of Canada, acc. no. 3684; catalogued and illustrated in N.G.C., *Catalogue of the Canadian School*, 1960, p. 353.

EXHIBITIONS: A.G.T., *Canadian sculpture*, 1928, no. 115; *S.S.C.*, 1929, no. 66 (plaster); *C.N.E.*, 1930, no. 224; Murray Bay, Manoir Richelieu, 1930 (July), no. 712.

Gift of the Canadian National Exhibition Association, 1966.

49/59

SIR FREDERICK BANTING (1891-1941)   **1947**

Bronze, 25" high.

NOTES: One of three busts, cast in 1947 from the plaster model, first exhibited in 1934. The other casts are in the collections of the University of Toronto, and of the National Gallery of Canada, acc. no. 5046; catalogued and illustrated in N.G.C., *Catalogue of the Canadian School*, 1960, p. 353.

Dr. Frederick Grant Banting (1891-1941), physician, who in 1921 together with Dr. C. H. Best discovered Insulin as a treatment for diabetes, was awarded the Nobel Prize for 1923, in recognition of this great contribution to medicine. In the same year he was appointed the first professor of medical research in the University of Toronto. He was created a knight commander of the civil division of the Order of the British Empire in 1934. A friend and supporter of the arts, Dr. Banting was also a painter of some merit. [see *Macmillan Dictionary of Canadian Biography*, 1963, p. 32-33].

EXHIBITIONS: *R.C.A.*, 1934, no. 205 (plaster); *R.C.A.*, 1935, no. 288 (plaster); *S.S.C.*, 1935, no. 226; *C.N.E.*, 1949, no. 23 (plaster); *N.G.C.*, *Contemporary Canadian sculpture*, 1950, no. 31 (plaster); Stratford, *Faces of Canada*, 1964 (reprod.).

REFERENCES: *Studio*, vol. CXXIX (Apr., 1945), p. 136 (reprod.); *Saturday Night*, vol. 62 (Sept. 14, 1946), p. 2 (reprod.); A.G.T., *50th anniversary* (1950), p. 36 (reprod.); *R.A.I.C. Journal*, vol. 27 (Jan., 1950), p. 31 (reprod.); A.G.T., *Painting and sculpture* (1959), p. 66 (reprod.); *Canadian Collector*, vol. I (Apr., 1966), p. 22 (reprod.), p. 23.

Gift from the Fund of the T. Eaton Co. Ltd. for Canadian Works of Art, 1950.

49/59　Sir Frederick Banting (1891-1941)

F. N. LOVEROFF (1894-　　)

BORN: Fred Nicholas Loveroff, Tiflis, Russia, June 8, 1893.

LIVES: Whereabouts unknown. Came to Canada with family as Doukhobors, settling in Saskatchewan, 1899.

STUDY: Toronto, Ontario College of Art, 1913, under G. A. Reid, J. W. Beatty and J. E. H. MacDonald.

SOCIETIES: A.R.C.A., 1920; O.S.A., 1921. [Both cancelled in 1933, when the artist took up residence in the U.S.A.].

Landscape painter.

1307

NORTHERN LAKE, LATE EVENING

Oil on panel, 8" x 10".
Signed (lower left): F.N. LOVEROFF-.

NOTES: Permanent loan from C.N.E. Association, 1929-65.

EXHIBITIONS: [?] Toronto, Robert Simpson Co., *O.S.A. small picture exhibition*, 1925 (Nov. 24 - Dec. 5), no. 131; *C.N.E.*, 1929, no. 601.

Gift of the Canadian National Exhibition Association, 1965.

64/87   **Untitled**

Doris McCarthy (1910-   )

BORN: Doris Jean McCarthy, Calgary, Alberta, July 7, 1910.

LIVES: Scarborough, Ontario.

STUDY: Toronto, Ontario College of Art, under Lismer, J. E. H. MacDonald and J. W. Beatty, 1926-30; London, England, Central School of Arts and Crafts, under John Skeaping and Fred Porter, 1935-36.

SOCIETIES: A.R.C.A., 1951; O.S.A., 1945, P.O.S.A. since 1964; C.S.P.W.C., Pres. 1957.

TEACHING: Instructor, Central Technical School, Toronto, since 1932.

2843

HEART'S EYE VIEW OF BARACHOIS   **1946**

Oil on canvas, 30" x 34".
Signed (lower right): D McCARTHY.

PROV.: the artist [OSA, 1946].

NOTES: Barachois is situated on the coast of the Gaspé peninsula, just north of Percé.

EXHIBITIONS: *O.S.A.*, 1946, no. 94.

Purchase, 1946.

2483   **Heart's Eye View of Barachois**

58/62

CHURCHYARD AT BIRTLEY 1958

Water colour on paper, 29$\frac{1}{4}$" x 21$\frac{3}{8}$" [sight].
Signed (lower right): DORIS McCARTHY.

PROV.: the artist [OSA, 1959].

NOTES: Birtley is a hamlet situated in Northumberland, England, northwest of Newcastle, near Wark-on-Tyne.

EXHIBITIONS: [?] Winnipeg, *4th Winnipeg show*, 1958, no. 72; *O.S.A.*, 1959, no. 62 (reprod.).

Canada Council Joint Purchase Award, 1959.

Harold W. McCREA
(1887-   )

BORN: Harold Wellington McCrea, Peterborough, Ontario, January 13, 1887.

LIVES: Toronto.

STUDY: Toronto, Central Ontario School of Art, under William Cruikshank; Chicago, Art Institute of Chicago.

Lived in Alberta, 1914-17.

SOCIETIES: O.S.A., 1925; Graphic Arts Society.

Painter of portraits, landscapes and historical scenes.

2479

OLD TIM

Oil on masonite, 9" x 7$\frac{1}{2}$".
Signed (lower right): McCREA.

NOTES: Label on reverse: OSA/Ontario Travelling Exhibition/1931-32. [Not in exhibition catalogue].

Bequest of Ambia L. Going, 1938.

2480

HORSES PLOUGHING

Oil on board, 14" x 18".
Signed (lower right): H W/McCREA.

NOTES: Label on reverse: OSA/63rd Annual Exhibition/1935/Title: Fall Ploughing [Not in exhibition catalogue].

Bequest of Ambia L. Going, 1938.

Grant MACDONALD
(1909-   )

BORN: Grant Kenneth Macdonald, Montreal, P. Q., June 27, 1909.

LIVES: Kingston, Ontario.

STUDY: Galt, Ontario, under Carl Ahrens, about 1928-29; Toronto, Ontario College of Art, part-time classes, 1930; New York Art Students' League, several sessions between 1930 and 1940, chiefly under George Bridgman; London, Heatherley's Art School, 1933.

SOCIETIES: A.R.C.A., 1954, R.C.A., 1965; O.S.A., 1950.

2863

H.M.C.S. HAIDA, SICK BAY 1945

Ink and red, brown, grey and blue wash on paper, 18" x 12".
Signed and dated (lower right): Grant Macdonald/RCNVR 45.

PROV.: [Eaton's Fine Art Galleries, Toronto].

NOTES: This drawing is an illustration for *Haida* [see ref. below].

EXHIBITIONS: Eaton's Fine Art Galleries, *Macdonald*, 1946 (Sept.) [no catalogue].

REFERENCES: Sclater, *Haida* [1947], opp. p. 102 (reprod. in colour with caption "Down below was a cluster of survivors").

Purchase, 1946.

2101

BARBADOS   **1932**

Oil on board, 8¹/₂″ x 10¹/₂″.
Dated (lower right): Mar/22.
Inscribed (on reverse): Barbados 1932.

PROV.: Thoreau MacDonald, Thornhill.

EXHIBITIONS: A.G.T., *MacDonald*, 1933, p. 16; [?] N.G.C., *MacDonald*, 1933, p. 30; Windsor, *Group of Seven*, 1952 (Oct. 1 - Nov. 12) [no catalogue]; A.G.T., N.G.C., *MacDonald*, 1965-66, no. 102 (reprod.).

Purchase, 1933.

2113

PALMS - BARBADOS   **1932**

Oil on board, 8¹/₂″ x 10¹/₂″.
Inscribed and dated (on reverse): Barbados '32.
Stamped (on reverse) [monogram].

PROV.: Thoreau MacDonald, Thornhill.

EXHIBITIONS: A.G.T., *MacDonald*, 1933, p. 16; [?], N.G.C., *MacDonald*, 1933, p. 30; Windsor, *Group of Seven*, 1952 (Oct. 1 - Nov. 12) [no catalogue]; A.G.T., N.G.C., *MacDonald*, 1965-66, no. 103 (reprod.).

Gift of Students' Club, Ontario College of Art, 1933.

Jock (J. W. G.) MACDONALD (1897-1960)

BORN: James Williamson Galloway Macdonald, Thurso, Caithness-shire, Scotland, May 31, 1897.

DIED: Toronto, December 3, 1960. Came to Canada (Vancouver), 1926.

STUDY: Edinburgh College of Art, 1920-22, under Charles Paine and John Platt.

Worked as fabric designer in Carlisle, 1922-25; first began to paint, 1926, in Vancouver.

SOCIETIES: A.R.C.A., 1959; O.S.A., 1949; C.S.P.W.C., 1948, Pres. 1953-54; C.G.P., charter member, 1933; B. C. Society of Artists, 1929, Pres. 1943-44; Painters Eleven, 1953.

TEACHING: Vancouver School of Art, head of design department, 1926-33; School of Decorative and Applied Arts, 1933-35; B. C. College of Art, co-director, 1933-35; Calgary, Provincial Institute of Technology and Art,

60/18

WINTER   **1938**

Oil on canvas, 22¹/₁₆″ x 18¹/₁₆″.
Signed and dated (lower right): J. W. G. MACDONALD/1938.
Inscribed (on reverse, on stretcher): TITLE "WINTER".

PROV.: Lawren Harris, Vancouver.

EXHIBITIONS: New York, *World's Fair*, 1939, section CGP, no. 38; A.G.T., *Macdonald retrospective*, 1960, no. 64 (lent by Dr. and Mrs. Lawren Harris); A.G.O. [circulating exhibition], *Canadian paintings of the 1930s*, 1967-68, no. 14.

Gift of Miss Jessie A. B. Staunton in memory of her parents, Mr. and Mrs. V. C. Staunton, 1961.

61/45

RUSSIAN FANTASY   **1946**

Water colour and ink on paper, 9⁷/₁₆″ x 13⁷/₁₆″ [sight].
Signed and dated (upper right): J. W. G. Macdonald. F. 1946.

PROV.: [Roberts Gallery, Toronto].

Director, Art Department, 1946-47; Toronto, Ontario College of Art, from 1947.

AWARDS: Government fellowship, 1954, to paint in Europe (while living in Vence, France, Macdonald knew Jean Dubuffet).

EXHIBITIONS: Roberts Gallery, *Macdonald*, 1962 (Jan. 5-20) [no catalogue].

REFERENCES: Griffith, *Watercolours* (1967), between p. 10 and 11 (reprod.).

Purchase, Peter Larkin Foundation, 1962.

49/64

THE WITCH
1948

Water colour and ink on paper, 15¼" x 18⅜".
Signed and dated (lower centre): MACDONALD – J. W. G./. 1948.

PROV.: the artist.

NOTES: Bought and exchanged for another 1948 water colour by Macdonald, entitled *Feathered Hat*.

EXHIBITIONS: A.G.T., *Macdonald retrospective*, 1960, no. 54.

Gift from the Albert H. Robson Memorial Subscription Fund, 1950.

61/42

THE MAGIC MOUNTAIN
1949

Water colour on paper, 14½" x 17½" [sight].
Signed and dated (lower left centre): J. W. G. MACDONALD - '49.

PROV.: [Roberts Gallery, Toronto].

EXHIBITIONS: Roberts Gallery, *Macdonald*, 1962 (Jan. 5-20) [no catalogue].

Purchase, Peter Larkin Foundation, 1962.

61/42   **The Magic Mountain**

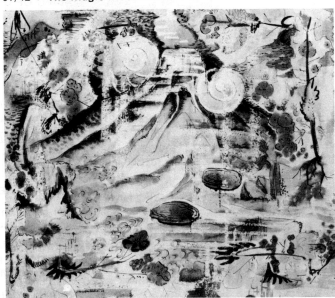

EXHIBITIONS: *C.S.P.W.C.*, 1959, no. 43.

REFERENCES: *Canadian Art*, vol. XVIII (May, 1961), p. 167 (reprod.; collection of Douglas Duncan); C.S.P.W.C., *42nd Annual Exhibition* (1967), p. 8 (reprod. [not exhibited]).

Gift of Douglas Duncan, 1962.

65/21

DAWNING MORROW   1959

Oil on canvas board, 16" x 20".
Signed and dated (lower left): JOCK · MACDONALD · 59 ·.
Inscribed (on reverse, in ink): ARTIST/Jock (J. W. C.) Macdonald – ARCA, CGP, P XI, OSA/4MAPLE AVENUE – TORONTO/TITLE – "DAWNING MORROW".

PROV.: [Dorothy Cameron Gallery, Toronto].

Purchase, 1965.

61/41   **Nature Evolving**

61/41

NATURE EVOLVING   1960

Oil on canvas, 44" x 54".
Signed and dated (lower left): Jock · Macdonald/60.

PROV.: [Roberts Gallery, Toronto].

EXHIBITIONS: *C.G.P.*, 1960-61, no. 45; Roberts Gallery, *Macdonald*, 1962 (Jan. 5-20), reprod. in exhibition brochure [no catalogue]; New York, Museum of Modern Art, 1963-64, under Macdonald, no. 4.

Purchase, Peter Larkin Foundation, 1962.

M. P. MACDONALD
(1879-1965)

BORN: Malcolm Philip Macdonald, Stornaway, Isle of Lewis (Outer Hebrides), Scotland, March 1, 1879.

DIED: Toronto, March, 1965. Came to Canada (Toronto) in 1909.

STUDY: Glasgow School of Art; Edinburgh University; Paris, Ecole des Beaux-Arts.

SOCIETIES: C.S.G.A.; Arts and Letters Club, Toronto.

Marine painter in oils and water colours, etcher.

2007

DOOMED

Dry-point, Imp.: $6^5/_8$" x $5^7/_{16}$". Paper: $10^1/_8$" x $7^7/_8$".
Signed (lower right, in pencil): M P Macdonald.
Inscribed (lower left, in pencil): Doomed.

EXHIBITIONS: *C.S.G.A.*, 1925, no. 200.

Purchase, 1931.

2008

HAULING HER IN

Dry-point, Imp.: $6^{15}/_{16}$" x $8^{13}/_{16}$". Paper: $9^1/_2$" x $12^7/_{16}$".
Signed (lower right, in pencil): M P Macdonald.
Inscribed (lower left, in pencil): Hauling her in.

EXHIBITIONS: *C.S.G.A.*, 1926, no. 192.

Purchase, 1931.

Manly MacDONALD
(1889-   )

BORN: Manly Edward MacDonald, Pointe Anne, Ontario, August 15, 1889.

LIVES: Toronto.

STUDY: Toronto, Ontario College of Art, under J. W. Beatty, and G. A. Reid; Buffalo, Albright Art School, under Ernest Fosbery; Boston, school of the Boston Museum of Fine Arts, under William Paxton and Philip Hale, 1912-13.

SOCIETIES: A.R.C.A., 1919, R.C.A., 1948; O.S.A., 1919; Ontario Institute of Painters.

AWARDS: R.C.A. scholarship, for travel in Europe, 1918.

Painted for the Canadian War Memorials, 1918.

Landscape painter.

Thoreau MacDONALD
(1901-   )

BORN: Toronto, April 21, 1901.

LIVES: Thornhill, Ontario.

STUDY: Under his father, J. E. H. MacDonald (q.v.), but largely self-taught.

SOCIETIES: C.G.P., founding member, 1933; Federation of Ontario Naturalists.

Painter, designer and illustrator.

2488
FRENCH PEASANT

Colour etching, Imp.: $5^7/_8$" x $3^{13}/_{16}$". Paper: $10^3/_{16}$" x $7^5/_8$".
Signed (lower right, in pencil): Manly MacDonald.
Inscribed (lower left, in pencil): French Peasant.

Bequest of Ambia L. Going, 1938.

55.36
ILLUSTRATIONS FOR WEST BY EAST   c. 1933

NOTE: The following (17) drawings were executed to illustrate the book of verse, *West by East and other poems*, by J. E. H. MacDonald, published in Toronto by The Ryerson Press in 1933. Five drawings illustrating the final edition are not in this collection, and acc. no. 55/36.17 was not used.

All the drawings are executed in ink on card.

The number and caption, where it occurs, that follow in square brackets each titled entry, refer respectively to the page in the published edition and to the poem to which the drawing is related.

THE DRAWINGS:

55/36.1
THE BURNISHED PLOUGH, $2^9/_{16}$" x $4^5/_8$".

[12 – "Spring Evening – Wartime"].

55/36.2
KITCHEN WINDOW, $3^7/_8$" x $6^5/_8$".

Signed (lower left): T M.
[24 – "Kitchen Window"].

55/36.3
AND HEAVY WAS THE LOWERED SKY, $2^9/_{16}$" x $6^5/_{16}$".

[34 – "Gallows and Cross"].

55/36.4

THE PLAIN, $3^7/_8$" x $6^{13}/_{16}$".

[36 – "Sunset"].

55/36.5

SUNFLOWER IN WINTER, $3^9/_{16}$" x $6^{11}/_{16}$".

Signed (lower left): T M.
[28 – "November Garden"].

55/36.6

ARMISTICE SILENCE, $3^9/_{16}$" x $5^1/_8$".

Signed (lower right): T M.
[14 – "Armistice Silence"].

55/36.7

GRAVEYARD CORNERS, $2^{15}/_{16}$" x $6^9/_{16}$".

Signed (lower right, on tombstone): T M.
[22 – "An Ode at Graveyard Corners"].

55/36.8

RURAL LANDSCAPE, $3^5/_8$" x $4^5/_8$".

[5].

55/36.9

COUNTRY CHURCH, $3^1/_2$" x $4^7/_{16}$".

[2].

55/36.10

LOG HOUSE, $4^1/_{16}$" x $7^3/_{16}$".

Signed (lower right): T M.
[33 – "Snow Dream"].

55/36.11

THE MILL, $3^{15}/_{16}$" x $6^3/_8$".

Signed (lower right): T M.
[10 – "The Constant Mill"].

55/36.12

THE DARK BARN BROODS, $4^{15}/_{16}$" x $7^1/_4$".

[1 – "West by East"].

55/36.13

THE MANGER, $3^3/_8$" x $5^3/_4$".

Signed (lower right): T M.
[35 – "The Manger"].

286

55/36.14

HORSE IN FARM LANDSCAPE, 2″ x 3³/₄″.

Signed (lower right): T M.
[18 – "February Faith"].

55/36.15

MARCH WIND, 2¹/₂″ x 5″.

[6 – "March Wind"].

55/36.16

TAPPING MAPLES, 4″ x 6⁷/₁₆″.

Signed (lower right): T M.
Inscribed (across bottom): WEST BY EAST.
[frontispiece].

55/36.17

FARM ROAD, (mounted on title page [but never actually published]). 2⁹/₁₆″ x 5³/₈″.

Signed (centre right): T M.

Gift of Edith and Lorne Pierce, 1955.

2707

HAWK OVER THE PASTURE   **1938-39**

Oil on canvas, 21¹/₄″ x 26¹/₈″.
Signed (lower left): Thoreau/MacDonald.
Inscribed (on stretcher, top): Red Tailed Hawk/Thoreau MacDonald/
25 Severn St. Toronto.

PROV.: the artist.

EXHIBITIONS: [?] *R.C.A.,* 1938, no. 140; *C.N.E.,* 1949, no. 40.

Purchase, 1942.

59/39

YOUNG MOOSE   **1958-59**

Wash drawing on paper, 9³/₄″ x 13¹/₂″.
Signed (lower left, in pencil): T. M.
Inscribed (lower right, in pencil): Young Moose/Thoreau MacDonald.

PROV.: the artist [AGT, 1960].

EXHIBITIONS: A.G.T., *Canadian Drawings,* 1960 (Apr. 22 - May 23).

Bequest of Charles S. MacInnes, 1960.

HOUSE NEAR LAKE CECEBE   **1959**

Pen and ink on cardboard, $9\frac{1}{8}$" x $12\frac{1}{4}$".
Signed and dated (lower right on border, in pencil): Thoreau Mac-Donald '59.
Inscribed (lower left on border, in pencil): Near Lake Cecebe.

NOTES: Lake Cecebe is situated northwest of Huntsville, Ontario.

REFERENCES: *Canadian Forum*, vol. XXXIX (July, 1959), p. 84 (reprod.).

Gift of Dr. Lorne Pierce, 1959.

Jean McEWEN (1923-)

BORN: Jean Albert McEwen, Montreal, P. Q., December 14, 1923.

LIVES: Montreal.

STUDY: Principally self-taught.
Began study in pharmacy at University of Montreal, but left in 1949 to devote his attention to painting.

SOCIETIES: A.R.C.A., 1964; Association des Artistes Non-Figuratifs, Montreal, Pres. 1960.

TRAVEL: Worked in Paris, 1951-53, then travelled in Spain, Holland and Italy.

AWARDS: First Prize of the Province of Quebec, 1961; Canada Council Award, 1961.

MEURTRIÈRE TRAVERSANT LE JAUNE   **1962**

Oil on canvas, 75" x 60".
Signed and dated (lower right): McEwen 62.
Inscribed (on reverse, upper right): Meurtriere traversant/le jaune/McEwen/-24-1-62-.
Inscribed (on reverse, lower left): McEwen 59 [sic]/Midi temps rouge [sic].

PROV.: [Gallery Moos, Toronto].

EXHIBITIONS: Gallery Moos, *McEwen*, 1962 (Apr. 26 - May 14) [no catalogue].

Gift from the McLean Foundation, 1962.

61/64   **Meurtrière traversant le jaune**
Colour reproduction, p. 552

R. Ta

BORN
Ontaric

DIED:

STUDY
1892].
Began
points
exhibit

SOCIE
Reside

TEACH
training
of Ana
and dir
Univers
1904.

AWAR
Swede
"Joy of
in Stoc
the wa

Sculpto

904

Florence H. McGILLIVRAY
(1864-1938)

BORN: Florence Helena McGillivray, Whitby, Ontario, 1864.

DIED: Ottawa, May 7, 1938.

STUDY: Toronto, Central Ontario School of Art, under Cruikshank, and later under J. W. L. Forster, L. R. O'Brien and F. McG. Knowles; Paris, Académie de la Grande Chaumière.

SOCIETIES: A.R.C.A., 1925; O.S.A., 1917; Society of Women Painters and Sculptors, New York, 1917; International Art Union, Paris.

TEACHING: Ontario Ladies' College, Whitby;

Pickering College.

TRAVEL: Europe, 1913-14.

Landscape painter.

2375
CONTENTMENT

Oil on cardboard, $16^1/_8$" x $12^7/_8$".
Signed (lower right): F. H. McGillivray.

EXHIBITIONS: [?] *O.S.A.*, 1916, no. 77; [?] *C.N.E.*, 1916. no. 391; London, *British Empire Exhibition*, 1924, Canadian section of fine arts, no. 163; A.A.M., *F. H. McGillivray*, 1928, no. 1.

REFERENCES: A.G.T., *Bulletin and annual report* (April 1937), p. 20 (reprod.).

Gift of Miss F. H. McGillivray, 1936.

2437
A CORNISH COVE

Water colour on paper, $10^1/_8$" x 13".
Signed (lower right [shadow writing]): F H McGillivray.

Bequest of Florence Helena McGillivray, 1937.

2438
IN HARBOUR, STONINGTON

Water colour on paper, 12" x 14".
Signed (lower right): FH McGillivray.
Inscribed (on reverse of cardboard mount): Stonington Harbour/ Conn. – U S A –.

NOTES: Stonington is situated at the eastern extremity of the Connecticut coast, near the Rhode Island state border.

Bequest of Florence Helena McGillivray, 1937.

50/75
STILL LIFE   1917

Oil on panel, $14^1/_4$" x 10".
Signed and dated (left, across bottom): F H McGillivray. 1917.

Gift of Herbert S. Palmer, 1951.

Charles MacGREGOR
(1893-   )

BORN: Edinburgh, Scotland, November 4, 1893.

LIVES: Calgary, since 1963. Came to Canada (Toronto) in 1924.

62/62
PORTRAIT OF MRS. CHARLES HAWKINS   c. 1932

Oil on canvas, 24" x 20".

PROV.: Mrs. Charles Hawkins, Toronto; [her daughter] Miss Maude Hawkins, Toronto.

J. W. McLAREN (1896-   )

BORN: Edinburgh, Scotland, August 11, 1896.

LIVES: Benmiller, Ont. Came to Canada in 1908.

STUDY: Edinburgh College of Art, 1910-14. Returning to Canada in 1915, he joined the services and fought abroad in World War I.

SOCIETIES: O.S.A., 1928; Graphic Arts Society, 1914; Arts and Letters Club, Toronto, 1922.

Illustrator, cartoonist.

Isabel McLAUGHLIN (1903-   )

BORN: Oshawa, Ontario, October 10, 1903.

LIVES: Toronto.

STUDY: Toronto, Ontario College of Art; Paris; and Mexico.

Influenced by members of the Group of Seven with whom she exhibited.

SOCIETIES: O.S.A., 1963; C.G.P., founding member, 1933.

1309

BOAT WORKS, OAKVILLE

Oil on board, $7^{11}/_{16}$" x $9^9/_{16}$" [sight].
Signed (lower right): McLaren.

NOTES: Permanent loan from C.N.E. Association, 1929-65.

EXHIBITIONS: *O.S.A. little pictures*, 1928, no. 271; *C.N.E.*, 1929, no. 608.

Gift of the Canadian National Exhibition Association, 1965.

49/62

BLOSSOM TIME

Oil on canvas, 24" x 32".

PROV.: the artist.

Gift from the Fund of the T. Eaton Co. Ltd. for Canadian Works of Art, 1950.

49/62   **Blossom Time**

52/25

SEPTEMBER FLOWERS   1952

Oil on canvas, 24" x 28".
Signed and dated (lower right): Isabel McLaughlin/1952.
Inscribed (on stretcher): September Flowers — Isabel McLaughlin/50. Balmoral Avenue, Toronto.

PROV.: the artist [CGP, 1952].

EXHIBITIONS: *C.G.P.*, 1952-53, no. 56.

Gift of the John Paris Bickell Bequest Fund, 1953.

Tom W. McLEAN (1881-1951)

BORN: Thomas W. McLean, Kendall, Ontario, November 17, 1881.

DIED: Toronto, December 8, 1951.

STUDY: Toronto, Central Ontario School of Art and Design.

Worked at Grip Ltd. where he was associated with some of the artists who later formed the Group of Seven; from 1912 to 1917 he was Manager of the Art Department at Bridgen's in Winnipeg.

SOCIETIES: Graphic Arts Club, founding member, 1903; C.S.G.A.; C.S.P.W.C.; Arts and Letters Club, Toronto.

TEACHING: Weston High and Vocational School, taught drawing.

Collaborated with C. W. Jefferys in illustrating the three volumes of the *Picture Gallery of Canadian History*, 1942.

Artist, illustrator.

For drawings to illustrate *Toronto's 100 Years*, 1934 see "Toronto's 100 Years", p. 457-462.

Pegi Nicol MacLEOD (1904-1949)

BORN: Margaret Kathleen Nichol [sic], Listowel, Ontario, January 4, 1904.

DIED: New York, February, 1949.

STUDY: Ottawa, under Franklin Brownell; Montreal, Ecole des Beaux-Arts.

Painted in Alberta, 1927; Skeena River, B. C., 1928; Toronto 1934-37, then moved to New York when she married. Painted the women's divisions of the armed forces, 1944-45.

SOCIETIES: C.G.P., 1933; C.S.P.W.C.

TEACHING: Conducted the Observatory Summer School, at the University of New Brunswick, 1940-48.

Signature in her mature period: Pegi Nicol MacLeod.

Landscape, figures, and genre subjects.

2525

JARVIS STREET SIDEWALK   c. 1936

Water colour on paper, $22^3/_4$" x $29^3/_4$" [sight].

PROV.: the artist [CSPWC, 1939].

EXHIBITIONS: *C.S.P.W.C.*, 1939; New York, *World's Fair*, 1939, section CSPWC, and SSC, no. 71; Rio de Janeiro, 1944, no. 35.

Purchase, 1939.

2766

NAVY CANTEEN, NEW YORK   1944

Water colour on paper, $22^1/_2$" x 30".

PROV.: the artist [CSPWC, 1944].

NOTES: In an undated letter from the artist, received June 14, 1944, the subject is described as follows:
"The United Services Canteen on 48th St., near Broadway, N. Y., where I go once a month to do portraits of uniformed men. It is an informal volunteer-run place with lounges, letter-writing rooms, a dance floor, and cafeteria. The food comes from a high school where the navy learns to cook. Five hundred signed-up volunteer hostesses are there every night. Each girl has to be there three nights of the week. There is an entrance and no dating allowed. It sounds dull and most of the boys are just off boats and often fall asleep in the canteen so the hostess has a dull time. The place is very popular."

EXHIBITIONS: *C.S.P.W.C.*, 1944, p. 4; *D.P.C.*, 1945, no. 204, p. 43 (reprod.); A.G.T., *Fifty years of painting in Canada*, 1949, no. 100.

REFERENCES: *Canadian Art*, vol. II (Mar. 1945), p. 102 (reprod.); *The Arts in Canada* (1957), p. 101; A.G.T., *Painting and sculpture* (1959), p. 82 (reprod.).

Purchase, 1944.

2766   **Navy Canteen, New York**

Duncan MacPHERSON
(1924-   )

BORN: Duncan Ian MacPherson, Toronto, Ontario, September 20, 1924.

LIVES: Toronto.

STUDY: London, England; school of the Boston Museum of Fine arts; Toronto, Ontario College of Art.

In 1948 his cartoons attracted the attention of Dick Hersey of the *Montreal Standard*, and led to various jobs doing cartoon illustrations, and finally to his position in 1959 as political cartoonist with the *Toronto Daily Star*, where he has remained ever since.

Served with the R.C.A.F., 1942-46.

Caricaturist, political cartoonist.

66/21

CANADA

Ink on cardboard, $16^3/_{16}$" x $16^1/_{16}$".
Signed (lower left): Macpherson Toronto Star.

PROV.: the artist.

Purchase, 1967.

66/22

JOHN G. DIEFENBAKER SPEAKING

Pencil and ink on paper, mounted on cardboard, $12^1/_8$" x $12^1/_8$".
Signed (lower right): Macpherson Toronto Star.

PROV.: the artist.

Purchase, 1967.

64/38

SMILE   1960

Pen and ink on board, $17^3/_4$" x 14".
Signed (lower left): Macpherson.

PROV.: the artist [AGT, 1965].

NOTES: Printed on editorial page, Toronto Daily Star, September 21, 1960.

EXHIBITIONS: A.G.T., *MacPherson*, 1965, no. 2.

Purchase, 1965.

64/37

TINY TIM   **1963**

Pen and ink on board, 16$^{15}/_{16}$" x 11$^{3}/_{4}$".
Signed (lower right): Macpherson TORONTO STAR.

PROV.: the artist [AGT, 1965].

NOTES: Printed on editorial page, *Toronto Daily Star*, December 24, 1963.

EXHIBITIONS: A.G.T., *MacPherson*, 1965, no. 17.

Purchase, 1965.

64/39

FEDERAL-PROVINCIAL CONFERENCE   **1964**

Pen and ink on board, 16$^{3}/_{4}$" x 17$^{3}/_{8}$".
Signed (lower right): Macpherson TORONTO STAR.
Inscribed (on flag) FEDERAL/PROVINCIAL CONFER[ENCE]; (figure on left) LAMONTAGNE; (figure, left centre) LA MARSH, (on her head band) CANADA/PENSION PLAN; (centre figure) PEARSON; (figure, right centre) GORDON, (on his head band) QUEBEC'S/FINANCIAL/DEMANDS.

PROV.: the artist [AGT, 1965].

NOTES: Printed on editorial page, *Toronto Daily Star*, April 1, 1964.

EXHIBITIONS: A.G.T., *MacPherson*, 1965, no. 22.

Purchase, 1965.

64/39   **Federal-Provincial Conference**

Charles Macdonald MANLY
(1855-1924)

BORN: Englefield Green, Surrey, England, 1855.

DIED: Toronto, April 3, 1924. Came to Canada (Toronto) in 1870.

STUDY: London, Heatherley School of Art; Dublin, Metropolitan School of Art, 1881-84.

SOCIETIES: A.R.C.A., 1890; O.S.A., 1876, P.O.S.A., 1903-05; Toronto Art Students' League, founding member, 1885; Mahlstick Club, Toronto, 1902; Arts and Letters Club, Toronto.

TEACHING: Toronto, Central Ontario School of Art and Design [O.C.A.], 1904 until his death.

Painter, graphic artist.

882
WILLOWS   1889

Water colour on paper, 21$^7/_8$" x 16$^1/_4$" [sight].
Signed and dated (lower left): C. M. Manly/89.

EXHIBITIONS: A.G.T., *Loan exhibition*, 1935, no. 243; *O.S.A.*, 1947, no. 152.

Gift of W. H. Cawthra, 1927.

882   **Willows**

Gilbert MARION (1933-   )

BORN: Montreal, P. Q., March 11, 1933.

LIVES: Montreal.

STUDY: Institut des Arts graphiques, Montreal, diploma, 1953 under Dumouchel; Ecole des Beaux-Arts, Montreal, diploma, 1961.

TEACHING: Institut des Arts graphiques, Montreal.

64/69
UNTITLED   1963

Linocut, 26" x 19$^{11}/_{16}$".
Signed and dated (lower right, in pencil): Gilbert Marion 63.
Numbered (lower left, in pencil): 3/6.

PROV.: [Dorothy Cameron Gallery, Toronto].

EXHIBITIONS: Dorothy Cameron Gallery, *Canadian printmaking today*, 1965 (Apr.) [exhibited but not in catalogue]; Hanover, N.H., Dartmouth College, *Eleven Canadian printmakers*, 1967, no. 55.

Gift from Anonymous Fund, 1965.

QUANTITÉ DÉTERMINÉE **1965**

Linocut, Imp.: 21¹/₂" x 34".
Signed and dated (lower right, in pencil): Gilbert Marion 65.
Inscribed and numbered (lower left, in pencil): "Quantité déterminée" 3/7.

PROV.: [Gallery Pascal, Toronto].

EXHIBITIONS: Musée du Quebec, *Graveurs du Québec*, 1966-67.

[NOTE: Impression of this print was exhibited also in Montreal at *Expo 67*, 1967, in The Canadian government pavilion.].

Anonymous Gift, 1966.

TEACHING:
at National

TRAVEL: 19
land, Engla
influenced b
Post-Impres
Painted for t

Painted mos
scape painti

John ME

BORN: Ferg

LIVES: Toror

STUDY: Tor

Waltraud MARKGRAF (1937-)

BORN: Hanover, Germany, 1937.

LIVES: Toronto. Came to Canada in 1960.

STUDY: Hanover, Werkkunstschule, graduating 1959.
Worked in Berlin for a year as a free lance graphic designer before coming to Canada.

AWARDS: Walter Gropius Foundation Scholarship, 1959.

Painter, graphic artist, known for her large drawings in pen and ink, and one colour, black.

For silk-screen print by Markgraf, see "Toronto 20", p. 453-457.

63/13   Un

Robert MARKLE (1936-   )

BORN: Robert N. Markle, Hamilton, Ontario, August 25, 1936.

LIVES: Toronto.

STUDY: Toronto, Ontario College of Art.

TEACHING: Since 1966, instructor, Toronto's New School of painting and sculpture.

64/41

SUSPENDED FIGURE I **1963**

Tempera on paper, 23" x 35".
Signed and dated (lower right): Markle '63.

PROV.: [Isaacs Gallery, Toronto].

EXHIBITIONS: Winnipeg, *9th Winnipeg show*, 1964, no. 75.

Anonymous gift in honour of J. W. G. (Jock) Macdonald, 1965.

64/40

FALLING FIGURE SERIES: MARLENE III **1964**

Charcoal on paper, 23" x 35".
Signed and dated (lower right): Markle '64.

PROV.: [Isaacs Gallery, Toronto].

EXHIBITIONS: Isaacs Gallery, *Meredith*, 1967. (Mar. 1-20) [no cata-logue]; Boston, Institute of Contemporary Art, *Nine Canadians*, 1967, no. 19.

REFERENCES: *artscanada*, vol. XXIV (Mar. 1967), artscan, p. 4 (reprod.).

Purchase, 1967.

66/23   **Seeker (Triptych)**
Colour reproduction, p. 558

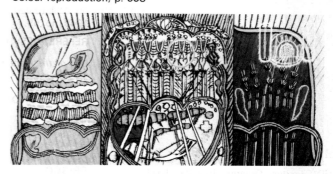

66/30

STUDY FOR "SEEKER"   **1966**

Coloured inks on paper, $16\frac{1}{8}$" x $12\frac{7}{16}$".
Signed (lower left): MEREDITH 66.

NOTES: Study for large triptych, *Seeker* in this collection; see accession no. 66/23.

Gift of the Isaacs Gallery, 1967.

For silk-screen print by Meredith, see "Toronto 20", p. 453-457.

David MILNE (1882-1953)

BORN: David Brown Milne, near Paisley, Bruce County, Ontario, January 8, 1882.

DIED: Toronto, December 26, 1953.

STUDY: New York, Art Students' League, about 1904, for six months.

SOCIETIES: C.G.P., 1939; C.S.P.W.C., 1939; C.S.G.A., 1944.

Did commercial art work in and around New York, until 1915, when he left New York and settled at Boston Corner in the lower Berk-shires. He returned to Canada in 1917 and joined the army; was appointed official war

57/24

THE BLUE ROCKER   **1914**

Oil on canvas, 20" x 20".

PROV.: Estate of the Artist [through Douglas Duncan].

NOTES: A painting of the same period and subject entitled *Interior with Paintings*, is in the collection of The Winnipeg Art Gallery; reprod. in *Winnipeg Art Gallery News Letter*, vol. VIII (Dec. 1966).

REFERENCES: *Canadian Art*, vol. XVI (Winter, 1959), p. 46 (reprod.).

Anonymous gift in memory of J. S. McLean, Esquire, 1958.

artist, painting in England and Flanders, 1918-19. From 1919 to 1928 he lived and painted between Ontario and upstate New York, then returned to Canada for good. From then on Milne spent much of his time in the Georgian Bay and Haliburton districts, with occasional extended visits to Toronto and area. He also painted in northern Ontario.

Painter of landscape, still life, genre, fantasy.

57/24   **The Blue Rocker**

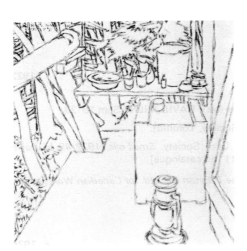

59/36   **Rustic Washroom**

2542

BOSTON CORNER, BERKSHIRE HILLS   **1920**

Oil on canvas, 18⁹⁄₁₆" x 22⁹⁄₁₆".
Signed and dated (lower right): DAVID B MILNE FEB 16 '20.

PROV.: [Picture Loan Society, Toronto].

EXHIBITIONS: N.G.C., and others, *Milne*, 1955-56, no. 10 (as Green Cedars, Boston Corners).

Purchase, 1940.

2542   **Boston Corner, Berkshire Hills**
Colour reproduction, p. 539

59/36

RUSTIC WASHROOM   **1921**

Brush drawing on paper, 15" x 16¹⁄₈" [sight].
Signed and dated (upper left): DAVID B MILNE/DARTS CAMP/ SEPT 9 '21.
Inscribed (on reverse, in ink): David Milne: Rustic Washroom/Sept. 9, 1921/(Dart's Camp, Adirondacks).

PROV.: [Picture Loan Society, Toronto].

Gift from the McLean Foundation, 1960.

51/67

COPAKE VILLAGE   **1922**

Oil on canvas, 12³⁄₁₆" x 16".
Signed (lower right): MILNE [see Notes below].
Inscribed and dated (lower right): COPAKE Nov 11-17 '22.
Inscribed (on stretcher): David Milne: "Copake Village" (N. Y.) (about 6 mi from /Boston/Corners).

PROV.: [Picture Loan Society, Toronto].

EXHIBITIONS: Laing Galleries, *Milne*, 1958 (Oct. 4-18) [no catalogue; exhibition announcement says all canvases of the period 1929-36, when Milne lived at Temagami, Palgrave and Six Mile Lake; ex collection His Excellency the Rt. Hon. Vincent Massey].

Gift from the McLean Foundation, 1958.

54/21

BLIND ROAD   1929-32

Colour dry-point, Imp.: $4^7/_8$" x $6^7/_8$".
Signed and numbered (lower left, in pencil): David B Milne/25.

PROV.: [Picture Loan Society, Toronto].

NOTES: Executed at Palgrave, Ontario.

Impressions of this print have been exhibited: *C.S.G.A.*, 1941; N.G.C., and others, *Milne*, 1955-56; Kingston, *Milne*, 1967.

Gift from J. S. McLean, Canadian Fund, 1955.

54/22

JOHN BROWN'S FARM   1929-32

Colour dry-point, Imp.: $6^{13}/_{16}$" x $8^{13}/_{16}$".
Signed (lower left, in pencil): David B. Milne.

PROV.: [Picture Loan Society, Toronto].

NOTES: Depicts the farm of 'John Brown's Body' fame, North Elba, N. Y.: executed at Palgrave, Ontario; an edition of 25.

Impressions of this print have been exhibited: *C.S.G.A.*, 1939; New York, *World's Fair*, 1939; N.G.C., and others, *Milne*, 1955-56; Kingston, *Milne*, 1967.

Gift from J. S. McLean, Canadian Fund, 1955.

58/18

THE CAMP   between 1929-36

Oil on canvas, 16" x 20".
Signed (lower centre): David Milne.

PROV.: Rt. Hon. Vincent Massey, Port Hope; [Laing Galleries, Toronto].

EXHIBITIONS: Laing Galleries, Milne, 1958 (Oct. 4-18) [no catalogue; exhibition announcement says all canvases of the period 1929-36, when Milne lived at Temagami, Palgrave and Six Mile Lake; ex collection His Excellency the Rt. Hon. Vincent Massey].

REFERENCES: *Canadian Art*, vol. XVII (Jan. 1960), p. 40 (reprod.).

Gift from the McLean Foundation, 1958.

51/88

LATE AFTERNOON   1930

Oil on canvas, 16" x 22".
Signed and dated (upper right): David B Milne 1930.

PROV.: [Mellors Galleries, Toronto]; Gerald Larkin, Toronto.

EXHIBITIONS: Kingston, and others, *Milne*, 1967, no. 28.

REFERENCES: *Canadian painting in the 20th century* (1961), pl. 5 (reprod. in colour).

Gift of Gerald Larkin, 1952.

51/88   Lake Afternoon

51/89

TRACK ON THE ICE   1937

Oil on canvas, $12^3/_8$" x $14^5/_{16}$".
Signed (left centre): David Milne/1937.

Inscribed (on reverse): ⑪ /TRACK ON THE ICE.

PROV.: [Mellors Galleries, Toronto]; Gerald Larkin, Toronto.

EXHIBITIONS: Mellors Galleries, *Recent pictures by David B. Milne*, 1938, no. 11.

Gift of Gerald Larkin, 1952.

2595   Snow in Bethlehem

2595

SNOW IN BETHLEHEM   1941

Water colour and ink on paper, 15" x $21^1/_2$".
Dated (lower right): August 1941.

PROV.: Douglas Duncan, Toronto.

EXHIBITIONS: *C.S.P.W.C.*, 1942; Andover, Mass., 1942, no. 49; *D.P.C.*, 1945, no. 231, p. 47 (reprod.); Washington, D. C., 1950, no. 56; Venice, *XXVI Biennale*, 1952, p. 199, no. 9; N.G.C., and others, *Milne*, 1955-56, no. 90; A.G.O. [circulating exhibition], *Canadian paintings of the 1930s*, 1967-68, no. 16.

51/3

CHURCH, TREE AND HOUSE   1951

Water colour on paper, 21¹/₄″ x 29⁵/₈″.
Inscribed (on reverse, in ink): CHURCH, TREE and HOUSE.
Inscribed (on reverse, in pencil): Jan. 1951.

PROV.: the artist [CNE, 1951].

EXHIBITIONS: *C.N.E.*, 1951, no. 87.

REFERENCES: Griffith, *Watercolours* (1967), between p. 4 and 5 (reprod.).

Gift from the Albert H. Robson Memorial Subscription Fund, 1951.

Michael MITCHELL (1921-   )

BORN: Michael Edward Mitchell, Toronto, January 3, 1921.

LIVES: Whereabouts unknown; was living in Westport, Connecticut in 1953.

SOCIETIES: C.G.P.; Westport Association of Illustrators.

47/3

STAR OF THE THREE RING CIRCUS   1947

Oil and egg tempera on masonite, 35⁷/₈″ x 26¹/₈″.
Signed (lower left): M. Mitchell.

PROV.: the artist [CGP, 1947].

EXHIBITIONS: *C.G.P.*, 1947-48, no. 70, reprod.; *C.N.E.*, 1949, no. 102.

REFERENCES: *R.A.I.C. Journal*, vol. 25 (Jan. 1948), p. 6 (reprod.).

Purchase, 1947.

Leo MOL (1915-   )

BORN: The Ukraine, January 15, 1915.

LIVES: Winnipeg. Came to Canada in 1948, and after a short time near Prince Albert, settled in Winnipeg.

STUDY: Vienna; Berlin; The Hague, Academy of Fine Arts.

SOCIETIES: A.R.C.A., 1966; S.S.C.; Manitoba Society of Artists, Pres. 1956-60.

AWARDS: R.A.I.C. Allied Arts Medallist, 1960.

Among his many commissions, he was awarded that of a monument to the Ukrainian hero-poet Taras Shevchenko, erected in Washington, D. C., and unveiled in June, 1964.

Sculptor, ceramist, stained glass designer.

58/16

TORSO   1954

Terra cotta, 14″ high.
Signed and dated (on right thigh): LM 54.

PROV.: the artist [SSC, 1958].

EXHIBITIONS: M.M.F.A., *74th annual spring exhibition*, 1957, no. 164 (honourable mention); *S.S.C.*, 1958, no. 37; A.G.T., *Four Canadians*, 1958, no. 1.

Gift from the McLean Foundation, 1958.

Guido MOLINARI (1933-   )

BORN: Montreal, October 12, 1933.

LIVES: Montreal.

STUDY: Montreal, Ecole des Beaux-Arts; Montreal Museum of Fine Arts, school of art and design, under Marion Scott.

62/27

MULTINOIR   1962

Acrylic on canvas, 44¹³/₁₆″ x 49¹/₈″.
Signed, dated and inscribed (on reverse, top): MOLINARI - 62 MULTINOIR.

SOCIETIES: Association des artistes non-figuratifs, Montreal; Société d'éducation par l'art.

AWARDS: Canada Council grant, 1962; Guggenheim Fellowship award, 1967.

From 1955 to 1957 Molinari directed his own gallery, L'Actuelle, in Montreal, the only one of its kind, dedicated to the exclusive exhibition of non-representational art.

Painter in the 'hard edge' tradition.

62/27 **Multinoir**

PROV.: [Jerrold Morris International Gallery, Toronto].

REFERENCES: Kilbourn (1966), p. 116 (reprod. in colour).

Gift from the McLean Foundation, 1963.

66/32

MUTATION SÉRIELLE VERTE-ROUGE   **1966**

Acrylic on canvas, 81" x 98".

PROV.: the artist.

EXHIBITIONS: Montreal, Galerie du Siècle, *Molinari "Mutation cinétique"*, 1966 (Mar. 14-28) [no catalogue].

Purchase, 1967.

66/32   **Mutation sérielle verte-rouge**
Colour reproduction, p. 558

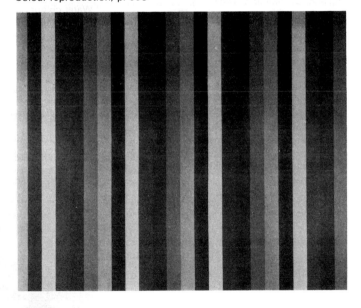

66/40

PARALLÈLE ROUGE, NOIRE   **1967**

Serigraph, Imp.: 21³/₄" x 18".
Signed and dated (lower right, in pencil): Molinari . 67.
Inscribed and numbered (lower left, in pencil): Parallele rouge, noire 7/100.

PROV.: [Gallery Pascal, Toronto].

EXHIBITIONS: Gallery Pascal, *Canadian Printmakers '67*, 1967 (May 4-30) [no catalogue].

Purchase, 1967.

63/12

BARGES DRAWN UP AT A WHARF

Pencil on paper, $4^1/_4$" x $6^9/_{16}$".

PROV.: Rt. Hon. Vincent Massey, Port Hope; [Laing Galleries, Toronto].

EXHIBITIONS: Laing Galleries, *Drawings by Morrice and Homer Watson*, 1963 (Oct.) [no catalogue].

Gift from the McLean Foundation, 1963.

773

MOROCCO, BUILDINGS AND FIGURES

Water colour on paper, 10" x $13^1/_2$" [sight].
Signed (lower right): Morrice.

EXHIBITIONS: N.G.C., *Morrice*, 1937-38, no. 17; London, Ont., *Morrice*, 1950 (Feb. 3-28) [no catalogue].

Purchase, 1925.

775

TOWN WITH LIGHTHOUSE BY THE SEA

Water colour on paper, $9^3/_{16}$" x $11^9/_{16}$" [sight].
Inscribed (on reverse, in ink): We guarantee this to be an original water colour by J. W. Morrice/W. Scott · Sons.
Stamped (on reverse): STUDIO/J. W. MORRICE.

EXHIBITIONS: N.G.C., *Morrice*, 1937-38, no. 16; London, Ont., *Morrice*, 1950 (Feb. 3-28) [no catalogue].

Purchase, 1925.

55/28

STREET IN NORTH AFRICAN TOWN

Oil on panel, 5" x $6^1/_{16}$".
Signed (lower left): Morrice.

PROV.: Madame Andjelka Ivanic, Belgrade.

REFERENCES: *Maclean's Magazine* (Apr. 25, 1959), p. 29 (reprod. in colour).

Gift from J. S. McLean, Canadian Fund, 1955.

47/1

RETURN FROM SCHOOL   1900-03

Oil on canvas, $18^1/_4$" x 29".
Signed (lower left): J. W. Morrice.

PROV.: Colonel and Mrs. James W. Woods, Ottawa (until 1941); Mrs. J. W. Woods, Ottawa; [Stevens Art Gallery Collection, Montreal, by 1943]; [Watson Art Galleries, Montreal].

NOTES: According to catalogue of Montreal exhibition, 1965 [see below], Morrice, in his notebooks, makes frequent reference to this painting as "Les Enfants canadiens". It has also been exhibited and published variously as *Ste. Anne de Beaupré, Winter*, as *Retraite en hiver*, and as *Effet de Neige*.

Another version, oil on panel, $9\frac{1}{4}$" x 13", is in the collection of Mr. and Mrs. Frazer Eliott, Montreal.

EXHIBITIONS: Toronto, *Canadian Art Club*, 1910, no. 42 (as St. Anne de Beaupré, Winter); A.A.M., *Canadian Art Club*, 1910, no. 39 (reprod., as Ste. Anne de Beaupré, Winter); A.A.M., *Morrice*, 1925, no. 111 (as Retreat of Winter; lent by Col. Woods); Paris, 1927, no. 135 (as Retraite en hiver; lent by Col. Woods); N.G.C., *Imperial Economic conference*, 1932, no. 7 (as Effet la Neige [sic]; lent by Mrs. J. W. Woods). N.G.C., *Morrice*, 1937-38, no. 131 (lent by Mrs. Woods); Montreal, Stevens Art Gallery, *Morrice*, 1943 (Oct.) [no catalogue; see *Montreal Gazette*, Oct. 16, 1943]; London, Ont., *Morrice*, 1950 (Feb. 3-28) [no catalogue]; Kitchener, *Canadian classic*, 1959, no. 10; M.M.F.A., *Morrice*, 1965, no. 10, p. 27 (reprod.).

REFERENCES: *Canadian Magazine*, vol. 28 (Jan. 1907), p. 220 (reprod., as A Quebec Pastoral); *Canadian Forum*, vol. V (June, 1925), p. 271 (as Retreat of Winter); Buchanan, *Morrice* (1936), pp. 32, 154; *Canadian Review of Music and Art*, vol. 2, nos. 7 and 8 (Aug., 1943), p. 22 (reprod.; Stevens Art Gallery Collection); *Vie des Arts*, no. 40 (Automne, 1965), p. 18 (reprod.); Pepper, *Morrice* (1966), pp. 55, 84, between p. 54 and 55 (reprod.).

Gift from the Reuben and Kate Leonard Canadian Fund, 1948.

47/1   **Return from School**
Colour reproduction, p. 536

55/29

SKETCH FOR "LA PLACE CHÂTEAUBRIAND, ST. MALO"
c. 1902-03

Oil on panel, $4\frac{7}{8}$" x 6".
Signed (lower left): Morrice.

PROV.: Madame Andjelka Ivanic, Belgrade.

MUNGITUK, see
Eskimo — MUNGITUK

Kathleen MUNN (1887-   )

BORN: Kathleen Jean Munn, Toronto, August 28, 1887.

LIVES: Toronto.

STUDY: Toronto, under F. McGillivray Knowles; New York, Art Students' League; Philadelphia, Pennsylvania Academy of Fine Arts.

A strong interest in Cubism may be seen in much of her work, done mostly in Toronto, and on her own.

2797

LAST SUPPER   **1938**

Pencil on paper, $15^5/_8$" x $19^7/_8$".
Signed (lower right): K. J. MUNN.

PROV.: the artist.

EXHIBITIONS: [?] New York, *World's Fair*, 1939, section CSGA, no. 102.

Purchase, 1945.

2798

CRUCIFIXION   **1938**

Pencil on paper, $19^7/_8$" x $15^5/_{16}$".
Signed (lower right): K. J. MUNN.

PROV.: the artist.

REFERENCES: *Culture*, vol. III (1942), p. 178.

Purchase, 1945.

2798   **Crucifixion**

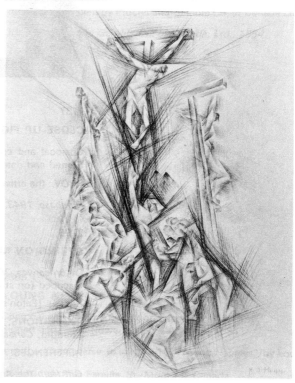

**MUNTZ, Laura, see
LYALL, Laura Muntz**

Rowley W. MURPHY
(1891-   )

BORN: Rowley Walter Murphy, Toronto, May 28, 1891.

LIVES: Toronto.

STUDY: Toronto, Ontario College of Art, under Emanuel Hahn and C. M. Manly, about 1909; Philadelphia, Pennsylvania Academy of Fine Arts, under Joseph Pennell and others, 1911-15.

SOCIETIES: A.R.C.A., 1941; O.S.A., 1941; F.C.A.; Arts and Letters Club, Toronto; C.S.G A

TEACHING: Instructor, Ontario College of Art, from 1927; also instructor, Artists' Workshop, Toronto, and MacDonald Hall, Guelph.
Official war artist with Royal Canadian Navy, 1941-42.

Marine painter, stained glass designer, illustrator.

2592

Jack N

BORN: N

LIVES: T

STUDY:
Louis Mu
48 in the
lithograpl
Paris, stu

SOCIETII
O.S.A., 1

TEACHIN
Toronto,
and 195
since 193

AWARDS
to study
Overseas
Council S

Official w
1944-46.

Painter, c

Robert MURRAY (1936-   )

BORN: Robert Gray Murray, Vancouver, B.C., March 2, 1936.

LIVES: New York.

STUDY: Regina College, School of Art, University of Saskatchewan, 1956-58; Mexico, Instituto Allende, San Miguel, 1958-59; artist's workshop, Emma Lake, Sask., with Barnett Newman, Will Barnet, John Ferren and Clement Greenberg; New York, Art Students' League, briefly in 1960.

TEACHING: Hunter College, New York, since 1966.

AWARDS: Canada Council grant, 1960, for study in New York, where he has lived ever since. At that time he turned to sculpture, having previously been concerned with painting.

Has carried out several commissions: one for the grounds of Saskatoon City Hall, 1960; another for International Sculpture Symposium, Long Beach State College, California, 1965; and in 1966, a 16' high aluminum sculpture for Expo '67, Montreal.

Sculptor.

For drawings to illustrate *Toronto's 100 Years*, 1934, see *Toronto's 100 Years*, p. 457-462.

65/60

TO   **1963**

Aluminum painted with enamel, in 2 parts: tubular column $106^3/_4$" high, planar column $108^1/_4$" high.
Stamped on each base: ROBERT MURRAY 1963 N Y.

PROV.: the artist.

NOTES: According to artist: "This work was fabricated at the facilities of Treitel-Gratz Co., New York, and is unique."

EXHIBITIONS: New York, Tibor de Nagy Gallery, *Shape and Structure 1965*, 1965 (Jan. 5-23) [no catalogue]; New York, Betty Parsons Gallery, *Murray*, 1965 (Mar. 30 - Apr. 17); New York, Whitney Museum of American Art, *Young America 1965*, 1965, no. 58; Toronto, David Mirvish Gallery, *Murray*, 1967 (May 4-28), reprod. on exhibition brochure [no catalogue].

REFERENCES: *Art News*, vol. 63 (Feb. 1965), p. 16; *Canadian Art*, vol. XXII, (Sept., 1965), pp. 53-54; *Canadian Art*, vol. XXIII (Oct., 1966), p. 48.

Gift from the Junior Women's Committee Fund, 1966.

65/12

DARK AND GLIDING QUEEN   **1964**

Lithograph, Imp.: 19$^5/_{16}$" x 14$^9/_{16}$". Paper: 25$^5/_8$" x 19$^7/_8$".
Signed (lower right, in pencil): J Nichols.
Numbered (lower left, in pencil): 5/50.

PROV.: [Picture Loan Society, Toronto].

NOTES: Edition of 59: impressions numbered 1 to 50, plus 9 artist's
proofs.

EXHIBITIONS: Picture Loan Society, *Nichols*, 1965 (Feb. 13-25)
[no catalogue].

Gift from Anonymous Fund, 1965.

65/13

INIMITABLE DANCER   **1964**

Lithograph, Imp.: 19$^5/_8$" x 14$^1/_4$". Paper: 25$^7/_8$" x 19$^7/_8$".
Signed (lower right, in pencil): J Nichols.
Inscribed (lower right, in pencil): A. P.

PROV.: [Picture Loan Society, Toronto].

NOTES: Edition of 20 artist's proofs only.

EXHIBITIONS: Picture Loan Society, *Nichols*, 1965 (Feb. 13-25)
[no catalogue].

Gift from Anonymous Fund, 1965.

65/14

GESTURE   **1964**

Lithograph, Imp.: 18$^1/_2$" x 14$^7/_8$". Paper: 24$^3/_4$" x 20$^7/_8$".
Signed (lower right, in pencil): J Nichols.
Inscribed (lower left, in pencil): AP.

PROV.: [Picture Loan Society, Toronto].

NOTES: Edition of 61: impressions numbered 1 to 45, plus 16 artist's
proofs.

EXHIBITIONS: Picture Loan Society, *Nichols*, 1965 (Feb. 13-25) [no
catalogue].

Gift from Anonymous Fund, 1965

65/15

VIEW FROM THE BARRIER   **1964**

Lithograph, Imp.: 14$^1/_2$" x 13$^3/_8$". Paper: 22$^1/_4$" x 17$^7/_8$".
Signed (lower right, in pencil): J Nichols.
Numbered (lower left, in pencil): 10/45.

PROV.: [Picture Loan Society, Toronto].

NOTES: Edition of 58: impressions numbered 1 to 45, plus 13 artist's
proofs.

EXHIBITIONS: Picture Loan Society, *Nichols*, 1965 (Feb. 13-25) [no catalogue].

REFERENCES: *Canadian Art*, vol. XXII (Sept. 1965), p. 14 (reprod.)

Gift from Anonymous Fund, 1965.

NICOL, Pegi, see MacLEOD, Pegi Nicol

NIVIAKSIAK, see Eskimo – NIVIAKSIAK

Graham N. NORWELL (1901-)

BORN: Graham Noble Norwell, Edinburgh, Scotland, December 11, 1901.

LIVES: Val David, P. Q. Came to Canada in 1914.

STUDY: Toronto, Ontario College of Art, about 1920, under Lismer, Beatty and Holmes.

SOCIETIES: O.S.A., 1924.

Landscape painter.

L. R. O'BRIEN (1832-1899)

BORN: Lucius Richard O'Brien, Shanty Bay, Ontario, August 15, 1832.

DIED: Toronto, December 13, 1899.

STUDY: Toronto, Upper Canada College. Painted in his youth, but entered an architect's office in 1847, and practised as a civil engineer. Turned to painting about 1870 and became a professional from about 1872. Was one of the first artists to paint western Canada in the early days of the railway.

SOCIETIES: R.C.A., charter member, 1880, First P.R.C.A., 1880-90; O.S.A., charter member, 1872.

Art editor and supervisor of publication of G. M. Grant's *Picturesque Canada* (1882).

Chiefly landscape painter.

1340

WINTER LANDSCAPE

Oil on canvas, 42″ x 48″.
Signed (lower right): NORWELL.

EXHIBITIONS: *R.C.A.*, 1923-24, no. 131 (as Gatineau; reprod.).

Purchase, 1930.

1945

SHACKS IN WINTER   1923

Cliche verre, Imp.: 7$^{15}/_{16}$″ x 8$^{15}/_{16}$″. Paper: 10$^3/_4$″ x 11$^1/_4$″.
Signed and dated (lower right, in pencil): G. N. Norwell – /23.
Numbered (lower left, in pencil): III/50.
Inscribed (lower right) [monogram].

Gift of the Artist, 1923.

590

MARSHES AT GRAND PRÉ

Oil on canvas, 20″ x 29$^1/_8$″.

NOTES: Label on reverse reads: Art Association of Montreal, Spring Exhibition, 189[ ]/as Eventide/owner D. E. Walker [sic] [see exhibitions below].

Label on reverse reads: Art Museum of Toronto, 4th loan exhibition, January 1911, property of Sir Edmund Walker [not in catalogue].

According to handwritten notes by F. S. Challener in library of Art Gallery of Ontario, this painting was exhibited in 1892 [not R.C.A., or O.S.A., 1892]; possibly O'Brien exhibition, H. S. Matthews Gallery, Toronto, December, 1892 [not verified].

EXHIBITIONS: A.A.M., *16th annual spring exhibition*, 1895, no. 85 (as Eventide [see Notes above]); A.G.T., *6th Loan exhibition*, 1920, no. 100; *O.S.A. retrospective*, 1922, no. 138.

Gift of Sir Edmund Walker, 1918.

Toni ONLEY (1928-   )

BORN: Douglas, Isle of Man, November 20, 1928.

LIVES: Victoria, B. C. Came to Canada (Brantford, Ont.,) in 1948, moving later to Vancouver.

STUDY: Douglas School of Fine Arts; Doon, Doon School of Fine Arts, under Carl Schaefer; Mexico, Instituto Allende, San Miguel, 1957-59, on a scholarship.

SOCIETIES: A.R.C.A., 1964; C.S.P.W.C.; B.C. Society of Artists.

AWARDS: Canada Council grant, 1963, to England.

65/65

QUIET SHORE

Etching, Imp.: $2\frac{1}{2}$" x $3\frac{3}{16}$".
Signed (lower right, in pencil): onley.
Inscribed (lower centre, in pencil): Quiet Shore.
Numbered (lower left, in pencil): 1/25.

PROV.: [Gallery Pascal, Toronto].

EXHIBITIONS: Gallery Pascal, *Canadian printmakers '66*, 1966 (Apr. 21 - May 12) [no catalogue].

[NOTE: Impression also exhibited, New York, Museum of Modern Art, *Canada '67*, 1967.].

Anonymous Gift, 1966.

64/25

LONDON SET NO. 13   1964

Dry-point and aquatint, Imp.: $11\frac{7}{8}$" x $14\frac{7}{8}$".
Signed and dated (lower right, in pencil): Onley. 64.
Numbered (lower left in pencil): 1/20.

PROV.: [Dorothy Cameron Gallery, Toronto].

EXHIBITIONS: Dorothy Cameron Gallery, *Onley*, 1965 (Jan. 8-25) [no catalogue]; Dorothy Cameron Gallery, *Canadian printmaking today*, 1965 (Apr.), reprod. in catalogue.

[NOTE: Impressions of this print have been exhibited also: Kelowna, B.C., Hambleton Galleries, 1964 (Oct. 9-24); Vancouver, B.C., New Design Gallery, 1964 (Nov. 2-19); Winnipeg, Fleet Gallery, 1964 (Dec. 10-31)].

REFERENCES: *Canadian Art*, vol. XXII (Sept. 1965), p. 11 (reprod.).

Gift from the Georgia J. Weldon Estate, 1965.

66/42

SILENT TWO   1966

Etching, Imp.: $9\frac{9}{16}$" x 12".
Signed (lower right, in pencil): Onley.
Inscribed (lower centre, in pencil): Silent Two.
Inscribed (lower left, in pencil): A/P.

PROV.: [Gallery Pascal, Toronto].

NOTES: This print was commissioned by the Canada Council in an edition of 50, with 14 artist's proofs, 10 of which were retained by the artist.

EXHIBITIONS: Gallery Pascal, *Canadian Printmakers '67*, 1967 (May 4-30) [no catalogue].

[NOTE: Impression of this print has been exhibited also, London, Ont., *Exhibition and sale of prints*, 1966 (Oct. 25-27)].

Purchase, 1967.

Leo Alan ORR (1919-　　)

BORN: July 24, 1919.

LIVES: Whereabouts unknown. Was resident in Toronto, 1941.

SOCIETIES: Experimental Art Group.

R. R. OSGOODE (1874-1946)

BORN: Ross Reverdy Osgood [sic], Dereham, Oxford Co., Ontario, June 17, 1874.

DIED: July, 1946, St. Thomas, Ontario.

Lived in St. Thomas most of his life. Served with the Canadian Engineers in France during World War I; was enlisted 1916, discharged, 1919.

His paintings appear to have been signed Osgoode [sic].

2564

PARK AVENUE IN RAIN

1940

Water colour and tempera on paper, $13^7/_8$" x $9^7/_8$".
Signed (lower right): LEO/ORR.

PROV.: the artist [CSPWC, 1941].

EXHIBITIONS: *C.S.P.W.C.*, 1941, no. 78.

Purchase, 1941.

2471

LANDSCAPE WITH TREE

Water colour on paper, $10^{15}/_{16}$" x 8".
Signed (lower left): R R Osgoode.

Bequest of Ambia L. Going, 1938.

2474

SHEEP BY MOUNTAIN LAKE

Oil on board, $9^1/_4$" x $12^1/_4$".
Signed (lower right): R. R. Osgoode.

NOTES: Label on reverse: ACADEMY BOA[RD]...ART METROPO-[LE]/TORONTO.

Bequest of Ambia L. Going, 1938.

2475

THREE DUCKLINGS

Water colour on paper, $4^3/_8$" x $7^1/_8$".
Signed (lower left): R R Osgoode.

Bequest of Ambia L. Going, 1938.

2472

ARRAS, FRANCE

Oil on canvas, $14^1/_4$" x 22".
Signed (lower left): R R Osgoode.

NOTES: Label on stretcher reads: The original sketch for this painting was made when I was with/the Canadian Engineers in France during the great war./The picture represents a Canadian battery of artillery going through/Porte Baudimont one of the entrances to the ancient city of Arras./R. R. Osgoode.

Bequest of Ambia L. Going, 1938.

Wm. J. PATTERSON
(1916-   )

BORN: William John Patterson, Belfast, Ireland, August 21, 1916.

LIVES: [Unknown].
Exhibited with the O.S.A. and other Canadian societies from 1935 to 1951, living in Toronto until 1951, at which time it is believed he was planning to go to Mexico.

Gordon E. PAYNE
(1890/91-   )

BORN: Gordon Eastcott Payne, Payne's Mills, Ontario, October 16, 1890/91.

LIVES: Hunt's Point, Queen's County, Nova Scotia.

STUDY: Buffalo, School of Fine Arts, Albright Art Gallery; Toronto, Ontario College of Art, 1910-14, under G. A. Reid, Beatty and Cruikshank.

SOCIETIES: O.S.A., 1925.
Formerly Director, Payne School of Art, Toronto.

Dora de PÉDERY-HUNT
(1913-   )

BORN: Dora de Pédery, Budapest, Hungary, November 16, 1913.

LIVES: Toronto. Came to Canada, 1948; married Albert Hunt.

STUDY: Budapest, Royal Academy of Applied Art, until 1943.

SOCIETIES: A.R.C.A., 1956; R.C.A., 1966; O.S.A., 1963; S.S.C., Pres. 1967.

AWARDS: Canada Council grant, 1958.
Has carried out a number of commissions to decorate various architectural edifices, especially churches.

Sculptor, working mostly in miniature; medalist.

2425

MIDNIGHT   1936

Water colour on paper, 18″ x 21$^7/_8$″ [sight].
Signed and dated (lower right): Patterson/36

PROV.: the artist [CSPWC, 1937].

EXHIBITIONS: *C.S.P.W.C.*, 1937, no. 85; New York, *World's Fair*, 1939, section CSPWC and SSC, no. 75.

Gift from Friends of Canadian Art Fund, 1937.

870

HOUSE IN THE TREES, CHESTER SPRINGS   1926

Pencil on paper, 11$^1/_{16}$″ x 12$^3/_4$″.
Signed and dated (lower left): Payne/.26.
Inscribed (lower right): House in the trees – /Chester Springs.

PROV.: the artist [CSGA, 1927].

EXHIBITIONS: *C.S.G.A.*, 1927, no. 441.

Purchase, 1927.

60/61

PORTRAIT OF C. S. BAND   1960

Bronze, with marble base, 3$^1/_{16}$″ [without base]. 4$^3/_4$″ [with base].
Signed (on back of head): H.

PROV.: the artist [SSC, 1961].

NOTES: Charles S. Band (1885–1969), Toronto business man and noted collector of Canadian and Eskimo art; President of the Art Gallery of Toronto, 1945-48 and 1964-65.

An edition of four heads in bronze, and four in tenastic.

EXHIBITIONS: Toronto, Laing Galleries, *Marion Scott, and Dora de Pédery-Hunt*, 1960 (Dec.) [no catalogue]; *S.S.C.*, 1961, no. 26 (one of four portrait heads); Toronto, O'Keefe Centre, *Canada Council exhibition*, 1961-62, no. 35.

Gift from the McLean Foundation, 1961.

60/62

"BABUSH"   1960

Bronze, with onyx base, 2$^1/_2$″ [without base]. 4$^3/_8$″ [with base].
Signed and dated (on back): H.60.

PROV.: the artist [SSC, 1961].

NOTES: An edition of four heads in bronze, and four in tenastic.

EXHIBITIONS: Toronto, Laing Galleries, *Marion Scott, and Dora de Pédery-Hunt*, 1960 (Dec.) [no catalogue]; *S.S.C.*, 1961, no. 26 (one of four portrait heads); Toronto, O'Keefe Centre, *Canada Council exhibition*, 1961-62, no. 35 (as Girl).

Gift from the McLean Foundation, 1961.

63/35

SUZANNA AND THE ELDERS   1961

Bronze medal, 3$\frac{1}{2}$" diameter.
Signed and dated (lower centre): Hunt 61.

PROV.: [Minotaur Gallery, Toronto].

NOTES: An edition of four casts, from the original modelled in plasticine; two others in the collections of Alan Jarvis, Toronto, and the Cabinet des Médailles, Brussels.

EXHIBITIONS: *S.S.C.*, 1961, no. 29 (one of three medals); Ottawa, Robertson Gallery, 1962 [no catalogue]; Minotaur Gallery, *International exhibition of medallic art*, 1963, no. 5; *R.C.A.*, 1963, no. 91; London, Ont., *Festival of Canadian art*, 1964 (Apr. 3-11), no. 80.

Purchase, 1964.

63/34

HEAD OF THE VIRGIN MARY   1963

Bronze medal, 2$\frac{3}{4}$" diameter.
Signed and dated (on right edge): H. 63.

PROV.: [Minotaur Gallery, Toronto].

NOTES: An edition of four casts, two of which are in the private Ottawa collections of Hamilton Southam, and Mrs. Arnold Smith.

EXHIBITIONS: Minotaur Gallery, *International exhibition of medallic art*, 1963, no. 9; N.G.C., *Exhibition and ballot sale of Canadian sculpture*, 1963, no. 78; Rome, Palazzo Braschi, *Esposizione internazionale della medaglia religiosa contemporanea*, 1963, no. 33.

Purchase, 1964.

63/33   **Head of Christ**

63/33

HEAD OF CHRIST   1963

Bronze medal, 2$\frac{5}{8}$" diameter.
Signed and dated (on right edge): H. 63.

PROV.: [Minotaur Gallery, Toronto].

NOTES: Edition of four casts, two of which are in the private Ottawa collections of Hamilton Southam, and Mrs. Arnold Smith.

EXHIBITIONS: Minotaur Gallery, *International exhibition of medallic art*, 1963, no. 8; N.G.C., *Exhibition and ballot sale of Canadian sculpture*, 1963, no. 79; Rome, Palazzo Braschi, *Esposizione internazionale della medaglia religiosa contemporanea*, 1963, no. 32.

Purchase, 1964.

REFERENCES: Morris, *Art in Canada* (n.d.), p. 40; *Universal Review*, vol. 4 (May - Aug., 1889), p. 183 (reprod.); *Toronto Evening Telegram*, (March 7, 1923), p. 12; MacTavish (1925), p. 175; Robson (1932), p. 78; A.G.T., *Painting and sculpture* (1959), p. 36 (reprod. in colour); Harper (1966), pp. 221, 225 (reprod. final canvas in the artist's studio); *artscanada*, vol. XXIV, no. 115 (Dec., 1967), on cover (detail reprod. in colour).

Gift of Sir Edmund Walker, 1918.

588 **The Tired Model**
Colour reproduction, p. 534

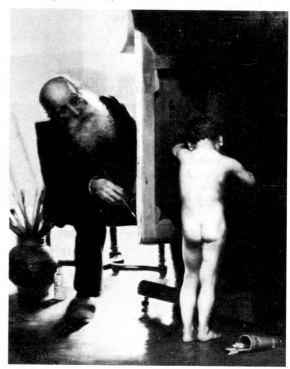

51/54

THE MODEL   1890

Oil on canvas, 21³/₈" x 14¹/₄".
Signed, dated and inscribed (lower left): d'après/Chaplin. Paul Peel 1890.

NOTES: Painting after Charles Chaplin (1825-1891), *Souvenirs*, exhibited in the *Salon de 1882*, no. 537, in the collection of the Musée de Dijon, France.

Formerly in the Luxembourg collection, it is catalogued in Léonce Bénédite, *The Luxembourg Museum, its paintings*, Paris, 1913, no. 112, where the dimensions are given as 72 x 50 cm.; and reproduced, pl. 41.

EXHIBITIONS: *C.N.E.*, 1954, no. 108.

Bequest of John Paris Bickell, 1952.

51/53 **The Little Shepherdess**

Alfred PELLAN (1906-)

BORN: Alfred Pelland [sic], Quebec, P. Q., May 16, 1906.

LIVES: Ville d'Auteuil [formerly Sainte-Rose], P. Q.

STUDY: Quebec, Ecole des Beaux-Arts, 1920-25; Paris, Ecole Supérieure des Beaux-Arts, under Lucien Simon, 1926-30, and visited the studios of the Grande Chaumière, Colarossi and Ransom academies from time to time.

53/43

LUXEMBOURG GARDENS, PARIS   **1890**

Oil on panel, 10$^1/_8$" x 13$^7/_8$".
Signed and dated (lower left): Paul Peel 1890.
Inscribed (on reverse of frame, in ink): Given by Paul Peel/to G. A. Reid.

NOTES: Rough sketch on reverse of panel.
Luxembourg Garden, no. 35 in the catalogue Oliver, Coate & Co., Toronto, *Paintings by Paul Peel*, sale, October 15, 1890, is said to have been sold to G. A. Reid for $65., according to *Toronto Evening Telegram*, March 7, 1923, p. 12.

Gift of Mary Wrinch Reid, 1954.

2135

THE YOUNG BIOLOGIST   **1891**

Oil on canvas, 46$^3/_4$" x 38$^7/_8$".
Signed and dated (lower left): PAUL PEEL,/1891 —.

PROV.: [Malloney's Art Gallery, Ltd., Toronto]; Theodore P. Loblaw, Toronto.

EXHIBITIONS: *C.N.E.*, 1930, no. 152 (lent by T. P. Loblaw).

REFERENCES; *Canadian Magazine* vol. XXXV (May, 1910), p. 53 (reprod., as The Unexpected Meeting, erroneously said to be "owned by Queen Alexandra"), p. 54.

Bequest of T. P. Loblaw, 1933.

51/53

THE LITTLE SHEPHERDESS   **1892**

Oil on canvas, 63$^1/_4$" x 44$^7/_8$".
Signed and dated (lower right): PAUL PEEL./1892.

NOTES: This painting has at times been referred to as *Daphnae*, but the information cannot be substantiated.

EXHIBITIONS: [?] A.G.T., *4th loan exhibition*, 1911, no. 185 (as The Shepherdess; property of E. Whaley, Esq.).

Bequest of John Paris Bickell, 1952.

56/7

FEMME D'UNE POMME   **1943**

Oil on canvas, 63$^3/_8$" x 51$^1/_{16}$".
Signed (lower right): A/PELLAN.

PROV.: the artist (until 1955); Mr. and Mrs. Charles S. Band, Toronto (1955-56).

EXHIBITIONS: Montreal, Art Centre, *Prisme d'Yeux*, 1948 [no catalogue; see ref. Robert, *Pellan* (1963), p. 52]; A.G.T., *50 years of painting in Canada*, 1949, no. 104 (lent by the artist); Boston, 1949, no. 77 (lent by the artist); Paris, Musée National d'Art Moderne, *Pellan*, 1955, no. 67, pl. 4 (reprod.); Los Angeles County Museum,

Was associated with Picasso, Léger, Miro and Max Ernst, before returning to Canada in 1940.

SOCIETIES: Prisme d'Yeux, Montreal, 1948.

TEACHING: Montreal, Ecole des Beaux-Arts, 1943-52.

AWARDS: Province of Quebec scholarship, 1926-30, for study in Paris; first prize, Première Exposition d'Art Mural, Paris, 1935; Canadian Government overseas fellowship, for research studies in France, 1952-55; Canada Council, 1958; Canada Council Medal, 1965. The first Canadian to be given a one-man show in Paris at the Musée d'Art Moderne, 1955.

Canada visits California, 1957, The Band collection [no catalogue]; Brussels, *Exposition universelle et internationale*, 1958, Art contemporain au Canada; Mexico, 1960, no. 146; C.N.E., *A tribute to women*, 1960; London, Ont., *Surrealism in Canadian painting*, 1964, no. 59; Charlottetown, and others, *Collection of Mr. and Mrs. Charles S, Band*, 1967, no. 27.

REFERENCES: *Canada from sea to sea* (1947), p. 79 (reprod. in colour); *Canadian Art*, vol. V (Winter, 1948), p. 104 (reprod.); *Here and Now*, vol. I (Jan. 1949), p. 63, no. 7 (reprod.); Buchanan (1950), p. 98; *Mayfair* (Apr. 1, 1955), (reprod., collection of Charles S. Band); *Art Quarterly*, vol. XX (Spring, 1957), p. 101 (reprod.), p. 104; *Canadian Art*, vol. XV (Jan. 1958), p. 57, no. 5 (reprod.): *Canadian Art*, vol. XVII (Jan. 1960), p. 19-20; Buchanan, *Pellan* (1962), p. 4; Robert, *Pellan* (1963), pp. 52, 81, 91, 90, pl. 221 (reprod.); *Canadian Art*, vol. XX (Nov. 1963), pp. 352-3 (reprod.); Harper (1966), p. 364, fig. 333 (reprod. in colour); *Vie des Arts*, no. 47 (Eté, 1967), p. 23.

Gift of Mr. and Mrs. Charles S. Band, 1956.

56/7   **Femme d'une pomme**
Colour reproduction, p. 546

64/24

LE GRAND CHAMP   **1964**

Oil on panel, 34" x 80".
Signed and dated (lower right): PELLAN/64.
Inscribed (on reverse): N° 441/TITRE — LE GRAND CHAMP/ FORMAT 34" x 80"/COLLECTION.

PROV.: [Roberts Gallery, Toronto].

EXHIBITIONS: Roberts Gallery, *Pellan*, 1964 (Nov. 10-21) [no catalogue].

Gift from the Georgia J. Weldon Estate, 1965.

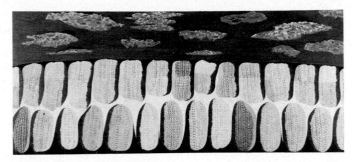

64/24   **Le grand champ**

2334

TOBACCO PATCH, ST. URBAIN   1934

Oil on canvas, 25" x 29".
Signed (lower right): G. PEPPER.

PROV.: the artist.

NOTES: St. Urbain is situated just north of Baie St. Paul on the north shore of the St. Lawrence, downstream from Quebec.

EXHIBITIONS: *O.S.A.*, 1934, no. 119; *C.N.E.*, 1934, no. 342; A.A.M., *Annual spring exhibition*, 1935, no. 250; A.G.T., *Loan exhibition*, 1935, no. 143 (lent by the artist); [?] London, Royal Institute Galleries, *Exhibition...by artists of the British Empire Overseas*, 1937, no. 23; San Francisco, 1939, p. 30, no. 20; *D.P.C.*, 1945, no. 169; A.G.O. [circulating exhibition], *Canadian paintings of the 1930s*, 1967-68, no. 19.

REFERENCES: A.G.T., *Bulletin* (March, 1936), reprod.; A.G.T., *Bulletin and annual report* (April, 1936), p. 6 (reprod.); *Studio*, vol. CXIV (Aug., 1937), p. 70 (reprod.); A.G.T., *Painting and sculpture* (1959), p. 73 (reprod.).

Purchase, 1935.

2334   **Tobacco Patch, St. Urbain**

George PEPPER (1903-1962)

BORN: George Douglas Pepper, Ottawa, Ontario, February 25, 1903.

DIED: Toronto, October 1, 1962.

STUDY: Toronto, Ontario College of Art, 1920-24; Paris, Académie de la Grande Chaumière, 1924-25.

SOCIETIES: A.R.C.A., 1942, R.C.A., 1955; O.S.A., 1934; C.G.P., founding member, 1933, Pres. 1959; C.S.P.W.C., 1947; Toronto, Arts and Letters Club.

TEACHING: Toronto, Ontario College of Art, from 1932 until his death; Vice-Principal from 1950.

Lived and worked in the Studio Building, Severn Street, Toronto, from 1932, for 17 years.

TRAVEL: Newfoundland, Labrador, St. Pierre and Miguelon, 1951; Spain and Morocco, 1955-56; voyage to eastern Arctic, three months, 1960; painted Eskimos during seven weeks at Povungnituk, 1961.

Official war artist, 1943-45.

Landscape and figure painter.

51/65

ESKIMO MOTHER AND CHILD

1951

Water colour on paper, 15⅝" x 21¾".
Signed and dated (lower left): G. Pepper 1951.

PROV.: the artist [CSPWC, 1952].

EXHIBITIONS: *C.S.P.W.C.*, 1952, no. 80.

REFERENCES: *C.S.P.W.C. 41st exhibition*, 1966-67, reprod. in catalogue [not exhibited].

Gift from the John Paris Bickell Bequest Fund, 1952.

PEPPER, Mrs. George, see DALY, Kathleen

Henri PERRÉ (1828-1890)

BORN: Strasbourg, Alsace, 1828.

DIED: Toronto. Came to Canada (Toronto), 1864.

STUDY: Dresden, Germany.

Fought in the war in Saxony, then fled to the U.S.A. in 1850, where he joined the Confederate Army and fought in the American Civil War. First visited Toronto about 1856, but only finally settled there in 1864, and lived for some time in rooms over the Ontario Society of Artists gallery.

SOCIETIES: O.S.A., 1874; R.C.A. charter member, 1880.

TEACHING: Toronto, Central Ontario School of Art and Design, for a time, from 1876.

TRAVEL: Travelled extensively in the United States, and spent some time in Chicago, c. 1869-71, whence he returned to Toronto following the great fire.

Influenced by the late Hudson River School.

Landscape painter.

63/6

CLIFF AND COVE

Water colour on paper, 17½" x 16⅜" [sight].
Signed (lower right): H. Perré.

Bequest of Lily M. Cowan, 1963.

63/6   **Cliff and Cove**

364

Llewellyn PETLEY-JONES
(1908-   )

BORN: Edmonton, August 23, 1908.

LIVES: Possibly, Wales, U. K.

STUDY: Independently in Paris, 1934-39, London, 1939-49, and Florence.

Returned to Canada in 1950, living in Vancouver from 1951-54.

TRAVEL: 1954 to Paris, on a commission from the Dominion Gallery, Montreal, to paint Paris.

50/1

REGATTA   1949

Oil on canvas, 25" x 30".
Signed (lower right): Petley.
Inscribed (on reverse): REGATTA 1949/Petley Jones.

PROV.: [Eaton's Fine Art Galleries, Toronto].

EXHIBITIONS: Eaton's Fine Art Galleries, *Petley-Jones*, 1950 (Mar. 20-30) [no catalogue]; *C.N.E.*, 1950, no. 120.

REFERENCES: A.G.T., *Accessions 1950-51*, reprod.

Gift from the Fund of the T. Eaton Co. Ltd. for Canadian Works of Art, 1950.

Ken PHILLIPS (1909-   )

BORN: J. Kenneth Phillips, Toronto, April 20, 1909.

LIVES: Cooksville, Ontario.

STUDY: Toronto, Ontario College of Art, under Arthur Lismer, C. W. Jefferys and Emanuel Hahn.

Commercial artist, working in Toronto for the Robert Simpson Co. Ltd.

2321

INTROSPECT   1935

Wood engraving, Imp.: 5" x 4". Paper: 13$\frac{1}{2}$" x 8$\frac{7}{8}$".
Signed (lower right, in pencil): Ken Phillips #1.
Inscribed (lower left, in pencil): Introspect.

PROV.: the artist [CSGA, 1935].

EXHIBITIONS: *C.S.G.A.*, 1935, no. 125; *C.N.E.*, 1935, no. 975; New York, *World's Fair*, 1939, section CSGA, no. 105.

Gift from Friends of Canadian Art Fund, 1935.

W. J. PHILLIPS (1884-1963)

BORN: Walter Joseph Phillips, Barton-on-Humber, Lincolnshire, England, October 25, 1884.

DIED: Victoria, B. C., July 5, 1963. Came to Canada (Winnipeg) in 1913.

STUDY: Birmingham School of Art, 1899-1902, under Edward Taylor.

SOCIETIES: A.R.C.A., 1921, R.C.A., 1933; C.P.E.; Manitoba Society of Artists; Society of Graver-Printers in Colour [G.P.C.], London, England; Society of Print Makers of California; C.S.P.W.C.

TEACHING: South Africa, six years prior to coming to Canada; Madison, University of Wisconsin, summers of 1917 and 1919; Winnipeg, St. John's Technical School, until 1924; Calgary, Provincial Institute of Technology and Art, 1941-49; Banff School of Fine Arts, 1940-59, when he retired to Victoria.

2352

SUBURBAN STREET   1920

Colour wood-cut, Imp.: 3$\frac{7}{16}$" x 5$\frac{15}{16}$". Paper: 5$\frac{1}{4}$" x 7".
Signed (lower right, in pencil): W J Phillips.
Inscribed (lower right) [monogram (5)].

PROV.: the artist.

NOTES: From a portfolio of (15) colour wood-cuts, *Winter Wood-Cuts*, by Walter J. Phillips, R.C.A., published in an edition limited to 100 copies, by Nelson and Sons, Toronto, 1936.

The original portfolio, the whereabouts of which is unknown, measured 16" x 12" x $\frac{5}{8}$", and each wood-cut was mounted on a sheet 15$\frac{1}{4}$" x 11$\frac{1}{2}$".

A copy of the text accompanying the portfolio is in the artist's file, Art Gallery of Ontario library.

REFERENCES: Scott, *Phillips* (1947), p. 55, no. 25 (dated 1920).

Purchase, 1936.

TRAVEL: 1924-25, ten months in England, when he became closely associated with William Giles, and the Japanese printmaker Y. Urushibara, who influenced Phillips' technique; extensive travel in Canada, painting mostly at Lake of the Woods, 1914-24; on the Prairies, 1925-35; and from 1936 in the Rockies.

AWARDS: 1960, Honorary degree of Doctor of Laws, University of Alberta.
Earned international fame for his colour wood-cuts.

Water colourist, printmaker.

2344

WINTER SUNSHINE 1920

Colour wood-cut, Imp.: $4^3/_{16}$" x $3^7/_8$". Paper: 5" x $4^5/_8$".
Signed (lower right, in pencil): W J Phillips.
Inscribed (lower right) [monogram (5)].

Prov.: the artist.

NOTES: From a portfolio of (15) wood-cuts [see above, accession no. 2352, *Suburban Street*, 1920].

REFERENCES: Scott, *Phillips* (1947), p. 55, no. 20 (dated 1920).

Purchase, 1936.

153

GLOAMING 1921

Colour wood-cut, Imp.: $9^5/_8$" x $8^1/_4$". Paper: $10^1/_2$" x 9".
Signed (lower right, in pencil): W. J. Phillips G.P.C.
Inscribed and dated (lower right) [monogram (8)].

NOTES: Permanent loan from C.N.E. Association, 1921-66.

EXHIBITIONS: *C.N.E.*, 1921, no. 424 (as Water Lilies), p. 75 (reprod., inscribed Gloaming).

REFERENCES: *American Magazine of Art*, vol. XV (Jan. 1924), pp. 723, 724; Phillips, *Technique of the colour wood-cut* (1926) between pp. 24 and 25 (detail reprod. in colour); Scott, *Phillips* (1947), p. 55, no. 26 (edition of 50).

Gift of the Canadian National Exhibition Association, 1966.

226

TWO LAKES 1921

Colour wood-cut, Imp.: $8^7/_{16}$" x $13^1/_8$".
Signed (lower right, in pencil): W. J. Phillips.
Inscribed and dated (lower left) [monogram (8)].

NOTES: Permanent loan from C.N.E. Association, 1922-66.

EXHIBITIONS: *C.N.E.*, 1922, no. 780.

REFERENCES: *American Magazine of Art*, vol. XV (Jan. 1924), p. 725; Scott, *Phillips* (1947), p. 55, no. 28 (edition of 50).

Gift of the Canadian National Exhibition Association, 1966.

2343

TREE SHADOWS ON SNOW 1922

Colour wood-cut, Imp.: 4" x 6". Paper: $5^1/_8$" x $7^1/_8$".
Signed (lower right, in pencil): W J Phillips.
Inscribed (lower right) [monogram (5)].

PROV.: the artist.

NOTES: From a portfolio of (15) wood-cuts [see above, acc. no. 2352, *Suburban Street*, 1920].

REFERENCES: Scott, *Phillips* (1947), p. 55, no. 35 (dated 1922).

Purchase, 1936.

191

LAKE OF THE WOODS   **1922**

Water colour on canvas, $19^5/_8$" x $15^5/_8$" [sight].
Signed and dated (lower left): W. J. Phillips A.R.C.A./1922.

NOTES: Permanent loan from C.N.E. Association, 1923-66.

EXHIBITIONS: *R.C.A.*, 1922, no. 164; *C.N.E.*, 1923, no. 222; *C.N.E.*, 1929, no. 515 (as Jack-Pine, Lake of the Woods); A.G.T., *50 years of painting in Canada*, 1949, no. 62.

Gift of the Canadian National Exhibition Association, 1965.

2348

SNOW BANK   **1923**

Colour wood-cut, Imp.: $4^7/_{16}$" x $3^3/_4$". Paper: $5^1/_8$" x $4^1/_2$".
Signed (lower right, in pencil): W J Phillips.
Inscribed (lower right) [monogram (5)].

PROV.: the artist.

NOTES: From a portfolio of (15) wood-cuts [see above, acc. no. 2352, *Suburban Street*, 1920].

REFERENCES: Scott, *Phillips* (1947), p. 56, no. 41 (dated 1923).

Purchase, 1936.

209

REST   **1923**

Colour wood-cut, Imp.: $7^{11}/_{16}$" x $11^5/_8$".
Signed (lower right, in pencil): W. J. Phillips.
Inscribed (lower left) [monogram (5)].

NOTES: Permanent loan from C.N.E. Association, 1923-66.

EXHIBITIONS: *C.N.E.*, 1923, no. 809.

[NOTE: Impressions of this print have been exhibited also: London, *British Empire Exhibition*, 1924; *Idem*, 1925; London, Whitechapel Art Gallery, 1925; Paris, 1927.]

REFERENCES: Scott, *Phillips* (1947), p. 56, no. 36 (dated 1923: edition of 100).

Gift of the Canadian National Exhibition Association, 1966.

2339

THE LILY   **1925**

Colour wood-cut, Imp.: $1^{15}/_{16}$" x $2^7/_8$". Paper: 3" x 4".
Signed (lower right, in pencil): W J Phillips.

PROV.: the artist.

NOTES: From a portfolio of (15) wood-cuts [see above, acc. no. 2352, *Suburban Street*, 1920].

Impression exhibited, *C.S.G.A.*, 1926, no. 219.

REFERENCES: Scott, *Phillips* (1947), p. 56, no. 50 (dated 1925).

Purchase, 1936.

2338

LITTLE LOG HOUSE   **1926**

Colour wood-cut, Imp.: $3^3/_8$" x $3^1/_2$". Paper: $4^3/_8$" x $4^1/_2$".
Signed (lower right, in pencil): W J Phillips.
Inscribed and dated (upper right) [monogram (3)].

PROV.: the artist.

NOTES: From a portfolio of (15) wood-cuts [see above, accession no. 2352, *Suburban Street*, 1920].

REFERENCES: Scott, *Phillips* (1947), p. 56, no. 58 (as Little White House).

Purchase, 1936.

2340

ALPINE MEADOW   **1926**

Colour wood-cut, Imp.: $3^1/_4$" x 4". Paper: $4^1/_{16}$" x 5".
Signed (lower right, in pencil): W J Phillips
Inscribed (lower right) [monogram (6)].

PROV.: the artist.

NOTES: From a portfolio of (15) wood-cuts [see above, acc. no. 2352, *Suburban Street*, 1920].
According to text from portfolio, this was sketched in the Rockies.

REFERENCES: Scott, *Phillips* (1947), p. 56, no. 57 (dated 1926).

Purchase, 1936.

2341

WINTER WOODS   **1926**

Colour wood-cut, Imp.: $3^3/_{16}$" x $3^5/_8$". Paper: 4" x $4^7/_{16}$".
Signed (lower right, in pencil): W J Phillips.
Inscribed (lower right) [monogram (6)].

PROV.: the artist.

NOTES: From a portfolio of (15) wood-cuts [see above, acc. no. 2352, *Suburban Street*, 1920].

REFERENCES: Scott, *Phillips* (1947), p. 56, no. 59 (dated 1926).

Purchase, 1936.

2444

MOUNTAIN TORRENT **1926**

Colour wood-cut, Imp.: $8^3/_4$" x $11^{15}/_{16}$". Paper: $10^1/_2$" x $14^5/_{16}$".
Signed (lower right, in pencil): W. J. Phillips.
Inscribed and numbered (lower left, in pencil): MOUNTAIN TORRENT
89/100.
Inscribed and dated (lower left) [monogram (1)].

EXHIBITIONS: New York, *World's Fair*, 1939, section CSGA, no. 106.

REFERENCES: Scott, *Phillips* (1947), p. 56, no. 55.

Purchase, 1937.

871

MOUNT SCHAEFFER **1927**

Colour wood-cut, Imp.: $8^3/_4$" x 10". Paper: $10^1/_8$" x $11^1/_4$".
Signed (lower right, in pencil): W J Phillips.
Numbered and inscribed (lower left, in pencil): Mount Schaeffer
29/100.
Inscribed (lower left): W. J. Phillips.

PROV.: the artist [CSGA, 1927].

EXHIBITIONS: *C.S.G.A.*, 1927, no. 452; *R.C.A.*, 1927-28, no. 331.

REFERENCES: Scott, *Phillips* (1947), p. 56, no. 62 (dated 1927).

Purchase, 1927.

1119

JIM KING'S WHARF, ALERT BAY, BRITISH COLUMBIA
1927

Colour wood-cut, Imp.: $10^3/_4$" x $8^1/_{16}$".
Signed (lower right, in pencil): W J Phillips.
Numbered (lower centre, in pencil): 65/100.
Inscribed (lower left, in pencil): Jim King's Wharf, Alert Bay, B. C.
Inscribed (lower right): W J Phillips.

PROV.: the artist.

EXHIBITIONS: *R.C.A.*, 1927-28, no. 329; *C.S.G.A.*, 1928, no. 417;
C.N.E., 1928, no. 951; N.G.C., *Annual*, 1928, no. 123.

REFERENCES: Scott, *Phillips* (1947), p. 23 (reprod. in colour), pp.
47, 57, no. 73 (dated 1927); *Canadian Art*, vol. IV (Mar. 1947) p. 55
(reprod. in colour).

Purchase, 1928.

2351

POM-POMS **1928**

Colour wood-cut, Imp.: $3^3/_4$" x $3^1/_4$". Paper: $4^1/_2$" x 4".
Signed (lower right, in pencil): W J Phillips.
Inscribed (lower left) [monogram (4)].

369

PROV.: the artist.

NOTES: From a portfolio of (15) wood-cuts [see above, acc. no. 2352, *Suburban Street*, 1920].

Impression exhibited, *C.P.E.*, 1929, no. 295.

REFERENCES: Scott, *Phillips* (1947), p. 57, no. 89 (dated 1928).

Purchase, 1936.

2347

THE STREAM IN WINTER

Colour wood-cut, Imp: $4^3/_{16}$" x $4^1/_2$". Paper: $4^{15}/_{16}$" x $5^1/_8$".
Signed (lower right, in pencil): W J Phillips.
Inscribed (lower right) [monogram (2)].

PROV.: the artist.

NOTES: From a portfolio of (15) wood-cuts [see above, acc. no. 2352, *Suburban Street*, 1920].

Purchase, 1936.

2439

ZINNIAS   **1928**

Colour wood-cut, Imp.: $10^1/_4$" x $10^1/_4$". Paper: $11^1/_2$" x $11^5/_8$".
Signed (lower right, in pencil): W J Phillips.
Numbered (lower left, in pencil): 98/100.
Inscribed (lower left) [monogram (6)].

PROV.: the artist.

EXHIBITIONS: *C.P.E.*, 1929, no. 300.

REFERENCES: Scott, *Phillips* (1947), p. 57, no. 87 (dated 1928).

Purchase, 1937.

1120

MAMALILICOOLA, B. C.   **1928**

Colour wood-cut, Imp.: 12" x $13^7/_8$".
Signed (lower right, in pencil): W J Phillips.
Inscribed and numbered (lower left, in pencil): MAMALILICOOLA B. C. 20/100.
Inscribed (lower right): W. J. Phillips.

PROV.: the artist [CSGA, 1928].

EXHIBITIONS: *C.S.G.A.*, 1928, no. 416.

[NOTE: Impressions of this print have been exhibited also: *C.N.E.*, 1928; *R.C.A.*, 1929; Vancouver, *All-Canadian exhibition*, 1932.]

REFERENCES: Scott, *Phillips* (1947), p. 19 (reprod.), p. 46 (described as "a faithful reproduction of the dilapidated water-front of a British Columbia coast Indian village, with totem poles aloft and two figures toiling up the stairway, the woman, as usual, bearing the burden..."), p. 57, no. 77 (dated, 1928).

Purchase, 1928.

1290

SNAKE ISLAND, LAKE WINNIPEG   **1928**

Water colour on paper, $15^1/_4$" x 20" [sight].
Signed and dated (lower left): W. J. Phillips 1928.

NOTES: Permanent loan from C.N.E. Association, 1928-65.

The title of this water colour, correct as above, has frequently been given erroneously as *Warren's Landing, Lake Winnipeg*.

A wood-engraving after the water colour, entitled *Snake Island*, and dated 1931, is reproduced in Paul Duval's *Canadian prints and drawings* (1952), pl. 32.

EXHIBITIONS: *C.N.E.*, 1928, no. 415; A.G.T., *Exhibition of Canadian sculpture...recent accessions*, 1928, no. 5 (erroneously entitled Warren's Landing, Lake Winnipeg); A.G.T., *Loan exhibition*, 1935, no. 247 (erroneously as Warren's Landing).

Gift of the Canadian National Exhibition Association, 1928.

1290   **Snake Island, Lake Winnipeg**

2442

KARLUKWEES, B. C.   **1929**

Colour wood-cut, Imp.: $10^1/_2$" x $12^1/_2$". Paper: $11^7/_8$" x $14^7/_{16}$".
Signed (lower right, in pencil): W J Phillips.
Inscribed (lower right): W. J. Phillips.
Inscribed and numbered (lower left, in pencil): KARLUKWEES B. C. 19/100.

PROV.: the artist.

EXHIBITIONS: *R.C.A.*, 1929, no. 280; *C.P.E.*, 1930, no. 293; N.G.C., *Annual*, 1930, no. 127; Vancouver, *All-Canadian exhibition*, 1932, no. 205.

REFERENCES: *Canadian Geographical Journal*, vol. XVII (Dec. 1938), p. 278 (reprod.); Scott, *Phillips* (1947), p. 27 (reprod. in colour), p. 47 (described as "a winter aspect of an Indian village or fishing station of the British Columbia coast..."), p. 57, no. 90 (dated 1929); *Canadian Art*, vol. 18 (Mar. 1961), p. 89 (reprod.).

Purchase, 1937.

2349

SOFT MAPLE   **1930**

Colour wood-cut, Imp.: 4" x 4$^1/_8$". Paper: 4$^1/_2$" x 4$^5/_{16}$".
Signed (lower right, in pencil): W J Phillips.
Inscribed (upper right) [monogram (6)].

PROV.: the artist.

NOTES: From a portfolio of (15) wood-cuts, [see above, acc. no. 2352, *Suburban Street*, 1920].

REFERENCES: Scott, *Phillips* (1947), p. 57, no. 99 (dated 1930).

Purchase, 1936.

2443

POPLAR BAY   **1930**

Colour wood-cut, Imp. 9$^5/_{16}$" x 13$^1/_8$". Paper: 10$^1/_2$" x 14$^1/_4$".
Signed (lower right, in pencil): W J Phillips.
Inscribed and numbered (lower left, in pencil): POPLAR BAY 48/100.
Inscribed and dated (lower right) [monogram (7)].

PROV.: the artist.

EXHIBITIONS: *C.P.E.*, 1931, no. 359; N.G.C., *Annual*, 1932, no. 239.

Purchase, 1937.

1974

RUIN, TSATSISNUKOMI   **1930**

Wood engraving, Imp.: 4$^5/_{16}$" x 4$^{15}/_{16}$". Paper: 11" x 8".
Signed (lower right, in pencil): W J Phillips.
Numbered (lower left, in pencil): 103/120.

NOTES: This and the following nine wood engravings are from a portfolio of ten wood engravings, *Essays in Wood*, published by Thomas Nelson & Sons, Toronto (1930).

EXHIBITIONS: *C.N.E.*, 1930, nos. 817-826 [entire set]; New York, *World's Fair*, 1939, section CSGA, no. 108.

REFERENCES: Scott, *Phillips* (1947), p. 53, no. 7.

Gift of the Artist, 1930.

1975

THE HOK-HOK, KARLUKWEES   **1930**

Wood engraving, Imp.: 6" x 4$^3/_8$". Paper: 10$^3/_4$" x 8".
Signed (lower right, in pencil): W J Phillips.

Numbered (lower left, in pencil): 103/120.

NOTES: [See Notes, accession no. 1974].

REFERENCES: Scott, *Phillips* (1947), p. 53, no. 3.

Gift of the Artist, 1930.

1976

ZUNUK   **1930**

Wood engraving, Imp.: 4$^7/_8$″ x 3$^7/_8$″. Paper: 8″ x 5$^1/_2$″.
Signed (lower right, in pencil): W J Phillips.
Numbered (lower left, in pencil): 103/120.

NOTES: [See Notes, accession no. 1974].

REFERENCES: Scott, *Phillips* (1947), p. 53, no. 5.

Gift of the Artist, 1930.

1977

THE CLOTHES-LINE, MAMALILICOOLA   **1930**

Wood engraving, Imp.: 4$^7/_8$″ x 4$^7/_8$″. Paper: 10$^7/_8$″ x 7$^7/_8$″.
Signed (lower right, in pencil): W J Phillips.
Numbered (lower left, in pencil): 103/120.

NOTES: [See Notes, accession no. 1974].

REFERENCES: Scott, *Phillips* (1947), p. 53, no. 9.

Gift of the Artist. 1930.

1978

DUG-OUT, ALERT BAY   **1930**

Wood engraving, Imp.: 2$^{15}/_{16}$″ x 4$^5/_8$″. Paper: 5$^1/_4$″ x 8″.
Signed (lower right, in pencil): W J Phillips.
Numbered (lower left, in pencil): 103/120.

NOTES: [See Notes, accession no. 1974].

REFERENCES: Scott, *Phillips* (1947), p. 53, no. 2.

Gift of the Artist, 1930.

1979

SHACKS ON THE BEACH, KARLUKWEES   **1930**

Wood engraving, Imp.: 5$^5/_8$″ x 4$^3/_4$″. Paper; 11″ x 8″.
Signed (lower right, in pencil): W J Phillips.
Numbered (lower left, in pencil): 103/120.

NOTES: [See Notes, accession no. 1974].

REFERENCES: Scott, *Phillips* (1947), p. 53, no. 6.

Gift of the Artist, 1930.

[NOTE: Impression of this print also exhibited, Rio de Janeiro, 1944.]
REFERENCES: Scott, *Phillips* (1947), p. 58, no. 117 (dated 1935).

Purchase, 1937.

2445

GIMLI NO. 2 1935

Colour wood-cut, Imp.: 7$^7/_8$" x 10". Paper: 9$^1/_4$" x 11$^1/_4$".
Signed (lower right, in pencil): W J Phillips.
Inscribed and numbered (lower left, in pencil): GIMLI NO. 2 38/100.
Inscribed (lower left): W J PHILLIPS.

PROV.: the artist.

EXHIBITIONS: *R.C.A.*, 1935, no. 340; *C.P.E.*, 1936, no. 83.

REFERENCES: Scott, *Phillips* (1947), p. 58, no. 115 (dated 1935).

Purchase, 1937.

2446

SIMOON, B. C. 1935

Colour wood-cut, Imp.: 6$^7/_8$" x 11". Paper: 8$^1/_4$" x 12$^1/_8$".
Signed (lower right, in pencil): W J Phillips.
Inscribed and numbered (lower left, in pencil): 42/100 SIMOON.

PROV.: the artist.

EXHIBITIONS: *C.P.E.*, 1936, no. 84; *R.C.A.*, 1937, no. 327.

[NOTE: Impressions of this print have been exhibited also: *C.P.E.*, 1950; Rio de Janeiro, 1944.]

REFERENCES: Scott, *Phillips* (1947), p. 45 (reprod.), p. 58, no. 120 (dated 1935).

Purchase, 1937

2345

AGAMEMNON CHANNEL, B. C. 1936

Colour wood-cut, Imp.: 3$^3/_{16}$" x 8$^1/_2$". Paper: 3$^{13}/_{16}$" x 9$^1/_4$".
Signed (lower right, in pencil): W J Phillips.

PROV.: the artist.

NOTES: From a portfolio of (15) wood-cuts [see above, acc. no. 2352, *Suburban Street*, 1920].

REFERENCES: Scott, *Phillips* (1947), p. 58, no. 121 (dated 1936; edition of 200).

Purchase, 1936.

2799 **Manitoba Harvest**

2799

MANITOBA HARVEST 1938

Water colour on paper, 14$^3/_8$" x 21$^1/_8$" [sight].
Signed (lower right centre): W J PHILLIPS.

REFERENCES: *Farmer's Magazine* (Dec. 1948), p. 11 (reprod.).

Purchase, 1945.

Claude PICHER (1927-   )

BORN: Quebec, May 30, 1927.

LIVES: Ile d'Orléans, P. Q.

STUDY: Quebec, Ecole des Beaux-Arts, under Jean-Paul Lemieux, 1945; New York, New School, under Julian Levi, 1948; Paris, Ecole National Supérieure, and Ecole du Louvre, 1948-49; France, Saint-Remy de Provence, with Albert Gleizes, 1950.

SOCIETIES: A.R.C.A., 1960.

ACTIVITY: Education and extension, Musée du Quebec, 1950-58, and Curator, 1964-65; National Gallery of Canada, eastern Canada liaison, 1958-62.

AWARDS: Province of Quebec scholarship for study in Europe, 1948-49, and 1949-50; Greenshields Foundation scholarship, 1955, to study abroad; Catherwood Foundation from Bryn Mawr University, to Mexico and Yucatan, 1958; Canada Council, 1961, 1964.

Painter, art critic.

60/20

LAKE BUSHES   1960

Oil on canvas, 30" x 44".
Signed and dated (lower right): PICHER 60.
Inscribed (on stretcher, top left): LAKE BUSHES.

PROV.: [Roberts Gallery, Toronto].

EXHIBITIONS: Roberts Gallery, *Bobak, Bergeron, Picher, Palmer,* 1960 (Nov. 4-17) [no catalogue].

Gift from the McLean Foundation, 1961.

60/20   **Lake Bushes**

Helen V. PIDDINGTON (1931-   )

BORN: Victoria, B. C., 1931.

LIVES: Paris, France.

STUDY: Vancouver, U.B.C., under B. C. Binning; London, Slade School, 1952-53, and Central School of Arts and Crafts, 1953-54; Ottawa Municipal Art Centre, with Gerald Trottier, 1955-58; Paris, Ecole Supérieure des Beaux-Arts, 1960-62; and Atelier 17, wirh S. W. Hayter, 1962-65.

AWARDS: Canada Council fellowship, 1962; Koerner Foundation grant 1963 and 1964.

65/66

POT ROUGE

Etching, $15\frac{1}{4}$" x $15\frac{1}{8}$".
Signed and inscribed (across bottom): Epreuve d'artiste Pot Rouge H. V. Piddington.

PROV.: [Gallery Pascal, Toronto].

EXHIBITIONS: Gallery Pascal, *Canadian printmakers '66,* 1966 (Apr. 21 - May 12) [no catalogue].

[NOTE: Impression also exhibited, *4th National Burnaby Print Show,* 1967.]

Anonymous Gift, 1966.

EXHIBITIONS: Montreal, *Quebec Provincial exhibition*, 1853 [no catalogue; see ref. *Anglo-American Magazine*, 1853]; Quebec, Palais de l'Exposition, *Salon du Terroir*, 1924 [no catalogue; see ref. Bellerive, 1925]; *D.P.C.*, 1945, no. 45; M.M.F.A., *French Canadian arts exhibition*, 1955; M.M.F.A., *Eleven artists in Montreal 1860-1960*, 1960, no. 19; Mexico, 1960, no. 82; Bordeaux, 1962, no. 26; London, *Commonwealth arts festival*, 1965, no. 319 (reprod.); Vancouver, *Images*, 1966, no, 31 (reprod.); N.G.C., *300 years of Canadian art*, 1967, no. 113, p. 71 (reprod.).

REFERENCES: *Almanach de l'action sociale catholique*, (n.d.), p. 47 (reprod.; traces provenance); *Anglo-American Magazine*, vol. III (July-Dec. 1853), p. 535 (mentioned in review of Quebec Provincial exhibition [see Exhibitions above]); Bellerive, *Artistes-peintres canadiens-français* (1925), p. 33 (says exhibited Salon du Terroir, 1924; property of Mme Paradis); Morisset, *Peintres et tableaux* (1936), vol. I, pp. 195-207, facing p. 198 (reprod.; mentions sketch [see Notes above]); Morisset, *Coup d'œil sur les arts en Nouvelle-France* (1941), p. 64; A.G.T., *Accessions 1942*, reprod.; *Art News*, vol XLI (Dec. 1, 1942), p. 35 (reprod.); Colgate (1943), p. 110 (erroneously dated 1869); Lambert (1947), pp. 37, 39ff, opp. p. 39 (reprod. in colour); *Canadian Art*, vol. V (Winter, 1948), p. 109 (reprod. in colour); Buchanan (1950), p. 18, pl. 4 (reprod.); A.G.T., *50th anniversary* (1950), p. 27 (reprod.); *R.A.I.C. Journal*, vol. 27 (Jan., 1950), p. 21 (reprod.); Wade, *French Canadians* (1955), opp. p. 289 (reprod.); *Vie des Arts*, no. 3 (May, 1956), p. 9 (reprod.), p. 12; *The arts in Canada* (1957), pp. 19, 20 (reprod. in colour); *Art Quarterly*, vol. XX (Spring, 1957), pp. 27, 28, fig. 10 (reprod.); A.G.T., *Painting and sculpture* (1959), p. 32 (reprod. in colour); *Art in America*, vol. 47, no. 3 (1959), p. 41 (reprod. in colour), p. 44; Morisset, *La peinture traditionnelle au Canada français* (1960), p. 108, opp. p. 97 (reprod.); *Encyclopedia Canadiana*, vol. 8 (1962), p. 96b (reprod. in colour); Hubbard (1963), pp. 57, 58, pl. 190 (reprod. in colour); Harper (1966), pp. 86-7, 90; *Antiques*, vol. XCII (July, 1967), p. 69 (reprod.), p. 70; *Burlington Magazine*, vol. CIX (Aug., 1967), p. 462, fig. 37 (reprod.).

Gift from the Albert H. Robson Memorial Subscription Fund, 1943.

2601 **La chasse aux tourtes**
Colour reproduction, p. 530

Joe PLASKETT (1918-   )

BORN: Joseph Francis Plaskett, New Westminster, B. C., July 12, 1918.

LIVES: Paris.

STUDY: Vancouver School of Art, night classes; San Francisco School of Art, 1946; New York, uner Hans Hofmann, 1946; Paris, under Léger, and others, 1949-51; London, Slade School, 1951-52.

SOCIETIES: C.G.P.; B. C. Society of Artists.

TEACHING: Winnipeg School of Art, acting director, 1947-49.

55/48

FOUNTAIN   1955

Pastel on paper, 13³/₈" x 19¹/₈".

PROV.: [Picture Loan Society, Toronto].

EXHIBITIONS: Picture Loan Society, *Plaskett*, 1956 (Apr. 7-20) [no catalogue].

Gift from J. S. McLean, Canadian Fund, 1956.

AWARDS: First Emily Carr scholarship, 1946, for study in United States; Canadian government overseas scholarship, 1954-55, to Europe; Canada Council grant, 1967.

55/48   **Fountain**

POOTAGOK, see
Eskimo — POOTAGOK

George RACKUS (1927-   )

BORN: George Kestutis Rackus, Lithuania, May 29, 1927.

LIVES: Cayuga, Ontario. Came to Canada as a child.

STUDY: Toronto, Ontario College of Art; Detroit, Wayne University; Paris, Ecole des Beaux-Arts; and under André Lhote in Paris, 1954.

Herbert RAINE (1875-1951)

BORN: Sunderland, England, December 2, 1875.

DIED: Montreal, May, 1951. Came to Canada (Montreal) early this century.

STUDY: Sunderland, apprenticed to Frank Carus, architect; Sunderland School of Art; Belfast School of Art; London, Royal Academy Schools.

Practised as an architect, and in his later years devoted his work to etching and water colour painting, and was noted for his scenes of old Montreal and rural Quebec.

SOCIETIES: A.R.C.A., 1916, R.C.A., 1925; Pen and Pencil Club, Montreal, 1916; Montreal Art Club.

Architect, etcher, painter in water colour.

61/59

OVERTURE TO SWAN LAKE   **1960**

Monotype, 17⅝" x 23³/₁₆" [sight].
Signed (lower right, in pencil): G. K. Rackus.
Inscribed, numbered and dated (lower left, in pencil): 1/1 Overture to Swan Lake/60.

PROV.: [Picture Loan Society, Toronto].

Gift from the McLean Foundation, 1962.

56/1

HOUSES ON THE HILL, BEAUPRÉ

Etching, Imp.: 7³/₈" x 11".
Signed (lower right, in pencil): Herbert Raine.
Inscribed (lower left, in pencil): Houses on the Hill. Beaupre.

Gift of Mrs. R. York Wilson, 1956.

56/2

THE HILL-CREST, BEAUPRÉ

Etching, Imp.: 7" x 9¹/₈".
Signed (lower right, in pencil): Herbert Raine.
Inscribed (lower left, in pencil): The Hill-Crest. Beaupré. P. Q.

Gift of Mrs. R. York Wilson, 1956.

NOTES: Title page reads: 7 x 30/Published by the Isaacs Gallery, 1966/ A portfolio of seven hand printed serigraphs/Limited to an edition of 30 sets.

EXHIBITIONS: Isaacs Gallery, *Rayner, 7 x 30*, 1966 (Dec. 6-22) [no catalogue].

Gift from the McLean Foundation, 1967.

For relief print by Rayner, see "Toronto 20", p. 453-457.

Donald REICHERT (1932-   )

BORN: Libau, Manitoba, January 11, 1932.

LIVES: Winnipeg.

STUDY: University of Manitoba School of Art, graduating, 1956; Instituto Allende, San Miguel, Mexico, 1958, under James Pinto and others.

SOCIETIES: Manitoba Society of Artists.

TEACHING: On the faculty of the University of Manitoba, since 1964.

AWARDS: Canada Council grant, 1962-63, to England.

Was artist-in-residence, University of New Brunswick 1961-62.

64/78

ALTAR XI   1964

Acrylic on masonite, 48" x 44".
Inscribed and dated (on stretcher, top): Don Reichert Nov. 1964. ALTAR — XI ACRYLIC 34.

PROV.: the artist.

EXHIBITIONS: Charlottetown, and others, *Directors' Choice*, 1967-68, no. 36.

Gift from Anonymous Fund and Canada Council Matching Grant, 1965.

64/78   **Altar XI**

G. A. REID (1860-1947)

BORN: George Agnew Reid, Wingham, Ontario, July 25, 1860.

DIED: Toronto, August 23, 1947.

STUDY: Toronto, Central Ontario School of Art, 1879-82, under Robert Harris, John A. Fraser, and others, and worked in the studios of Norman-Fraser, Toronto; Philadelphia, Pennsylvania Academy of Fine Arts, 1882-85, under Thomas Eakins; Paris, Julian Academy, under Benjamin Constant, and at Colarossi Academy, 1888-9.

SOCIETIES: O.S.A., 1885, P.O.S.A. 1897-1902; A.R.C.A., 1885, R.C.A., 1890, P.R.C.A. 1906-09; C.S.P.W.C.; C.P.E., Pres. 1935; Canadian Society of Applied Art.

TEACHING: Ontario College of Art, 1890-1928, principal from 1912.

Worked for the Canadian War Memorials, 1918.

TRAVEL: Europe, 1885; Spain, 1896, and upon other occasions.

Painter, muralist.

65/42 **Self Portrait**
Colour reproduction, p. 532

66/5
NUDE STUDY

Oil on canvas, 11³/₄" x 9".

NOTES: Oil sketch removed from Reid scrap book in the study collection of the Art Gallery of Ontario.

Gift of Mary Wrinch Reid, 1957.

66/6
MOTHER AND BABY

Oil on canvas, 7¹/₂" x 6".

NOTES: Oil sketch removed from Reid scrap book in the study collection of the Art Gallery of Ontario.

Gift of Mary Wrinch Reid, 1957.

66/7
HEAD OF A WOMAN

Oil on canvas, 13³/₄" x 9¹/₂".
Signed (centre right): G. A. REID.

NOTES: Oil sketch removed from Reid scrap book in the study collection of the Art Gallery of Ontario.

Gift of Mary Wrinch Reid, 1957.

65/42
SELF PORTRAIT   1884

Oil on panel, 6¹/₄" x 5¹/₄".
Inscribed and dated (on reverse, in pencil): G. A. Reid/Self Portrait/Philadelphia/1884.

PROV.: Mary Wrinch (Mrs. G. A.) Reid, Toronto.

NOTES: Painted while the artist was a student at the Pennsylvania Academy of Fine Arts.

REFERENCES: Miner, *Reid* (1946), p. 24 (reprod.), p. 207; Harper (1966), pp. 225, 229, fig. 204 (reprod.; collection of Mary Wrinch Reid).

Gift of the Reuben Wells Leonard Estate, 1966.

63/39
GOSSIP   1888

Oil on canvas, 60" x 40".
Signed and dated (lower right): G. A. REID. 1888.

PROV.: J. F. W. Ross, Toronto; Academy of Medicine, Toronto.

EXHIBITIONS: *R.C.A., and O.S.A.,* 1888, no. 116.

91

1917

Oil on canvas, 41" x 52¼".
Signed and dated (lower left): G. A. Reid 1917.

NOTES: Permanent loan from C.N.E. Association, 1917-65.

Sometimes entitled *Sewers*, and *Red Cross Workers*.

Sketch for the painting was exhibited in the *O.S.A. small pictures*, 1917, and *R.C.A.*, 1918. Its present whereabouts is not known.

EXHIBITIONS: *O.S.A.*, 1917, no. 112; *C.N.E.*, 1917, no. 196, p. 60 (reprod.).

REFERENCES: Miner, *Reid* (1946), p. 203 (described as "Women Red Cross volunteers...seen sewing at machines in the artist's studio").

Gift of the Canadian National Exhibition Association, 1965.

107

THE BLUE PRINT   **1919**

Oil on canvas, 40" x 30".
Signed and dated (lower left): G. A. REID. 1919.

NOTES: Permanent loan from C.N.E. Association, 1920-65.

EXHIBITIONS: *R.C.A.*, 1919, no. 134 (reprod.); *C.N.E.*, 1920, no. 111.

REFERENCES: MacTavish (1925), p. 97; Miner, *Reid* (1946), p. 202.

Gift of the Canadian National Exhibition Association, 1965.

53/35

SELF PORTRAIT   **1936**

Oil on cardboard, 36" x 30".
Signed and dated (lower right): G. A. Reid. 1936.
Inscribed (upper left): GEORGE · AGNEW · REID · 1936.

NOTES: Label on reverse: Frame designed and made/by G. A. Reid.

A head and shoulders study for the portrait, seated to left of picture, head slightly to right, eyes to spectator, measuring 20" x 16", is in the collection of the Ontario College of Art, Toronto; listed in Miner, *Reid* (1946), p. 205. According to Miner, a second study was at that time in the Peel Memorial Collection, Brampton. This collection formed by the late Perkins Bull, has since been dispersed to collections in Peterborough and Ottawa.

EXHIBITIONS: *R.C.A.*, 1936, no. 171; *C.N.E.*, 1938, no. 176; *O.S.A.*, 1941, no. 133; *O.S.A.*, 1944, no. 149; Quebec, *O.S.A.*, 1944, no. 113; *O.S.A.*, 1948, Reid Memorial, no. 207.

REFERENCES: Miner, *Reid* (1946), p. 183 (reprod.), p. 205.

Gift of Mary Wrinch Reid, 1954.

53/40
YELLOW WOODS 1938

Oil on board, 12" x 14".
Signed (lower right): G. A. REID.
Signed and dated (lower right): G. A. REID 1938.

NOTES: Label on reverse: Frame designed/carved and made by/G. A. Reid.

EXHIBITIONS: [?] *C.N.E.*, 1926, no. 314 (as Afternoon Sunlight) [not verified; exhibition label on reverse]; *O.S.A.*, 1948, Reid memorial, no. 225.

REFERENCES: Miner, *Reid* (1946), p. 208.

Gift of Mary Wrinch Reid, 1954.

Isobelle Chestnut REID (1905-   )

BORN: Fredericton, N. B., May 27, 1905.

LIVES: Toronto.

STUDY: Toronto, Ontario College of Art, c. 1923, under Arthur Lismer, J. E. H. Mac-Donald, J. W. Beatty, and others.

TRAVEL: Spain, 1960-61.

2734
1942 1942

Oil on insulite, 23$^7/_8$" x 23".

PROV.: the artist [AGT, 1943].

EXHIBITIONS: A.G.T., *Non-Jury show*, 1943, p. 13.

REFERENCES: *Saturday Night*, vol. 58 (Apr. 17, 1943), p. 2 (says "inspired presumably by the sorrows of the Ukraine").

Purchase, 1943.

Mary Hiester REID (1854-1921)

BORN: Reading, Pennsylvania, April 10, 1854.

DIED: Toronto, October 4, 1921. Came to Canada (Toronto) in 1886 as Mrs. George A. Reid.

STUDY: Philadelphia, Pennsylvania Academy of Fine Art, under Thomas Eakins, 1883-85; Paris, Colarossi Academy, under Dagnan-Bouvert, Rixens, Comtois and others, 1888-9.

SOCIETIES: O.S.A., 1887; A.R.C.A., 1893.

Painter of flowers and still life; landscapes, gardens, interiors; mural decoration and some figure work.

635
BURNING LEAVES, WYCHWOOD

Oil on canvas, 30$^3/_{16}$" x 25".
signed (lower left): M. H. REID.

NOTES: Frequently exhibited under the title *Autumn Fires*, and *Autumn Fires, Wychwood Park*.

EXHIBITIONS: *O.S.A.*, 1914, no. 125; *R.C.A.*, 1916, no. 195; N.G.C., *Central Canada Exhibition*, 1917, no. 142; Toronto, Heliconian Club, 1920, no. 11; A.G.T., *Memorial...Reid*, 1922, no. 109; *O.S.A. retrospective*, 1922, no. 150; A.G.T., *Inaugural*, 1926, no. 252; A.G.T., *Loan exhibition*, 1935, no. 145.

REFERENCES: *Studio*, vol. LXII (July, 1914), p. 147.

Bequest of Mary H. Reid, 1922.

665
A STUDY IN GREYS

Oil on canvas, 25$^3/_{16}$" x 30$^1/_8$".
Signed (lower left): MARY H. REID.
Inscribed (on reverse, in pencil): A Study in Grays/M. H. Reid.

Moe REINBLATT (1917-   )

BORN: Montreal, June 20, 1917.

LIVES: Montreal.

STUDY: Art Association of Montreal School of Fine Art and Design.

SOCIETIES: C.S.G.A.

TEACHING: Since 1945 on teaching staff of School of Fine Art and Design, Montreal Museum of Fine Arts.

Official Canadian war artist with the R.C.A.F.

Jack REPPEN (1933-1964)

BORN: Toronto, 1933.

DIED: Toronto, June, 1964.

STUDY: Toronto, Northern Vocational School; Ontario College of Art, evenings.

Began his career as a caricaturist of sports personalities.

SOCIETIES: O.S.A., 1962.

Executed several mural commissions, one in 1960 in the Prudential Insurance Company of America, Head Office, Toronto, where he was art director when he died.

TRAVEL: 1961, to Mexico; 1962, to France on a mural commission for the Constellation Hotel, Malton, Ontario; 1963, to Yucatan, Mexico.

Painter, cartoonist, caricaturist (for *Toronto Daily Star*), and commercial artist.

2730

A.F.M. (REAR ELEVATION)   1942

Water colour and wash on paper, 25$\frac{1}{8}$" x 19$\frac{1}{16}$".
Signed (lower right): M. REINBLATT.
Inscribed (lower right): A.F.M./END ELEV.

PROV.: the artist [HH, 1942].

EXHIBITIONS: University of Toronto, Hart House, *Canadian armed forces art exhibition*, 1942, no. 355.

Purchase, 1943.

63/69

LONG BEFORE THEN   1963

Mixed media on acetate, 40" x 30".
Signed and dated (lower right): reppen '63.

PROV.: Estate of the artist.

Anonymous Gift, 1964.

63/69   Long Before Then
Colour reproduction, p. 554

392

Cecil RICHARDS (1907-   )

BORN: Cornwall, England, January 5, 1907.

LIVES: Winnipeg, Manitoba, Came to Canada (Toronto) in 1925.

STUDY: In England, Farnham, Penzance School of Art; Guilford Arts School, Surrey; Toronto, Ontario College of Art; Bloomfield, Illinois, Cranbrook Academy of Art, four years, and became an assistant to Carl Milles.

SOCIETIES: A.R.C.A., 1957, R.C.A., 1965; S.S.C.

TEACHING: Cranbrook Academy, summers; Flint, Michigan, Institute of Art; University of Texas; University of British Columbia, summers; since 1950, instructor of sculpture, Winnipeg School of Art.

TRAVEL: 1958-59 in Europe.

Sculptor.

53/50

THE PROPHET   1950

Serpentine, 12½" x 8½".

PROV.: the artist [AGT, 1954].

EXHIBITIONS: A.G.T., *Bowman, Cahen, McCloy, and Richards*, 1954, no. 7.

REFERENCES: *Canadian Art*, vol. XII (Winter, 1955), p. 56 (reprod.).

Gift from the Fund of the T. Eaton Co. Ltd. for Canadian Works of Art, 1954.

53/50   **The Prophet**

Jean-Paul RIOPELLE (1923-   )

BORN: Montreal, P. Q., October 7, 1923.

LIVES: Vanves, a suburb of Paris, France.

STUDY: No formal training.

From 1936 to 1944 Riopelle was a figurative landscape painter; in 1944 he adopted a non-figurative style, "tachisme" [action painting], and became associated with the *Automatistes*, a Montreal group led by Paul-Emile Borduas (q.v.), with whom he exhibited in 1946.

53/23

COUPS SUR COUPS   1953

Oil on canvas, 28¾" x 39½".
Signed and dated (lower right): Riopelle/53.

PROV.: [Pierre Matisse Gallery, New York].

EXHIBITIONS: Pierre Matisse Gallery, *Riopelle*, 1954, no. 7; Venice, *XXVII biennale*, 1954, p. 207, no. 10, pl. 56 (reprod); A.G.T., *Paris Today*, 1957; Australia, 1957, no. 46; N.G.C., and others, *Riopelle*, 1962-63, no. 19.

2862   **Marian**

2762

TREES AND LAKE, ST. ALPHONSE   **1941 or '42**

Oil on masonite, 21¼" x 25½".
Signed (lower right): G. Roberts.

PROV.: A. Y. Jackson, Toronto.

EXHIBITIONS: N.G.C., *Coronation exhibition*, 1953, no. 63.

Gift from the Albert H. Robson Memorial Subscription Fund, 1944.

51/52

LAURENTIAN LANDSCAPE NEAR ST. ALPHONSE   **1943**

Water colour and pencil on paper, 19½" x 26¾" [sight].
Signed (lower right, in pencil): G. Roberts.

PROV.: the artist [HH, 1951].

EXHIBITIONS: University of Toronto, Hart House, *Roberts*, 1951 (Dec.) [no catalogue].

Gift from the Fund of the T. Eaton Co. Ltd. for Canadian Works of Art, 1952.

2862

MARIAN   **1946**

Oil on canvas, 38⅛" x 28⅜".
Signed (lower right): G. Roberts.

PROV.: [Dominion Gallery, Montreal].

NOTES: The sitter is the artist's wife.

Purchase, 1946.

51/18

THE ST. LAWRENCE, PORT-AU-PERSIL   **1951**

Oil on masonite, 11⅞" x 15¹⁵⁄₁₆".
Signed (lower right): G. Roberts.

PROV.: the artist.

NOTES: Label on reverse: The St. Lawrence/Port-au-Persil/ (18)

Gift from the Fund of the T. Eaton Co. Ltd. for Canadian Works of Art, 1951.

52/15   **Pleasant Island, Georgian Bay**
Colour reproduction, p. 548

52/15

PLEASANT ISLAND, GEORGIAN BAY   **1952**

Oil on masonite, 32" x 48".
Signed and dated (lower right): G. Roberts/1952.

PROV.: [Dominion Gallery, Montreal].

EXHIBITIONS: Dominion Gallery, *Roberts*, 1952 (Oct. 7-21) [no catalogue]; Australia, 1957, no. 40; Fredericton, *Roberts*, 1960, no. 5; Stratford, *Canada on canvas*, 1963.

REFERENCES: A.G.T., *Painting and sculpture* (1959), p. 78 (reprod.); *Canadian Art*, vol. XVII (July, 1960), p. 246.

Gift from the Fund of the T. Eaton Co. Ltd. for Canadian Works of Art, 1952.

William ROBERTS (1921-   )

BORN: William Griffith Roberts, Nelson, B. C., July 25, 1921.

LIVES: Milton, Ontario.

STUDY: Vancouver School of Art; Ontario College of Art, but mainly self-taught.

SOCIETIES: A.R.C.A., 1957; O.S.A., 1956; C.S.P.W.C.; C.G.P.

TEACHING: Ontario College of Art, instructor, 1958; Resident artist, University of Western Ontario, 1963-64.

TRAVEL: England, France and Spain, 1953.

AWARDS: Canada Council grant, 1967, to England and Wales.

60/56

SECRET HOUSE NO. 6   1960

Pen and ink on grey paper, $11^{15}/_{16}$" x $17^{13}/_{16}$".
Signed and inscribed (lower right): WILLIAM ROBERTS/SECRET HOUSE NO. 6.

PROV.: [Roberts Gallery, Toronto].

EXHIBITIONS: Roberts Gallery, *Cox, and Roberts*, 1961 (May 11-24) [no catalogue]; A.G.T., *Drawings*, 1963, p. 8.

Canada Council Joint Drawings Purchase Fund, 1961.

60/55

LOST WALL   1961

Oil on board, $15^3/_4$" x $25^1/_4$".
Signed and inscribed (upper left): WILLIAM ROBERTS/LOST WALL.

PROV.: [Roberts Gallery, Toronto].

EXHIBITIONS: Roberts Gallery, *Cox, and Roberts*, 1961 (May 11-24) [no catalogue].

Gift from the McLean Foundation, 1961.

60/55   **Lost Wall**

REFERENCES: *Educational Record of the Province of Quebec*, vol. LXXI (July - Sept., 1955), p. 151; Lee, *Robinson* (1956), p. 36 (reprod.), p. 37.

Gift from the Fund of the T. Eaton Co. Ltd. for Canadian Works of Art, 1950.

841

RETURNING FROM EASTER MASS   1922

Oil on canvas, 27½" x 33½".
Signed and dated (lower left): ALBERT ROBINSON. 22.

PROV.: the artist [AGT, 1926].

NOTES: Painted from studies made at Cacouna, P. Q., where the artist sketched in 1921, in company with A. Y. Jackson.

A sketch for the painting, 8½" x 10½", dated 1921, was bequeathed by Dr. J. M. MacCallum in 1944 to the National Gallery of Canada; reproduced, N.G.C., *Catalogue of the Canadian School* (1960), p. 267, acc. no. 4745.

According to T. R. Lee [see ref. 1956] the artist originally made a gift of this painting to a neighbour in return for many kindnesses.

EXHIBITIONS: A.A.M., *40th spring exhibition* 1923, no. 182; *R.C.A.*, 1923-24, no. 147 (reprod.); A.G.T., *Group of Seven, and painting...French Canada*, 1926, no. 223; A.G.T., *Canadian painting*, 1926, no. 40; Buffalo, *Exhibition of paintings by Canadian artists*, 1928, no. 47; St. Louis, 1930, no. 51; A.G.T., *Summer*, 1935, no. 44, p. 22 (reprod.); A.G.T., *Loan exhibition*, 1935, no. 147; London, Tate, 1938, no. 190, pl. 9 (reprod.); *D.P.C.*, 1945, no. 157; Washington, 1950, no. 74 (reprod.); Hamilton, *Inaugural*, 1953-54, no. 47; Hamilton, *Robinson retrospective*, 1955, no. 10, on cover (reprod. in colour); Mexico, 1960, no. 121; Hamilton, *Some artists who have lived and worked in Hamilton*, 1967, no. 68 (reprod. [also on cover]).

Gift from the Reuben and Kate Leonard Canadian Fund, 1926.

841   **Returning from Easter Mass**

50/7

FISHING BOATS, BAIE ST. PAUL   **1922**

Oil on panel, $8^9/_{16}$" x $10^5/_8$".
Signed (lower left): A H Robinson.
Inscribed (on reverse): A H R/No. 1/Fishing Boat Baie St. Paul.

PROV.: [West End Art Gallery, Montreal].

EXHIBITIONS: West End Art Gallery, *Robinson*, 1950 (Mar. 28 -
Apr. 8) [no catalogue]; Hamilton, *Robinson retrospective*, 1955,
no. 49; Kitchener, *Canadian classic*, 1959, no. 22.

REFERENCES: Lee, *Robinson* (1956), p. 32 (reprod.).

*Gift from the Fund of the T. Eaton Co. Ltd. for Canadian Works of
Art, 1950.*

50/6

QUEBEC   **1923**

Oil on panel, $8^1/_2$" x $10^9/_{16}$".
Signed and dated (lower left): Albert Robinson. 23.
Inscribed (on reverse): No. 12/Quebec/35°°/A. H. Robinson.

PROV.: [West End Art Gallery, Montreal].

EXHIBITIONS: West End Art Gallery, *Robinson*, 1950 (Mar. 28 -
Apr. 8) [no catalogue].

REFERENCES: Lee, *Robinson* (1956), p. 22 (reprod.).

*Gift from the Fund of the T. Eaton Co. Ltd. for Canadian Works of
Art, 1950.*

52/6

STUDY FOR "THE OPEN STREAM"   **1924**

Oil on panel, $8^1/_2$" x $10^9/_{16}$".
Signed and dated (lower right): Albert H. Robinson. 1924.
Inscribed (on reverse, in pencil): Sketch/for the /canvas/sol[d]
[   ] [Fr]ance.

PROV.: [Continental Galleries Inc., Montreal]; Mr. William Gibbs,
Montreal; [Continental Galleries, Inc., Montreal.].

NOTES: Sketch for the large canvas, *The Open Stream*, acquired for
the Luxembourg collection, from the Canadian exhibition at the
Musée du Jeu de Paume, Paris, 1927; now in the collection of the
Musée National d'Art Moderne, Paris.

Formerly entitled *The Breaking River*, the above title has been adopted
in accordance with records signed by the artist.

Painted at Baie St. Paul.

EXHIBITIONS: Hamilton, *Robinson retrospective*, 1955, no. 51 (as
The Breaking River).

REFERENCES: Lee, *Robinson* (1956), p. 22 (reprod.; erroneously said
to be the painting in the Paris collection).

*Gift from the Fund of the T. Eaton Co. Ltd. for Canadian Works of Art,
1952.*

1339

ST. TITE DES CAPS 1928

Oil on canvas, 27¹/₂″ x 33¹/₄″.
Signed (lower left): Albert h. Robinson.
Dated and inscribed (lower right): St. Tite des Cap. [sic] 28.

PROV.: the artist.

NOTES: St. Tite des Caps is situated just inland from the north shore of the St. Lawrence, northeast of Ste. Anne de Beaupré.

EXHIBITIONS: St. Louis, 1930, no. 52; A.G.T., *Summer*, 1935, no. 43; Hamilton, *Robinson retrospective*, 1955, no. 29; Kitchener, *Canadian classic*, 1959, no. 24; Stratford, *Canada on canvas*, 1963.

REFERENCES: Lee, *Robinson* (1956), p. 10 (reprod.); Harper (1966), p. 315.

Purchase, 1929.

1339   **St. Tite des Caps**
Colour reproduction, p. 542

William **RONALD** (1926-   )

BORN: Stratford, Ontario, August 13, 1926.

LIVES: Toronto.

STUDY: Toronto, Ontario College of Art, under Jock Macdonald, Carl Schaefer, Will Ogilvie, and others; in New York, under Hans Hofmann.
Lived and painted in New York from 1955-65.

SOCIETIES: Painters Eleven, 1953.

AWARDS: Hallmark art award, 1952; Guggenheim award for Canadian painting, 1956.

63/14

THE SPORTSMAN 1952

Mixed media on masonite, 25¹¹/₁₆″ x 35⁹/₁₆″.
Signed and dated (lower right): William/RONALD '52.

PROV.: the artist [AGT, 1963].

EXHIBITIONS: *O.S.A.*, 1952, no. 89; University of Toronto, Hart House, *Ronald*, 1954 [no catalogue]; A.G.T., *17th annual exhibition and sale*, 1963, no. 130.

REFERENCES: *Canadian Art*, vol. XI (Winter, 1954), p. 51 (reprod.).

Gift from the McLean Foundation, 1963.

54/19 **In Dawn the Heart**

54/19

IN DAWN THE HEART **1954**

Oil on canvas, 72$\frac{1}{8}$" x 39$\frac{7}{8}$".
Signed and dated (lower left): RONALD '54.

PROV.: the artist.

NOTES: This painting won for the artist the Guggenheim International Award for Canadian painting, 1956.

EXHIBITIONS: Toronto, Roberts Gallery, *Painters Eleven*, 1955 (Feb. 11-26) [no catalogue]; University of Toronto, Hart House, *Ronald*, 1955 (Feb. 28 - Mar. 13) [no catalogue]; New York, Guggenheim Museum, *Guggenheim International Award*, 1956; Vancouver, University of British Columbia, *Eight Ontario painters*, 1961.

REFERENCES: *Canadian Art*, vol. XIII (Winter, 1956), p. 255 (reprod.); A.G.T., *News and Notes*, vol. I (Jan., 1957), p. 3 (reprod.); *Vic des Arts*, no. 6 (May, 1957), p. 26 (reprod.); *Canadian Art*, vol. XIV (Winter, 1957), p. 78; Gardner, *Art through the ages* (1958), p. 728 (reprod.); A.G.T., *Painting and sculpture* (1959), p. 87 (reprod.).

Gift from J. S. McLean, Canadian Fund, 1955.

59/8

EXODUS II **1959**

Oil on canvas, 60" x 60".
Signed and dated (lower right): RONALD '59.
Inscribed (on reverse, upper right): RONALD/9-29-59/'EXODUS'.

PROV.: [Samuel M. Kootz Gallery Inc., New York].

EXHIBITIONS: Kootz Gallery, *Ronald*, 1959 (Oct. 21 - Nov. 7) [no catalogue].

REFERENCES: A.G.T., *News and Notes*, vol. IV (May, 1960), p. 3 (reprod.).

Purchase, Membership Endowment, 1960.

59/8 **Exodus II**

403

61/71

NO. 256 **1960**

Water colour on paper, 18" x 24".
Signed and dated (lower right): RONALD 60.

PROV.: [Isaacs Gallery, Toronto].

Purchase, 1962.

62/57

GINZA **1962**

Oil on canvas, 72" x 54".
Signed, dated and inscribed (on reverse, upper right): 72" x 54"/
PAINTED/NOV. 4 - 1962/RONALD '62.
Inscribed (on reverse, upper left): 'GINZA'.

PROV.: [Isaacs Gallery, Toronto].

EXHIBITIONS: New York, Kootz Gallery, *Ronald*, 1963 (Jan. 2-19)
[no catalogue]; Isaacs Gallery, *Ronald*, 1963 (Mar. 21 - Apr. 10) [no
catalogue].

REFERENCES: *Canadian Art*, vol. XX (Nov., 1963), p. 337 (reprod.).

Purchase, 1963.

62/57 **Ginza**
Colour reproduction, p. 551

63/28

HERRONTON WOOD **1963**

Oil on canvas, $51\frac{1}{8}$" x $88\frac{1}{4}$".
Signed and dated (on reverse, upper left): RONALD/SEPT. 63/ 51" x 90".
Inscribed (on reverse, upper right): 'HERRONTON WOOD'.

PROV.: [Samuel M. Kootz Gallery Inc., New York].

EXHIBITIONS: Kootz Gallery, *Ronald*, 1963 (Dec. 3-21) [no catalogue].

Gift from the McLean Foundation, 1964.

For linocut and monotype by Ronald, see "Toronto 20", p. 453-457.

Robert ROSS (1902-   )

BORN: Toronto, December 29, 1902.

LIVES: Toronto.

STUDY: Toronto, Ontario College of Art, 1921, under C. M. Manly, Beatty, Reid, Lismer, Varley; and sculpture under Emanuel Hahn.

TEACHING: Toronto, Central Technical School, for over 30 years, and presently teaching life and portrait drawing.

1943-45; draughtsman at de Haviland aircraft works.

2567

STUDY OF DEER **1934**

Pencil on paper, $10\frac{1}{2}$" x $14\frac{1}{2}$".
Signed and dated (upper left): ROSS. 34.

PROV.: the artist [CSGA, 1941].

EXHIBITIONS: *C.S.G.A.*, 1941, no. 123.

REFERENCES: Duval (1952), pl. 26 (reprod.).

Purchase, 1941.

G. Horne RUSSELL (1861-1933)

BORN: George Horne Russell, Banff, Scotland, April 18, 1861.

DIED: St. Stephen, N. B., June 24, 1933. Came to Canada (Montreal) in 1890.

STUDY: Aberdeen School of Art; South Kensington Art Schools, London, and under Andrew Burnett, Alphonse Legros and Sir George Reid.

SOCIETIES: A.R.C.A., 1909, R.C.A., 1918, P.R.C.A. 1922-26; Pen and Pencil Club, Montreal, 1912.

Portrait painter, marine and landscape painter. Described in Harper (1966), p. 318, as "painter of fashionable Montreal society...and seascapes of their holiday resorts."

102

CARTING SEAWEED

Oil on canvas, 32" x 47".
Signed (lower right): G Horne Russell.

NOTES: Permanent loan from C.N.E. Association, 1919-65.

EXHIBITIONS: *R.C.A.*, 1918, no. 167; *C.N.E.*, 1919, no. 136.

Gift of the Canadian National Exhibition Association, 1965.

102   **Carting Seaweed**

Henry SANDHAM (1842-1910)

BORN: J. Henry Sandham, Montreal, 1842.

DIED: London, England, June 21, 1910.

STUDY: Montreal, Notman's photographic studios, in association with Fraser, Vogt, Jacobi, and Way.

SOCIETIES: R.C.A., charter member, 1880; O.S.A., 1873; Society of Canadian Artists, Montreal, founding member, 1867.

Directed the St. John, N. B., office of Notman's in the late 1870's.

TRAVEL: Visited England in 1880; was living in Boston from 1881. Made his reputation in the United States as an illustrator for Scribner's, Harper's and Century magazines during the 1880's and '90's. Late in life he returned to England.

Landscape painter, and illustrator.

2167

CLIFF AND BOATS 1872

Water colour on paper, 26$^1/_{16}$" x 33$^3/_4$".
Signed and dated (lower left): Hy Sandham/1872.

PROV.: [D. M. Henderson and Co., Toronto, sale, February 28, 1934, to Wenroth]; Mr. S. Wenroth, Toronto.

NOTES: In notes by F. S. Challener in the archives of the Art Gallery of Ontario, the painting is referred to by the title, *On the Nova Scotia Coast.*

EXHIBITIONS: A.G.T., *Loan exhibition*, 1935, no. 148; C.N.E., 1939, no. 198; London, Ont., *Milestones*, 1942, no. 18.

Purchase, 1934.

2167   **Cliff and Boats**

47/11

FISHING BOATS, BAY OF FUNDY 1885

Oil on canvas, 17" x 31".
Signed and dated (lower right): Hy Sandham/1885.

Bequest of John Ross Robertson, 1947.

47/11   **Fishing Boats, Bay of Fundy**

408

Jerry SANTBERGEN (1942-   )

BORN: Klundert, the Netherlands, March 9, 1942.

LIVES: Toronto. Came to Canada (Regina) about 1954.

STUDY: Regina Art School, principally under McKay.

Moved to Toronto, November, 1966, following about three months in New York.

AWARDS: Canada Council, 1967.

66/28

PAINTING   1966

Acrylic on canvas, 2 triangular panels hung as a diamond, 41″ greatest width, 4″ to 7$\frac{1}{2}$″ depth.
Inscribed (on stretcher): [1] SANTBERGEN (1).
                          [2] BORN HOLLAND 42 Pt. ACR. ON.
CANVAS 1966 (2).

PROV.: the artist.

EXHIBITIONS: Toronto, Pollock Gallery, *Santbergen*, 1967 (Apr. 2-15) [no catalogue].

Gift of Reeves and Sons (Canada) Ltd., 1967.

66/28   **Painting**

Anne SAVAGE (1897-   )

BORN: Annie (Anne) Douglas Savage, Montreal, 1897.

LIVES: Montreal.

STUDY: Art Association of Montreal, under William Brymner and Maurice Cullen; Minneapolis School of Art.

SOCIETIES: C.G.P., founding member, 1933, Pres. 1960.

TEACHING: Montreal, Baron Byng High School, from about 1921; later supervisor of art for Protestant School Board, Montreal; organized children's classes at Art Association of Montreal.

Landscape painter.

2831

THE WOOD   1938

Oil on canvas, 30$\frac{3}{8}$″ x 25$\frac{1}{4}$″.
Signed (lower left): A D SAVAGE.

PROV.: the artist.

EXHIBITIONS: A.A.M., *Summer exhibition*, 1939, no. 42; [?] A.G.T., *Savage, Heward, Robertson, and Seath*, 1940 (Feb.); New York, Riverside Museum, *Canadian women artists*, 1947, no. 63.

Purchase, 1946.

Carl SCHAEFER (1903-   )

BORN: Carl Fellman Schaefer, Hanover, Ontario, April 30, 1903.

LIVES: Toronto.

STUDY: Toronto, Ontario College of Art, 1921, under J. E. H. MacDonald, Arthur Lismer, Robert Holmes, and G. A. Reid, though largely self-taught in landscape painting.

SOCIETIES: A.R.C.A., 1949, R.C.A., 1964; C.S.P.W.C., Pres. 1938-41; C.G.P., 1936; C.S.G.A., 1932.

TEACHING: Toronto, Central Technical School, 1929-48; Ontario College of Art, since 1948.

AWARDS: John Simon Guggenheim Memorial fellowship for creative painting, 1940 [the first Canadian to receive this honour]; spent the year in Vermont.

Official war artist with R.C.A.F., 1943-46

Chiefly landscape painter, best known for his water colours.

2423

BEFORE RAIN, PARRY SOUND   1935

Water colour on paper, 15$\frac{1}{2}$" x 22".
Signed and dated (lower left): Carl Schaefer, 1935.

PROV.: the artist [CSPWC, 1937].

EXHIBITIONS: *R.C.A.*, 1935, no. 231; *C.S.P.W.C.*, 1937, no. 93, p. 4 (reprod.); *D.P.C.*, 1945, no. 171; A.G.T., and Ontario Department of Education, 1951, no. 35.

REFERENCES: A.G.T., *Bulletin* (Apr., 1937), p. 1 (reprod.); *Studio*, vol. CXIV (Aug., 1937), p. 69 (reprod.); A.G.T., *Bulletin and annual report* (Apr., 1938), reprod.; *New World Illustrated* (Aug., 1940), p. 26 (reprod. in colour); *Studio*, vol. CXXII (July, 1941), p. 16 (reprod. in colour); *Idem*, vol. CXXIII (Feb., 1942), p. 49; Colgate (1943), p. 104 (reprod.); McRae (1944), p. 48 (reprod.); *The Arts in Canada* (1957), pp. 96, 97 (reprod.); A.G.T., *Painting and sculpture* (1959), p. 72 (reprod.).

Gift from Friends of Canadian Art Fund, 1937.

2320

APPLES   1935

Wood engraving, Imp.: 4" x 6$\frac{3}{8}$". Paper: 7$\frac{1}{16}$" x 7$\frac{3}{16}$".
Signed and dated (lower right, in pencil): Carl Schaefer 35.
Numbered (lower left, in pencil): 1/35.

PROV.: the artist [CSGA, 1935].

EXHIBITIONS: *C.S.G.A.*, 1935, no. 145, p. 6 (reprod.); *C.N.E.*, 1935, no. 1000; New York, *World's Fair*, 1939, section CSGA, no. 119.

REFERENCES: A.G.T., *Bulletin* (May, 1935), p. 4 (reprod.); *New World Illustrated* (Aug., 1940), p. 27 (reprod.); *Canadian Art*, vol. CXVII (Mar., 1960), p. 67.

Gift from Friends of Canadian Art Fund, 1935.

53/51

STORM OVER THE FIELDS   1937

Oil on canvas, 27$\frac{3}{16}$" x 37".
Signed and dated (lower left): Carl Schaefer/1937.

PROV.: the artist [AGT, 1954].

NOTES: Water colour study for this in the J. S. McLean collection, Toronto, is illustrated on p. 445 in *Canadian Art*, vol. XIX (Nov., 1962).

EXHIBITIONS: *O.S.A.*, 1938, no. 156; A.G.T., *Clark, and Schaefer*, 1954, no. 15; Stratford, *Canada on canvas*, 1963; A.G.T., [circulating exhibition], *Canadian paintings of the 1930s*, 1967-68, no. 21.

REFERENCES: *Canadian Art*, vol. XV (Mar., 1960), p. 66 (McLean study reprod.; says painted at Hanover, Ontario), p. 67.

Gift from J. S. McLean, Canadian Fund, 1954.

53/51   **Storm over the Fields**

2572

VIEW OF NORWICH, VERMONT   **1940**

Water colour on paper, 15$\frac{1}{2}$" x 22$\frac{1}{2}$".
Signed and dated (lower left): C F S 1940/Nov. 21.

PROV.: the artist.

NOTES. For chalk study by the same title in this collection, see below, acc. no. 60/33.

EXHIBITIONS: Quebec, *Exposition...O.S.A.*, 1944, no. 118.

REFERENCES: Griffith, *Water colours* [1967], between pp. 3 and 4 (reprod.); C.S.P.W.C., *42nd annual exhibition* (1967), p. 9 (reprod. [not exhibited]).

Purchase, 1941.

2572   **View of Norwich, Vermont**

60/33

VIEW OF NORWICH, VERMONT
1940

Black chalk on paper, $21\frac{1}{8}$" x $30\frac{5}{8}$".
Signed and dated (lower left): C. Schaefer 40.

PROV.: [Picture Loan Society, Toronto].

NOTES: Probably study for water colour by the same title in this collection [see above, acc. no. 2572].

EXHIBITIONS: [?] *C.S.G.A.*, 1942.

Canada Council Joint Drawings Purchase Fund, 1961.

2571

NEW ENGLAND HOUSE
1941

Water colour on paper, $15\frac{1}{2}$" x $22\frac{1}{2}$".
Signed and dated (lower left): C. Schaefer 41/Mar. 27.

PROV.: the artist.

Purchase, 1941.

2709

RAILROAD BRIDGE, WHITE RIVER JUNCTION
1941

Lithograph, Imp.: $7\frac{7}{8}$" x $10\frac{7}{8}$". Paper: $13\frac{1}{8}$" x 15".
Signed and dated (lower right, in pencil): C. Schaefer 41.
Numbered (lower left, in pencil): 1 -4/10.
Inscribed (across bottom in pencil): Railroad Bridge at White River Junction.

PROV.: the artist.

NOTES: Executed in Vermont.

EXHIBITIONS: A.G.T., *Canadian prints*, 1949.

REFERENCES: A.G.T., *Accessions 1943*, reprod.; Duval (1952), pl. 55 (reprod.).

Purchase, 1943.

2708

ELECTRIC WELDER, SHEET SHOP
1942

Ink and wash on paper, $11\frac{3}{4}$" x $17\frac{15}{16}$".
Signed, dated and inscribed (lower right): Electric Welder/ C. Schaefer/ 24.4.42 —.

PROV.: the artist.

NOTES: Depicts war-time production at the John Inglis Company, Toronto.

EXHIBITIONS: A.G.T., *War record drawings*, 1943.

REFERENCES: *Canadian Art*, vol XVII (Mar., 1960), p. 68.

Purchase, 1943.

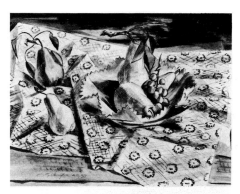

55/39 **Still Life, Yellow**
Colour reproduction, p. 549

55/39

STILL LIFE, YELLOW   **1955**

Water colour on paper, 15″ x 22″ [sight].
Signed and dated (lower left): C. Schaefer 4.9.55.

PROV.: the artist [RCA, 1955].

EXHIBITIONS: *R.C.A.*, 1955-56, no. 73 (reprod.); Dallas, 1958.

REFERENCES: *Canadian Art*, vol. XVII (Mar., 1960), p. 70 (reprod.).

Gift from J. S. McLean, Canadian Fund, 1956.

62/31

THE CUTTER, WELLINGTON COUNTY   **1962**

Pen and ink on blue paper, 11$\frac{5}{8}$″ x 17$\frac{3}{8}$″ [sight].
Signed, dated and inscribed (lower left): The Cutter, Wellington C./C Schaefer.26.6.62.

PROV.: [Roberts Gallery, Toronto].

EXHIBITIONS: Roberts Gallery, *Schaefer*, 1963 (Feb. 20 - Mar. 2) [no catalogue].

Gift from the McLean Foundation, 1963.

62/46

BARN RUINS, ESQUESING TOWNSHIP, WELLINGTON COUNTY   **1962**

Water colour, pen and ink on paper, 14$\frac{9}{16}$″ x 21$\frac{9}{16}$″ [sight].
Signed, dated and inscribed (lower left): Barn Ruins, Esquesing Township/Wellington County · Halton/C Schaefer. 16·9·62.

PROV.: [Roberts Gallery, Toronto].

EXHIBITIONS: Roberts Gallery, *Schaefer*, 1963 (Feb. 20 - Mar. 2) [no catalogue].

Gift from the McLean Foundation, 1963.

62/30

BIRDS' NESTS   **1963**

Pen and ink on green paper, 12$\frac{1}{2}$″ x 17$\frac{13}{16}$″ [sight].
Signed, dated and inscribed (lower right): Birds' Nests/C Schaefer 26.1.63.

PROV.: [Roberts Gallery, Toronto].

EXHIBITIONS: Roberts Gallery, *Schaefer*, 1963 (Feb. 20 - Mar. 2) [no catalogue].

Gift from the McLean Foundation, 1963.

STUDY: Montreal, school of the Montreal Museum of Fine Arts, under Arthur Lismer, and privately under Alfred Pinsky; Paris, Atelier 17, under William Hayter, and Ecole des Beaux-Arts.

TEACHING: Professor of graphic arts, Mount Allison University, Sackville, N. B., since 1963.

TRAVEL: Extensively in Europe and Russia; Grenoble, France, 1958-59, working at Institute of Decorative Arts and Architecture.

AWARDS: Canada Council grant, 1967, to work in Kyoto, Japan.

Graphic artist.

NOTES: The portfolio, in white cardboard, measures $15^3/_4$" x $12^3/_4$". Each engraving is accompanied by an engraved verse from *The Song of Solomon*, the reference to which follows each title in brackets.

On title page: "Dedicated to my son/Alexis".

Published by the Upstairs Gallery, October, 1961, Toronto.

THE ENGRAVINGS:

61/47.1

THE SONG OF SONGS: Thou are all fair, my love; there is no spot in thee [IV: 7], Imp.: $9^7/_{16}$" x $6^7/_{16}$".

61/47.2

THE SONG OF SONGS: How beautiful are thy feet with sandals, O prince's daughter! [VII: 1], Imp.: $9^7/_{16}$" x $6^7/_{16}$".

61/47.3

THE SONG OF SONGS: Behold his bed which is Solomon's, three-score valiant men are about it, of the valiant of Israel. They all hold swords, being expert in war [III: 7-8], Imp.: $9^7/_{16}$" x $6^7/_{16}$".

61/47.4

THE SONG OF SONGS: I will rise now, and go about the city in the streets, and in the broad ways I will seek him whom my soul loveth [III: 2], Imp.: $9^{15}/_{16}$" x $6^7/_{16}$".

61/47.5

THE SONG OF SONGS: His left hand is under my head, and his right hand doth embrace me [II: 6], Imp.: $10^{15}/_{16}$" x $5^{15}/_{16}$".

61/47.6

THE SONG OF SONGS: Thy cheeks are comely with rows of jewels, thy neck with chains of gold [I: 10], Imp.: $9^{15}/_{16}$" x $6^7/_{16}$".

61/47.7

THE SONG OF SONGS: I am my beloved's, and my beloved is mine [VI: 3], Imp.: $9^{15}/_{16}$" x $6^7/_{16}$".

61/47.8

THE SONG OF SONGS: The watchmen that went about the city found me, they smote me, they wounded me; the keepers of the walls took away my veil from me [V: 7], Imp.: $9^7/_{16}$" x $6^7/_{16}$".

61/47.9

THE SONG OF SONGS: Come with me from Lebanon, my spouse, with me from Lebanon: look from the top of Amana, from the top of Shenir and Hermon [IV: 8], Imp.: $9^{15}/_{16}$" x $6^1/_2$".

61/47.10

THE SONG OF SONGS: I charge you O ye daughters of Jerusalem that ye stir not up nor awaken my love till he please [VIII: 4], Imp.: $9^7/_{16}$" x $6^7/_{16}$".

61/47.11

THE SONG OF SONGS: Solomon had a vineyard at Baal-Hamon [VIII: 11], Imp.: $9^7/_{16}$″ x $6^7/_{16}$″.

61/47.12

THE SONG OF SONGS: Make haste, my beloved, and be thou like a roe or to a young hart upon the mountains of spices [VIII: 14], Imp.: $9^7/_{16}$″ x $6^7/_{16}$″.

61/47.13

THE SONG OF SONGS: Return, return, O Shulamite; return, return, that we may look upon thee [VII: 13], Imp.: $9^{15}/_{16}$″ x $6^7/_{16}$″.

61/47.14

THE SONG OF SONGS: His left hand should be under my head and his right hand should embrace me [VIII: 3], Imp.: $9^7/_{16}$″ x $6^7/_{16}$″.

61/47.15

THE SONG OF SONGS: For lo, the winter is past, the rain is over and gone; The flowers appear on the earth; the time of the singing of birds is come [II: 11-12], Imp.: $6^7/_{16}$″ x $9^{15}/_{16}$″.

Gift of Dr. and Mrs. M. K. Bochner, 1962.

Ellen SIMON (1916-   )

BORN: Toronto, 1916.

LIVES: New York.

STUDY: Toronto, Ontario College of Art, 1934-36, under Yvonne Housser, Carmichael, Alfsen, Pepper, and others; New York, Art Students' League, 1936-40, under Harry Sternberg, Soyer, and Kantor; New York, New School for Social Research, under Will Barnet; Toronto, in the studios of Yvonne Williams, stained glass; also under Joep Nicolas.

SOCIETIES: C.S.G.A.

Worked mostly in lithography and book illustration, until 1942, when she turned to stained glass design, in which area she has carried out many commissions both in Canada and the United States. Numerous stained glass windows in Toronto and other Canadian centres have been executed in cooperation with Miss Yvonne Williams.

TEACHING: New York, Riverside Church, since 1965; has also worked with art therapy in several New York hospitals.

Stained glass designer, printmaker, illustrator.

2710

DISHWASHERS

Lithograph, Imp.: 13″ x $18^1/_2$″. Paper: $15^3/_4$″ x $11^7/_{16}$″.
Signed (lower right, in pencil): Ellen Simon.

PROV.: the artist.

Purchase, 1943.

PROV.: [Gallery Pascal, Toronto].

EXHIBITIONS: Gallery Pascal, *Canadian printmakers '66*, 1966 (Apr. 21 - May 12) [no catalogue].

Purchase, 1966.

66/45

HORIZONTAL RED   **1967**

Serigraph, Imp.: 23$^1/_2$" x 19$^3/_4$".
Signed (lower right, in pencil): Gordon Smith.
Numbered (lower left, in pencil): 3/30.

PROV.: [Gallery Pascal, Toronto].

EXHIBITIONS: Gallery Pascal, *Canadian Printmakers '67*, 1967 (May 4-30) [no catalogue].

[NOTE: Impression of this print exhibited also: New York, Museum of Modern Art, *Canada '67*, 1967 (May 2 - June 4).].

Purchase, 1967.

62/9

MAN TURNING   **1961**

Stone, 22" (incl. base).
Incised (on base, left of figure): (1984).

PROV.: [Isaacs Gallery, Toronto].

EXHIBITIONS: Isaacs Gallery, *Smith*, 1962 (May 17 - June 5) [no catalogue].

REFERENCES: *Canadian Art*, vol. XIX (July, 1962), p. 293 (reprod. as Man).

Purchase, 1962.

62/9   **Man Turning**

John Ivor SMITH (1927-   )

BORN: London, England, January 28, 1927.

LIVES: Montreal.

STUDY: Montreal Museum of Fine Arts school of art and design, under Arthur Lismer, and Jacques de Tonnancour; Montreal, Ecole des Beaux-Arts; but mainly self-taught.

SOCIETIES: S.S.C.

TEACHING: Montreal, Sir George Williams University, Assistant professor, Fine Arts Department, since 1966.

TRAVEL: Italy, 1957-58, sculpting.

AWARDS: Canada Council grant, 1957 [forfeited]; Canada Council grant, 1967.

Sculptor.

424

John SNOW (1911-   )

BORN: John Harold Thomas Snow, Vancouver, B. C., December 12, 1911.

LIVES: Calgary, Alberta.

STUDY: Calgary, Institute of Technology and Art; and life drawing with Maxwell Bates, 1947-49.

SOCIETIES: A.R.C.A., 1965; C.S.G.A.; Alberta Society of Artists.

TRAVEL: United Kingdom, North Africa, Sicily, Italy and India, during World War II.

Graphic artist, mostly lithography.

64/71

BLUE FLOWERS

Lithograph, Imp.: $15^3/_4$" x $19^7/_8$".
Signed (lower right, in pencil): John Snow.
Inscribed (lower left, in pencil): Blue Flowers.
Numbered (lower centre, in pencil): 6/21.

PROV.: [Dorothy Cameron Gallery, Toronto].

EXHIBITIONS: Dorothy Cameron Gallery, *Canadian printmaking today*, 1965 (Apr.) [exhibited but not in catalogue].

Gift from Anonymous Fund, 1965.

Michael SNOW (1929-   )

BORN: Toronto, December 10, 1929.

LIVES: New York, since 1962.

STUDY: Toronto, Ontario College of Art.

TRAVEL: Europe (Italy and Belgium), 1954-55, painting and playing jazz piano.

AWARDS: Canada Council grants, 1959, and 1966-67.

Painter, sculptor, film maker, jazz musician.

61/61

ROLLED WOMAN I   1961

Canvas, and cardboard cylinders in wooden case, $30^1/_8$" x $25^1/_8$".
Signed and dated (upper right): SNOW '61.
Inscribed (on reverse, upper left): ROLLED WOMAN I/CANVAS, PLYWOOD, OIL, ETC./SNOW '61.

PROV.: [Isaacs Gallery, Toronto].

EXHIBITIONS: Isaacs Gallery, *Snow*, 1962 (Mar. 15 - Apr. 3) [no catalogue].

Gift from the McLean Foundation, 1962.

61/61   **Rolled Woman I**

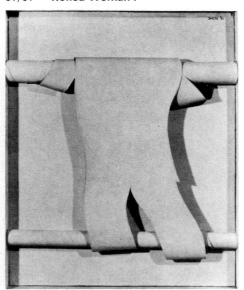

Owen STAPLES (1866-1949)

BORN: Stoke-sub-Hamdon, Somerset, England, September 3, 1866.

DIED: Toronto, December 5, 1949. Came to Canada (Hamilton) in 1870; moved with his family to Rochester, N. Y., in 1877, and remained in the United States until 1885, when he returned to Canada and settled in Toronto.

STUDY: Rochester Art Club, under Horatio Walker, and others; New York, Art Students' League, 1883; Philadelphia, Pennsylvania Academy of Fine Arts, 1884, under Thomas Eakins, and Thomas Anshutz; Toronto, under G. A. Reid, 1885.

SOCIETIES: O.S.A., 1892; Toronto Art Students' League, 1884-88; C.P.E., 1918, Pres.; C.S.P.W.C., founding member, 1926; Arts and Letters Club, Toronto, charter member, 1908.

TRAVEL: England and France, 1908.

Made cartoons and illustrations for *The Evening Telegram*, Toronto, for many years, from 1887 to 1947.

Painter, etcher, illustrator, newspaper cartoonist.

574

INGLENOOK

Etching, Imp.: $3^{11}/_{16}$" x $4^3/_8$".
Signed (lower right, in pencil): Owen Staples.

Gift of the Artist, 1915.

575

LOG HOUSE

Etching, Imp.: $6^1/_2$" x $8^5/_8$".
Signed (lower right, in pencil): Owen Staples.

EXHIBITIONS: [?] *O.S.A.*, 1913, no. 147 (as A Log House of 1800).

Gift of the Artist, 1915.

577

JULIET

Etching, Imp.: $4^1/_2$" x $3^3/_{16}$". Paper: $6^9/_{16}$" x $5^3/_{16}$".
Signed (lower right, in pencil): Owen Staples.
Inscribed (lower left): O Staples.
Inscribed (lower centre): JULIET.

Gift of the Artist, 1915.

578

SLEEPING LEOPARD

Etching, Imp.: $3^1/_8$" x $6^1/_2$". Paper: $5^1/_4$" x $9^1/_2$".
Signed (lower right, in pencil): Owen Staples.
Inscribed (lower right): Staples.
Inscribed (lower centre): THE SLEEPING LEOPARD.

EXHIBITIONS: [?] *O.S.A.*, 1913, no. 148.

Gift of the Artist, 1915.

1436

CLOVELLY

Etching, Imp.: $5^7/_8$" x $6^7/_8$". Paper: $9^1/_4$" x $11^1/_8$".
Signed (lower right, in pencil): Owen Staples.

EXHIBITIONS: [?] Toronto, Studio of the artist, *Exhibition of sketches and small pictures*, 1917 (Nov. 10-17), no. 72 (A Clovelly Cottage).

Gift of Sir Edmund Walker Estate, 1926.

61/33

FLOWER GARDEN

Pastel on paper, $12^{13}/_{16}$" x $9^{13}/_{16}$".
Signed (lower left): Owen Staples.

428

PROV.: Miss Dorothy Staples, Toronto; Mrs. Stephen DuBrul, Detroit, Michigan.

EXHIBITIONS: [?] *C.N.E.*, 1921, no. 241 (The Garden).

Gift from the McLean Foundation; 1962.

61/34

DAHLIAS

Pastel on paper, 12⁷/₈″ x 9¹³/₁₆″ [sight].

PROV.: Miss Dorothy Staples, Toronto; Mrs. Stephen DuBrul, Detroit, Michigan.

Gift from the McLean Foundation, 1962.

61/35

ROSE AND DELPHINIUM

Pastel on paper, 13¹/₈″ x 10¹/₈″.
Signed (lower right): Owen Staples.

PROV.: Miss Dorothy Staples, Toronto; Mrs. Stephen DuBrul, Detroit, Michigan.

Gift from the McLean Foundation, 1962.

576

CONSTRUCTION OF THE UNION BANK   **1915**

Etching, Imp.: 8″ x 6¹/₂″.
Inscribed (lower right): Owen/Staples.

EXHIBITIONS: [?] Toronto, Studio of the artist, *Exhibition of sketches and small pictures*, 1917 (Nov. 10-17), no. 68 (as Steel Construction).

REFERENCES: Duval (1952), pl. 15 (reprod.; dated 1915).

Gift of the Artist, 1915.

275   **Exhibition Park from the Water**

275

EXHIBITION PARK FROM THE WATER   **1924**

Water colour on paper, 13³/₈″ x 20¹/₄″ [sight].
Signed and dated (lower left): Owen Staples 1924.

NOTES: Permanent loan from C.N.E. Association, 1925-65.

EXHIBITIONS: *O.S.A.*, 1925, no. 215; *C.N.E.*, 1925, no. 343; A.G.T., *Loan exhibition*, 1935, no. 249; Hamilton, *Some artists who have lived and worked in Hamilton*, 1967, no. 75 (reprod.).

Gift of the Canadian National Exhibition Association, 1965.

61/6

LANDSCAPE 1908

Oil on cardboard, 8¹/₂" x 10⁵/₈".
Signed (lower right): Suzor-Coté.
Inscribed (on reverse): 2 September 1908/"Le Castel Ryan"/ 5¹/₂ hrs.
après Midi/Oak Ridge Virginia USA/M A Suzor-Coté.

EXHIBITIONS: London, Ont., *Canadian Impressionists*, 1965, no. 35.

REFERENCES: A.G.T., *The Gerald R. Larkin Bequest 1961*.

Bequest of Gerald R. Larkin, 1961.

276   **Femmes de Caughnawaga**

276

FEMMES DE CAUGHNAWAGA 1924

Bronze, 17¹/₄" high, 22" long.
Signed and dated (on base, upper side): M. Suzor-Coté 1924.
Inscribed (on base, front): FEMMES/de CAUGHNAWAGA.
Stamped (on base): COPYRIGHT/CANADA & US 1925.

NOTES: Permanent loan from C.N.E. Association, 1925-66,

Caghnawaga, Quebec, is an Indian reserve on the south bank of the
St. Lawrence River, opposite Lachine.

According to R. H. Hubbard [see ref. 1963], this work is directly
inspired by Carl Milles' bronze *Dutch Women*; reproduced in *Studio*,
vol. L (Aug., 1910), p. 211.

Other casts are in the collections of the National Gallery of Canada,
acc. no. 3367; the Montreal Museum of Fine Arts; and the Vancouver
Art Gallery.

EXHIBITIONS: A.A.M., *41st spring exhibition*, 1924, no. 326; *R.C.A.*,
1924, no. 245; A.A.M., *42nd spring exhibition*, 1925, no. 402; *C.N.E.*,
1925, no. 359; N.G.C., *Special exhibition of Canadian art*, 1926, no.
157; Paris, 1927, no. 223; A.G.T., *Exhibition of Canadian sculpture*,
1928, no. 128; *S.S.C.*, 1929, no. 71; A.G.T., *Works by senior painters
in Canada*, 1937, no. 70; London, Tate, 1938, no. 244 (reprod.).

REFERENCES: Chauvin (1928), pp. 87, 89 (reprod.); Colgate (1943),
pp. 124, 125 (reprod.); *Canadian Review of Music and Art*, vol. 2, nos.
9 and 10 (Oct., 1943), p. 14 (reprod. artist at work on "Three Indians");
Gour, *Suzor-Coté* (1950), opp. p. 16 (reprod.), pp. 18, 21; *Saturday
Night*, vol. 69 (Feb. 27, 1954), p. 5 (reprod.); *The Arts in Canada*
(1957), p. 66 (reprod.), p. 67; Hubbard (1963), p. 81.

Gift of the Canadian National Exhibition Association, 1966.

2100

MARIA CHAPDELAINE 1925

Bronze, 15³/₈".
Signed and dated (on base): M. Suzor-Coté/1925.
Inscribed (on base, front): Maria Chapdelaine.

PROV.: Arthur Coté, Montreal.

2100   **Maria Chapdelaine**

NOTES: Subject drawn from Louis Hémon's novel, *Maria Chapdelaine* (1916), a Canadian classic, portraying the hardships of the French-Canadian pioneer, settling the Lake St. John area in the late 19th century. [see Norah Story, *The Oxford companion to Canadian history and literature*, 1967, p. 353].

According to Gérard Morisset, the statuette was first modelled at the same time Suzor-Coté executed drawings to illustrate the first edition of Hémon's novel, that is, 1915-16; cast in bronze in 1925 [letter from Mr. Morisset, Quebec, January 12, 1954].

EXHIBITIONS: *R.C.A.*, 1925, no. 275; *R.C.A.*, 1926-27, no. 168; *R.C.A.*, 1928-29, no. 175; N.G.C., *Annual*, 1929, no. 156; A.G.T., *Works by senior painters in Canada*, 1937, no. 71, p. 29 (reprod.); Kitchener, *Canadian classic*, 1959, no. 8.

REFERENCES: Chauvin (1928), p. 83 (reprod.), p. 87; A.G.T., *Bulletin and annual report* (Mar., 1933), p. 15 (reprod.); Colgate (1943), p. 124; *New Frontiers* (Winter, 1953), p. 26 (reprod.); *Saturday Night*, vol. 69 (Feb. 27, 1954), p. 5 (reprod.).

Purchase, 1933.

51/59

L'ESSOUCHEUR   ?1925

Bronze, 15³/₄" high, 21" long.
Signed (on base): M. A. SUZOR-COTE.
Inscribed (on base): L'ESSOUCHEUR.
Stamped (front of base): COPYRIGHT/CANADA & UNITED STATES.
Stamped (right front of base): ROMAN BRONZE WORKS N-Y.

NOTES: According to Gérard Morisset, the statuette was modelled sometime between 1917 and 1922; cast in bronze in 1925 [letter from Mr. Morisset, Quebec, January 12, 1954].

EXHIBITIONS: *R.C.A.*, 1927-28, no. 269; N.G.C., *Annual*, 1928, no. 146; Vancouver, *All-Canadian exhibition*, 1932, no. 236.

REFERENCES: Chauvin (1928), p. 82; Gour, *Suzor-Coté* (1950), p. 18; *Saturday Night*, vol. 69 (Feb. 27, 1954), p. 5 (reprod.).

Bequest of John Paris Bickell, 1952.

51/60

LE BÛCHERON   ?1925

Bronze, 18³/₈" high.
Signed (on base): A SUZOR COTE.
Inscribed (on base): LE BUCHERON.
Stamped (on base): COPYRIGHT/CANADA & UNITED STATES.

NOTES: According to Gérard Morisset, the statuette was modelled sometime between 1917 and 1922; cast in bronze in 1925 [letter from Mr. Morisset, Quebec, January 12, 1954].

EXHIBITIONS: *R.C.A.*, 1927-28, no. 268.

REFERENCES: Chauvin (1928), p. 82.

Bequest of John Paris Bickell, 1952.

PROV.: [Dominion Gallery, Montreal]; Mr. and Mrs. E. P. Taylor, Toronto.

EXHIBITIONS: Montreal, International Fur and Leather Workers Union, *Taylor*, 1955 (Jan.) [no catalogue]; Dominion Gallery, *Taylor*, 1955 (Nov. 17-30) [no catalogue].

Gift of Mr. and Mrs. E. P. Taylor, 1956.

Mashel TEITELBAUM (1921-)

BORN: Saskatoon, Saskatchewan, 1921.

LIVES: Toronto.

STUDY: Early self-taught; California School of Fine Arts, with Clyfford Still, 1950-51, and Mills College, with Max Beckman, summer of 1951.

TEACHING: University of Manitoba, School of Fine Arts, 1960; conducted avant-garde New School in Toronto, 1961.

TRAVEL: Europe, 1959-60.

For embossed print by Teitelbaum, see "Toronto 20", p. 453-457.

Lionel THOMAS (1915-)

BORN: Lionel Arthur John Thomas, Toronto, April 3, 1915.

LIVES: Vancouver.

STUDY: Toronto, John Russell School of Fine Art; Provincetown, Mass., with Hans Hofmann, 1947; San Francisco, California School of Fine Art, under Mark Rothko, 1949-50.

SOCIETIES: C.G.P.; B. C. Society of Artists; F.C.A.; Pacific Art Association.

TEACHING: Vancouver School of Art, 1944-50; University of British Columbia, from 1950.

AWARDS: Emily Carr Trust Fund scholarship, 1949-50.

Has carried out many mural and architectural sculpture commissions.

Painter, muralist, and sculptor.

52/55

TREE FORMS 1951

Oil on canvas, 20" x 26".
Signed (lower left): Lionel Thomas.

PROV.: the artist [AGT, 1953].

EXHIBITIONS: Vancouver, University of British Columbia, *Thomas*, 1951, no. 49, on front cover (reprod.); A.G.T., *Scott, and Thomas*, 1953, no. 10.

Gift from the John Paris Bickell Bequest Fund, 1953.

52/55 **Tree Forms**

**THOMPSON, Ernest Seton, see
SETON, Ernest Thompson**

George THOMSON (1868-1965)

BORN: Near Claremont, Ontario, February 10, 1868; elder brother to Tom Thomson; grew up at Leith, Ontario.

DIED: Owen Sound, July 21, 1965.

STUDY: Seattle, University of Washington, law, 1901; New York, Art Students' League, 1906-07; Old Lyme, Connecticut, under Du-Mond.

First took up painting in 1906.

SOCIETIES: O.S.A., 1933.

Lived in New Haven, Conn., from about 1910 until 1926 when he returned to Canada to live in Owen Sound.

Landscape painter.

2335

APPROACHING SPRING   **1932**

Oil on canvas, 20" x 24".
Signed and dated (lower right): Geo. Thomson '32.

PROV.: [J. Merritt Malloney Gallery, Toronto]; W. Muir Twaddle, Toronto.

EXHIBITIONS: London, Ont., *Thomson*, 1951 (Oct. 19 - Nov. 18) [no catalogue].

REFERENCES: A.G.T., *Bulletin and annual report* (Apr., 1937), p. 16 (reprod.).

Gift of W. Muir Twaddle, 1935.

Tom THOMSON (1877-1917)

BORN: Thomas John Thomson, near Clare-mont, Ontario, August 4, 1877; grew up at Leith, near Owen Sound.

DIED: By drowning, Canoe Lake, Algonquin Park, July, 1917; buried at Leith, where later a cairn was erected to him.

STUDY: Largely self-taught, having developed an interest in sketching in crayon and water colour while working as a commercial artist in Seattle, 1901-05.

Returned to Toronto, 1905, where he continued to work at commercial studios, with Grip Limited, 1908-12, and there became associated with MacDonald, Lismer, Varley, and Carmichael, all founding members of the Group of Seven, some years later. Worked at Rous and Mann, from 1912 until 1914, when he turned all his attention toward painting.

SOCIETIES: O.S.A., 1914.

When the Studio Building opened on Severn Street in 1914, Thomson shared a studio with Jackson, and later with Franklin Carmichael.

By 1915, Thomson was spending most of the year in Algonquin Park, where he had become an accomplished guide, only returning to

848

A NORTHERN LAKE

Oil on panel, 8½" x 10½".
Stamp of the Thomson studio, lower left [see Note, following Biography].

EXHIBITIONS: Toronto, Mellors Galleries, *Thomson*, 1937, no. 41.

Gift from the Reuben and Kate Leonard Canadian Fund, 1927.

850

WILD CHERRY TREES IN BLOSSOM

Oil on panel, 8½" x 10½".
Stamp of the Thomson studio, lower right [see Note, following Biography].

EXHIBITIONS: Toronto, Mellors Galleries, *Thomson*, 1937, no. 43; Windsor, *Group of Seven*, 1948, no. 43.

Gift from the Reuben and Kate Leonard Canadian Fund, 1927.

851

PINE TREE

Oil on panel, 8½" x 10½".
Stamp of the Thomson studio, lower left [see Note, following Biography].

Toronto, and his shack beside the Studio Building, in winter to paint canvases from his numerous rapid sketches.

Landscape painter.

[NOTE: The stamp of the Thomson studio, "TT" with the year, 1917, enclosed in a circle, was designed by J. E. H. MacDonald, about 1919, and impressed on all the works by Thomson that could be found after his death. (letter from Thoreau MacDonald, January 28, 1966)]

853   **Bateaux**

EXHIBITIONS: Toronto, Mellors Galleries, *Thomson*, 1937, no. 44; Windsor, *Group of Seven*, 1948, no. 41; A.G.T., and Ontario Department of Education, 1951, no. 28.

Gift from the Reuben and Kate Leonard Canadian Fund, 1927.

852

AUTUMN FOLIAGE

Oil on panel, 8½" x 10½".
Stamp of the Thomson studio, lower right [see Note, following Biography].

EXHIBITIONS: Toronto, Mellors Galleries, *Thomson*, 1937, no. 35; London, Ont., *Tom, and George Thomson*, 1957, no. 43; Montreal, *Expo '67*, 1967, Painting in Canada, no. 4 (reprod.).

REFERENCES: Hubbard, *Thomson* (1962), pl. 27 (reprod.); Ballantyne, *Expo '67 Art* (1967), p. 18.

Gift from the Reuben and Kate Leonard Canadian Fund, 1927.

853

BATEAUX

Oil on panel, 8½" x 10½".
Stamp of the Thomson studio, lower left [see Note, following Biography].
Inscribed (on stretcher, in pencil): 5. Bateaux Rouges 48. Harkness [?].

EXHIBITIONS: Toronto, Mellors Galleries, *Thomson*, 1937, no. 36; A.G.T., *Comparisons*, 1957, no. 81.

REFERENCES: Robson, *Thomson* (1937), pl. VII (reprod. in colour); *Canadian Geographical Journal*, vol. XVII (Dec., 1938), p. 288 (reprod. in colour); *Canadian Review of Music and Art*, vol. I, no. 6 (Oct., 1942), p. 9 (reprod.); A.G.T., *Programme 1947-48*, reprod. in colour; Canadian Pulp and Paper Association, *With Palette and Brush* (1954), reprod. in colour; A.G.T., *Painting and sculpture* (1959), p. 41 (reprod. in colour).

Gift from the Reuben and Kate Leonard Canadian Fund, 1927.

856

BURNT COUNTRY

Oil on panel, 8½" x 10½".

EXHIBITIONS: Toronto, Mellors Galleries, *Thomson*, 1937, no. 39.

Gift from the Reuben and Kate Leonard Canadian Fund, 1927.

857

ALGONQUIN PARK

Oil on panel, 8½" x 10½".
Signed (lower right): TOM THOMSON.

Stamp of the Thomson studio, lower right [see Note, following Biography].
Inscribed (on stretcher, in pencil): Algonquin Park   Mac Callum.

EXHIBITIONS: Toronto, Mellors Galleries, *Thomson*, 1937, no. 40; Ste. Anne de Bellevue, Que., MacDonald College, *Semi-centenary exhibition*, 1955, no. 19; London, Ont., *Tom, and George Thomson*, 1957, no. 42; Windsor, *Thomson*, 1957, no. 15.

Gift from the Reuben and Kate Leonard Canadian Fund, 1927.

862

AUTUMN BIRCHES

Oil on panel, 8¹/₂" x 10¹/₂".
Stamp of the Thomson studio, lower right [see Note, following Biography].

EXHIBITIONS: Windsor, *Thomson*, 1948, no. 40; Vancouver, *Group of Seven*, 1954, no. 71; Ste. Anne de Bellevue, Que., MacDonald College, *Semi-centenary exhibition*, 1955, no. 18; London, Ont., *Tom, and George Thomson*, 1957, no. 40; Windsor, *Thomson*, 1957, no. 16.

Gift of Mr. and Mrs. Lawren Harris, 1927.

863

BLACK SPRUCE AND MAPLE

Oil on panel, 8¹/₂" x 10¹/₂".
Signed (lower right): TOM THOMSON.

EXHIBITIONS: Rio de Janeiro, 1944, no. 185; Vancouver, *Group of Seven*, 1954, no. 70.

Gift of Mr. and Mrs. Lawren Harris, 1927.

864

A RAPID

Oil on panel, 8¹/₂" x 10¹/₂".
Stamp of the Thomson studio, lower right [see Note, following Biography].

EXHIBITIONS: Stratford, and Saint John, *Ten decades, ten painters*, 1967, no. 17.

Gift of Mr. and Mrs. Lawren Harris, 1927.

53/13

THE SHACK

Oil on panel, 8⁵/₈" x 10⁵/₈".
Inscribed (on reverse): Tom Tomson's [sic] Shack in the/North Country/Tom Tomson [sic] The property of A. J. Boughton.

864   A Rapid

PROV.: Mrs. A. J. Boughton, Toronto.

EXHIBITIONS: A.G.T., *Walker - Thomson*, 1941, lent by A. Boughton.

Gift from the Fund of the T. Eaton Co. Ltd. for Canadian Works of Art, 1953.

2449

DROWNED LAND   **1912**

Oil on canvas board, 6³/₄" x 9⁵/₈".
Signed (lower right): Tom Thomson.

PROV.: [Mellors Galleries, Toronto].

EXHIBITIONS: Mellors Galleries, *Thomson*, 1937, no. 90; London, Ont., *Milestones*, 1942, no. 44; Vancouver, *Group of Seven*, 1954, no. 68; London, Ont., *Tom, and George Thomson*, 1957, no. 44; Windsor, *Thomson*, 1957, no. 13; Stratford, and Saint John, *Ten decades, ten painters*, 1967, no. 16.

Purchase, 1937.

2449   **Drowned Land**

2188

THE MARSH, LAKE SCUGOG   **1913**

Oil on canvas, 11" x 17".
Signed (lower right): T. T.

PROV.: S. H. F. Kemp, Toronto.

NOTES: According to letter of November 21, 1934, from Mr. Kemp, "The picture is not his preliminary sketch but a later painting from the sketch. It depicts a marsh or swamp on the edge of Lake Skugog (or Scugog) with evening settling down."

The painting was given by the artist to his friend Mr. Kemp, in the fall of 1913.

444

founding me
Arts and Let

TRAVEL: Sr
York, Detroit
bia, 1913.

In Toronto, I
of the Don

Founded Th
Toronto, of
1890s.

In 1904, The
as a staff a

Engraver.

EXHIBITIONS: A.G.T., *Walker - Thomson*, 1941; London, Ont., *Tom, and George Thomson*, 1957, no. 41.

REFERENCES: Robson, *Thomson* (1937), p. 9; Harper (1966), p. 272.

Purchase, 1934.

854

TIMBER CHUTE   1915

Oil on panel, 8$^1/_2$" x 10$^1/_2$".
Stamp of the Thomson studio, lower left [see Note, following Biography].

NOTES: Believed to have been painted on the upper Petawawa River.

EXHIBITIONS: Toronto, Mellors Galleries, *Thomson*, 1937, no. 37; Windsor, *Group of Seven*, 1948, no. 42.

REFERENCES: *Canadian Review of Music and Art*, vol. I, no. 4 (May, 1942). p. 10.

Gift from the Reuben and Kate Leonard Canadian Fund, 1927.

2563

FLOWERS   1916

Oil on panel, 8$^3/_8$" x 10$^1/_2$".

PROV.: Rev. J. S. Lawson, Dean of Emanuel College, University of Toronto.

EXHIBITIONS: A.G.T., *Walker - Thomson*, 1941; London, Ont., *Milestones*, 1942, no. 43; Vancouver, *Group of Seven*, 1954, no. 69; Windsor, *Thomson*, 1957, no. 14; London, *Commonwealth arts festival*, 1965, no. 334.

REFERENCES: Robson, *Thomson* (1937), pl. II (reprod. as Wild-flowers; collection of J. S. Lawson); *Canadian painting in the twentieth century* (1961), pl. I (reprod. in colour).

Gift from the Albert H. Robson Memorial Subscription Fund, 1941.

2563   **Flowers**

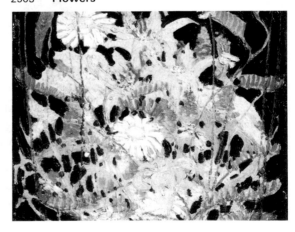

51/1   The Pink Necklace
Colour reproduction, p. 546

48/26

BLACK TABLE AND RUBBER PLANT   1948

Oil on canvas, 33³/₈″ x 45″.
Signed and dated (upper left): de Tonnancour. 11 . 4 . 48.

PROV.: the artist [CGP, 1949].

EXHIBITIONS: *C. G. P.*, 1949, no. 55; A.G.T., *Fifty years of painting in Canada*, 1949, no. 108; Boston, 1949, no. 95, p. 36 (reprod.); Venice, *XXIX biennale*, 1958, p. 221, no. 25.

REFERENCES: *A.G.T., Accessions 1948-49*, reprod.; *Art News*, vol. XLVIII (Summer, 1949), p. 41 (reprod.); A.G.T., *50th anniversary* (1950), p. 33 (reprod.); *R.A.I.C. Journal*, vol. 27 (Jan., 1950), p. 27 (reprod.); Canadian Museum Association, *Canadian paintings* (1950), reprod.; *Saturday Review* (June 7, 1952), p. 38 (reprod.); Park, *Culture of Contemporary Canada* (1957), p. 135; A.G.T., *Painting and sculpture* (1959), p. 85 (reprod.); Hubbard (1960), pl. 112 (reprod.); Hubbard (1963), p. 122; Brieger, Vickers, and Winter, *Art and Man, III* (1964), p. 174, fig. 196 (reprod.); Morris, *Modern Art* (1965), pp. 36, 44, pl. 4 (reprod.); *Vie des Arts*, no. 46 (Spring, 1967), p. 49, fig. 8 (reprod.).

Gift from the Albert H. Robson Memorial Subscription Fund, 1949.

48/26   **Black Table and Rubber Plant**

52/34

THE WILLOWS   1952

Oil on canvas, 13¹/₄″ x 16¹/₄″.
Signed and dated (lower right): de Tonnancour 52.

PROV.: the artist.

NOTES: Another version, measuring 24" x 30", formerly in the collection of J. J. Vaughan, Toronto, is in the collection of the University of Alberta, Calgary; reproduced in Vancouver Art Gallery, *de Tonnancour*, 1966, no. 19.

EXHIBITIONS: M.M.F.A., Gallery XII, *Archambault, and de Tonnancour*, 1956 (Jan. 20 - Feb. 5) [no catalogue].

REFERENCES: *Canadian Art*, vol. XI (Winter, 1954), p. 71 (reprod.).

Gift from the Fund of the T. Eaton Co. Ltd. for Canadian Works of Art, 1953.

60/1

SCRUBBY FIELDS, NOVEMBER   **1959**

Oil on masonite, 36" x 48".
Signed and dated (lower left centre): De Tonnancour 59.

PROV.: [Laing Galleries, Toronto].

EXHIBITIONS: Laing Galleries, *de Tonnancour*, 1960 (Apr. 30 - May 14) [no catalogue]; Stratford, *Canada on canvas*, 1963.

Gift from the McLean Foundation, 1960.

TORONTO 20   **1965**

Portfolio of graphics by (20) Toronto artists.

NOTES: Portfolio, in grey cloth, measures $27\frac{1}{4}$" high, $21\frac{1}{4}$" wide, and $1\frac{1}{8}$" deep.

Front leaf inscribed: © ART PUBLICATIONS 1965/PRINTED AT UNIVERSITY OF TORONTO PRESS/PRODUCED AND DESIGNED BY E. DEL JUNCO AND H. KURSCHENSKA.

In introduction by Emilio del Junco, arch. M.R.A.I.C., the portfolio is described as "a record of art in Toronto in 1965".

Publication sponsored by: Art Gallery of Toronto, Art Publications, Dorothy Cameron Gallery, The Isaacs Gallery, The David Mirvish Gallery, Moos Gallery, The Jerrold Morris International Gallery.

Dennis BURTON (1933-   **)**
For biography see p. 52.

65/34

THE PRINTS:

(1)
UNTITLED

Monotype on blue cardboard, 20" x 16".
Signed, dated, and numbered (lower left, in pencil): 1 DENNIS BURTON 9·28·65.

R. W. MURPHY (1891-   )
For biography see p. 329.

2194

THE VENETIAN BRIDGE, ISLAND PARK [57]

2195

THE BLOCK-HOUSE ON THE ISLAND [51]

2196

THE SECOND HORSE FERRY TO THE ISLAND,
ABOUT 1843-1850 [55]

2197

THE ISLAND LIGHTHOUSE, 1808 [52]

2198

MODERN HARBOUR DEVELOPMENT [145]

2199

YACHT RACING AT THE CANADIAN
NATIONAL EXHIBITION [117]

2200

THE EASTERN GAP [53]

Stanley TURNER (1883-   )
For biography see p. 470.

2225

MASSEY HALL, ERECTED 1894 [107]

2226

CHURCH OF THE HOLY TRINITY, 1847 [126]

2227

FIRST CHRISTIAN SCIENCE CHURCH,
ST. GEORGE STREET, 1915 [133]

2228

BOND STREET CONGREGATIONAL CHURCH, 1878 [132]

2229

THE VICE-REGAL PARTY ARRIVING
AT THE WOODBINE [119]

2230

THE GOODERHAM FOUNTAIN,
CANADIAN NATIONAL EXHIBITION [147]

2231

**ST. PAUL'S ROMAN CATHOLIC CHURCH,
QUEEN AND POWER STREETS [128]**

2232

**ST. PAUL'S SCHOOL ROOM
(THE OLD CHURCH), 1860 [127]**

2233

**OLD UPPER CANADA COLLEGE,
SIMCOE AND KING STREETS, 1829-1891 [64]**

2234

**BUILDING OF TORONTO HYDRO-ELECTRIC SYSTEM,
CARLTON STREET AT YONGE, ERECTED 1933 [139]**

2235

**ANNUAL SKATING CARNIVAL AT THE
MAPLE LEAF GARDENS [121]**

2236

ROYAL LYCEUM THEATRE, KING STREET, 1873 [105]

2237

JARVIS STREET COLLEGIATE INSTITUTE, 1922 [63]

2238

**KINGS COLLEGE, ERECTED 1842;
DEMOLISHED 1886 [65]**

2239

ST. JAMES CATHEDRAL, 1853 [125]

2240

**THE FIRST METHODIST CHURCH,
KING AND JORDAN STREETS, 1818-1832 [129]**

2241

**A LOCOMOTIVE BOILER FROM GOOD'S FOUNDRY,
1855 (FROM A DRAWING IN "THE DAILY COLONIST")
[73]**

2242

**THE OLD BLUE SCHOOL,
ADELAIDE AND CHURCH STREETS, 1816-1829 [60]**

EXHIBITIONS: Toronto, Laing Galleries, *Drawings by Town*, 1959 (Sept. 19 - Oct. 2) [no catalogue].

Anonymous Gift in memory of Pearl McCarthy, 1964.

63/70   Bacchante Threatened by Panther

60/22

QUEEN ELIZABETH I   1960

Brush, pen and ink on paper, 29$^5/_8$" x 21$^9/_{16}$" [sight].
Signed and dated (lower right): Town - 4 - 10 - 60.

PROV.: [Laing Galleries, Toronto].

EXHIBITIONS: A.G.T., *Drawings*, 1963, p. 8.

Canada Council Joint Drawings Purchase Fund, 1961.

60/45

ENTER THE EMPRESS   1960

Oil and lucite on canvas, 82" x 68".
Signed and dated (lower right): Town 60.

PROV.: [Laing Galleries, Toronto].

EXHIBITIONS: Laing Galleries, *Town*, 1961 (Feb. 25 - Mar. 8) [no catalogue].

REFERENCES: *Art Quarterly*, vol. 24 (Autumn, 1961), p. 307 (reprod.).

Gift from the McLean Foundation, 1961.

61/66

GREAT SEAL NO. 1   1961

Oil and lucite on canvas, 73$^1/_2$" x 82$^1/_2$".
Signed and dated (upper right): Town — 61 —.

PROV.: [Jerrold Morris International Gallery, Toronto].

446 W

NOTES: Another version entitled *Great Seal*, oil on canvas, 74" x 82$\frac{1}{4}$", dated 1961, is in the collection of Mr. and Mrs. Percy Waxer, Toronto; reproduced in colour, Elizabeth Kilbourn, *Great Canadian painting* (1966), p. 28.

EXHIBITIONS: Jerrold Morris International Gallery, *Town*, 1962, reprod. in exhibition brochure [no catalogue]; New York, Trabia-Morris Gallery, *Art of the Americas*, 1962, reprod.; Vancouver, *Town*, 1964.

REFERENCES: *Canadian Art*, vol. XXIII (Jan., 1966), p. 55.

Purchase, Corporations' Subscription Endowment, 1962.

61/66   **Great Seal No. 1**

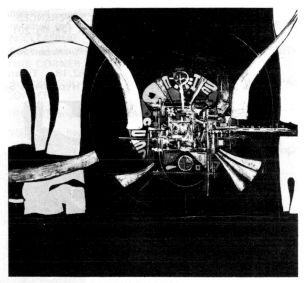

61/67

IN MEMORY OF TED POPE, AND THE NIGHT OF THE CEMENT TEEPEES   **1961**

Ink on linen, and collage on masonite, 96" x 48".
Signed and dated (lower right): Town – 61 –.
Signed twice more (on reverse): Town 61 –.

PROV.: [Jerrold Morris International Gallery, Toronto].

NOTES: Ted Pope, an avid skier and sportscar enthusiast, was a producer with the Canadian Broadcasting Corporation. He was killed in his sportscar at Mosport, August 12, 1960. A friend of the artist, he and Town often engaged in comedy routines, one of which centred around a fabricated incident in Pope's childhood involving "cement teepees". In recollection of this occasion, the artist dedicated his collage to the memory of Ted Pope.

EXHIBITIONS: Jerrold Morris International Gallery, *Town*, 1962 (Apr. 13 - May 5) [no catalogue].

Purchase, Corporations' Subscription Endowment, 1962.

2306 Virgin and Child

**UNKNOWN, Montreal,
mid-18th century**

EXHIBITIONS: A.G.T., *5th biennial...architecture and allied arts, (and) exhibition of traditional arts of French Canada*, 1935, no. 537 (Cap Tourmente school, about 1700; lent by Marius Barbeau); London, Tate, 1938, no. 255; Detroit, Arts of French Canada, 1946-47, no. 5 (dated c. 1705), pl. I (reprod.); Columbus, Ohio, *Colonial Americas* [see *Monthly Bulletin*, vol. 18, Oct., 1947, no. 88, pl. VI, reprod.]; M.M.F.A., *French Canadian arts*, 1955, no. 44; A.G.T., *Religious art*, 1963, no. 23, pl. VII (reprod.).

REFERENCES: A.G.T., *Bulletin* (Mar., 1935), reprod., dated c. 1700; A.G.T., *Accessions 1935*, reprod.; A.G.T., *Bulletin and annual report* (Apr., 1936), p. 2 (reprod.); Barbeau, *Quebec, where ancient France lingers* (1936), p. 44 (reprod.; Cap Tourmente); Barbeau, *Québec, où survit l'ancienne France* (1937), p. 25 (reprod.); Lasnier, and Barbeau, *Madones canadiennes* (1944), p. 205 (suggests attribution to Ursulines), p. 206 (reprod.); *Saturday Night* (July 24, 1954), p. 5 (reprod.); *The Arts in Canada* (1957), p. 45; A.G.T., *Painting and sculpture* (1959), p. 46 (reprod.); Hubbard (1963), p. 35, pl. 38 (reprod. as anonymous).

Gift of Gerald Larkin, 1935.

2307

VIRGIN AND CHILD   **c. 1750**

Wood, with traces of polychrome, 64" high.

PROV.: Victor Morin, Montreal.

NOTES: Formerly attributed to Paul Labrosse; changed to Unknown, Montreal, mid-18th century, 1967.

472

2307   Virgin and Child
Colour reproduction, p. 527

This work has been attributed by Marius Barbeau [see ref. 1936] to Paul Labrosse, dit Paul Jourdain (1697-1769), a sculptor working in Montreal and district from 1704. Dr. Barbeau has elsewhere attributed it to Charles Chaboillez (1638?-1706), before 1708 [see ref. 1944]. A third attribution has also been made, suggesting the hand of Philippe Liébert (1732-1804).

The sculpture is said to have been found in a ditch near the church of Saint-Laurent, a parish a few miles north of Montreal, dating from 1800. Dr. Barbeau believes that it came originally from the old Notre-Dame in Montreal, which was demolished in 1840.

EXHIBITIONS: A.G.T., *5th biennial...architecture and allied arts, (and) exhibition of traditional arts of French Canada*, 1935, no. 586 (lent by Victor Morin); Detroit, *Arts of French Canada*, 1946-47, no. 27 pl. IV (reprod.); Columbus, Ohio, *Colonial Americas* [see *Monthly Bulletin*, vol. 18, Oct., 1947, no. 87]; M.M.F.A., *French Canadian arts*, 1955, no. 43; London, *Commonwealth Arts Festival*, 1965, no. 292 (reprod.); N.G.C., *300 years of Canadian art*, 1967, no. 23, p. 19 (reprod.).

REFERENCES: A.G.T., *Bulletin* (Mar., 1935), reprod.; A.G.T., *Bulletin and annual report* (Apr., 1936), p. 2 (reprod.); Barbeau, *Quebec, where ancient France lingers* (1936), p. 47 (reprod.); Barbeau, *Québec, où survit l'ancienne France* (1937), p. 28 (reprod.); Lasnier, and Barbeau, *Madones canadiennes* (1944), pp. 239, 240 (reprod.); *Magazine of art*, vol. 38 (Mar., 1945), p. 99 (reprod.); *Studio*, vol. CXXIX (Apr., 1945), p. 133 (reprod.); *Canadian Art*, vol. IV (Nov., 1946), p. 17 (reprod.); *Art Quarterly* (Autumn, 1946), p. 340 (reprod.); *Magazine of Art*, vol. 40 (Feb., 1947), p. 49 (reprod.), p. 50; McInnes (1950), between pp. 84, 85 (reprod.); A.G.T., *50th anniversary* (1950), p. 12 (reprod.); *R.A.I.C. Journal*, vol. 27 (Jan., 1950), p. 30 (reprod.); *The Arts in Canada* (1957) p. 26 (reprod.); Barbeau, *J'ai vu Québec* (1957), reprod.; and English ed. (1957), reprod.; A.G.T., *Painting and sculpture* (1959), p. 46 (reprod.); Hubbard (1960), pl. 10 (reprod.); *Journal of the Royal Society of Arts* (Nov., 1962), p. 923ff; Hubbard (1963), p. 40, pl. 55 (reprod.); Brieger, Vickers and Winter, *Art and Man*, III (1964), p. 135, fig. 143 (reprod.).

Gift of Walter C. Laidlaw, 1935.

**UNKNOWN, Canadian,
1st half 19th century**

65/77

PORTRAIT OF ELIZA JONES

Oil on canvas, 28½" x 24¹/₁₆".

PROV.: Mr. and Mrs. Henry John Boulton; Henry John Boulton, Jr.;
Mrs. Henry John Boulton, Jr.; H. Rudyerd Boulton; Benjamin R. and
Elfrida Boulton, Toronto.

NOTES: Eliza Jones (d. 1868) became the wife of the Hon. Henry
John Boulton (1790-1870) [q.v. above, acc. no. 65/76].

*Gift of Benjamin R. and Elfrida Boulton in memory of their father,
H. Rudyerd Boulton, 1955.*

65/77   **Portrait of Eliza Jones**

55/37

PORTRAIT OF MRS. D'ARCY BOULTON, JR.

early 1830s

Oil on canvas, 34¹/₈" x 30¹/₄".

PROV.: Mr. and Mrs. D'Arcy Boulton, Jr., The Grange, Toronto; Mr.
and Mrs. William Henry Boulton, The Grange, Toronto; Mr. and Mrs.
Goldwin Smith, The Grange, Toronto; Goldwin Smith, The Grange,
Toronto; Mrs. John Robison Cartwright [eldest granddaughter of the
sitter]; Misses Cartwright, Toronto.

55/37 **Portrait of Mrs. D'Arcy Boulton, Jr.**
Colour reproduction, p. 528

**UNKNOWN, Canadian,
2nd half 19th century**

NOTES: Mrs. D'Arcy Boulton, Jr. (1789-1863), the former Sarah Anne Robinson, was born at L'Assomption in Lower Canada, the daughter of Christopher Robinson, and sister to Sir John Beverley Robinson, Chief Justice of Upper Canada. She married D'Arcy Boulton, Jr., in 1808, the same year in which D'Arcy acquired Park Lot 13, the property on which The Grange was built in 1817.

On the basis of the lady's costume, the painting has been dated in the early 1830s.

Bequest of Mabel Cartwright, 1955.

64/11

KEYSTONE HEAD (MALE)   c. 1862

Limestone, $29^1/_2$" x 22" x 29".

PROV.: Ontario Bank, Toronto; [Teperman and Sons Ltd., Toronto].

NOTES; This and the following sculptured keystone once decorated the Ontario Bank (demolished c. 1964), situated on the northeast corner of Scott and Wellington Streets, Toronto, erected in 1862, Joseph Sheard and William Irving, architects.

Photographs of the Ontario Bank building and three of the keystones are reproduced on pp. 166-67 of Eric Arthur's *Toronto: No Mean City*, 1964, where the bank is dated 1875.

In Appendix C, "Buildings of Architectural Distinction and Historical Significance of the 19th Century and Still Standing, January 1963", of Arthur's *St. Lawrence Hall 1850-1967*, 1963, p. 33, no. 29, the date of the bank is given as 1862.

In Robertson's *Landmarks of Toronto*, vol. 3, 1898, pp. 43-4, it is evident that the bank was not erected by 1856, but was standing by 1866.

Purchase, 1964.

64/12

KEYSTONE HEAD (FEMALE)   c. 1862

Limestone, $29^1/_2$" x 22" x 29".

PROV.: Ontario Bank, Toronto; [Teperman and Sons Ltd., Toronto].

64/88   **The Oakdales' Reunion**

61/70

OF AUTUMN   **1961**

Oil and ink on paper, 38$\frac{1}{4}$" x 35".
Signed and dated (lower right): urquhart 10/61.

PROV.: [Isaacs Gallery, Toronto].

EXHIBITIONS: *C.S.P.W.C.*, 1961, no. 99 (reprod.); Louisville, Ky., *19 Canadian painters*, 1962, no. 52.

REFERENCES: *Canadian Art*, vol. XIX (Mar., 1962), p. 107 (reprod.).

Purchase, 1962.

65/43.1-5

THE MEN OF NUMBERS   **1964**

Series of (5) drawings in pen and ink with wash on paper, each a different version of the same subject.

PROV.: [Isaacs Gallery, Toronto].

NOTES: All versions are variously inscribed with numerals, arabic and roman, letters, and some abbreviated words, "pos.", etc.

The drawings
65/43.1

MEN OF NUMBERS, VERSION NO. 1   **1964**

10" x 9$\frac{1}{4}$".
Signed and dated (lower right centre): urquhart 1/1964.

EXHIBITIONS: London, University of Western Ontario, *Urquhart and Curnoe*, 1964 (Nov. 9-27) [no catalogue]; *C.S.G.A.*, 1965, no. 79, on cover (reprod.).

Gift from the Georgia J. Weldon Estate, 1965.

65/43.2

MEN OF NUMBERS, VERSION NO.2   **1964**

$7^{13}/_{16}$" x $6^{3}/_{16}$"
Signed and dated (lower centre): urquhart 1964.

EXHIBITIONS: London, University of Western Ontario, *Urquhart and Curnoe*, 1964 (Nov. 9-27) [no catalogue]; Calgary, *5th annual Calgary graphics exhibition*, 1966, no. 22.

Gift from the Georgia J. Weldon Estate, 1965.

65/43.2   **Men of Numbers, Version No. 2**

65/43.3

MEN OF NUMBERS, VERSION NO. 3   **1964**

$10^{5}/_{8}$" x $8^{7}/_{8}$".
Signed and dated (lower right centre): urquhart 4/64.

EXHIBITIONS: London, University of Western Ontario, *Urquhart and Curnoe*, 1964 (Nov. 9-27) [no catalogue].

Gift from the Georgia J. Weldon Estate, 1965.

65/43.4

MEN OF NUMBERS, VERSION NO. 4   **1964**

$9^{15}/_{16}$" x $6^{9}/_{16}$".

EXHIBITIONS: London, University of Western Ontario, *Urquhart and Curnoe*, 1964 (Nov. 9-27) [no catalogue].

Gift of the Georgia J, Weldon Estate, 1965.

57/18

LANDSCAPE pre-1912

Water colour on paper, 10$^1/_4$" x 12$^3/_4$".

Gift of Barker Fairley, 1958.

50/72

ST. QUENTIN c. 1918

Water colour on paper, 7" x 9$^1/_2$".
Signed (lower right): F H Varley.
Dated (on reverse): 1918.

PROV.: H. L. Rous, Toronto.

Gift from the Fund of the T. Eaton Co. Ltd. for Canadian Works of Art, 1951.

57/17   **Portrait of Margaret Fairley**

57/17

PORTRAIT OF MARGARET FAIRLEY 1921

Oil on canvas, 30$^3/_8$" x 22$^{11}/_{16}$".
Signed and dated (upper right): F. H. VARLEY 21.

NOTES: Margaret Fairley, wife of Professor Barker Fairley [q.v., p. 109].

EXHIBITIONS: A.G.T., *Group of Seven*, 1921, no. 50; Buffalo, *Exhibition of paintings by Canadian artists*, 1928, no. 48 (lent by Prof. Fairley); Stratford, *Faces of Canada*, 1964, reprod.; Windsor, *Varley retrospective*, 1964, no. 12; N.G.C. [travelling exhibition], *Canadian painting 1850-1950*, 1967-68, no. 46, p. 25 (reprod.).

REFERENCES: *Canadian Art*, vol. XVI (Winter, 1959), p. 46 (reprod.); *Canadian painting in the twentieth century* (1961), pl. 3 (reprod. in colour); *artscanada*, vol. XXIV (Jan., 1967), p. 10 (reprod.).

Gift of Mrs. Fairley, 1958

2852

PORTRAIT OF MRS. E. 1921

Oil on canvas, 40$^5/_8$" x 34".
Signed (lower right): F. H. Varley.

EXHIBITIONS: A.G.T., *Group of Seven*, 1921, no. 49; *C.N.E.*, 1921, no. 256, p. 49 (reprod.); Winnipeg, *Canadian art of today*, 1921, no. 34; N.G.C., *Retrospective...Group of Seven*, 1936, no. 180 (lent by Ernest Ely); *C.N.E.*, 1939, no. 220 (lent by Ernest Ely); *C.N.E.*, 1952, no. 22; A.G.T., and others, *Varley*, 1954-55, no. 13; Chautauqua, N. Y., *Group of Seven*, 1963.

Gift of Mrs. E. F. Ely, 1946.

51/62

SPLIT ROCK, GEORGIAN BAY   **1922**

Oil on panel, $8^3/_4$" x $10^3/_{16}$".
Signed (lower right): [VAR]LEY.
Inscribed (on reverse): Split Rock, Georgian Bay/by F. H. Varley,
Sept. 1922.

PROV.: Mrs. Peter Sandiford, Toronto.

EXHIBITIONS: [?] *O.S.A. small paintings*, 1922, no. 200.

*Gift from the Fund of the T. Eaton Co. Ltd. for Canadian Works of
Art, 1952.*

60/28

ART STUDENT, VANCOUVER   **1930**

Pencil on paper, $10^3/_8$" x $6^7/_8$" [sight].
Signed (lower left): VARLEY.

PROV.: [Roberts Gallery, Toronto].

EXHIBITIONS: Roberts Gallery, *Varley*, 1961 (Jan. 5-18) [no cata-
logue].

Canada Council Joint Drawings Purchase Fund, 1961.

2593

DHÂRÂNA   **1932**

Oil on canvas, 34" x 40".
Signed (lower right): VARLEY.

PROV.: the artist.

EXHIBITIONS: *R.C.A.*, 1932, no. 194; Vancouver, *First annual B. C.
artists' exhibition*, 1932, no. 47; N.G.C., *Annual*, 1933, no. 268;
N.G.C., *Retrospective...Group of Seven*, 1936, no. 190 (lent by the
artist); N.G.C. [circulating exhibition], *Southern Dominions*, 1936,
no. 98 (reprod.); Johannesburg, *Empire exhibition*, 1936, no. 897;
London, Ont., *Group of Seven*, 1946, no. 31; Vancouver, *Group
of Seven*, 1954, no. 74; A.G.T., and others, *Varley*, 1954-55, p.
11, no. 18, pl. 6 (reprod.); Mexico, 1960, no. 119; London, Ont.,
Master Canadian painters and sculptors, 1963-64, no. 46 (reprod.);
Windsor, *Varley retrospective*, 1964, no. 23; Port Arthur, *Group of Seven
and Lake Superior*, 1964, no. 32; A.G.T. [circulating exhibition],
Canadian paintings of the 1930s, 1967-68, no. 25.

REFERENCES: *Art Digest*, vol. VII (Mar. 15, 1933), p. 6; *Canadian
Art*, vol. V (Autumn, 1947), p. 3 (reprod.); Buchanan (1950), p. 43
(explains the title as a "Buddhist term signifying the power to project
oneself into one's surroundings"); *Canadian Art*, vol. XII (Autumn,
1954), p. 8; A.G.T., *Painting and sculpture* (1959), p. 56 (reprod.);

PROV.: [Roberts Gallery, Toronto].

EXHIBITIONS: Roberts Gallery, *Varley*, 1961 (Jan. 5-18) [no catalogue].

Gift from the McLean Foundation, 1961.

53/21

WOMAN'S HEAD   **1953**

Pencil, red, and green chalk, heightened with white on paper, 11$\frac{1}{4}$" x 8$\frac{1}{4}$" [sight].
Signed (lower right): VARLEY (and) [fingerprint].
Inscribed (on reverse): Head (red chalk)/Oct. 1953/F. H. Varley.

PROV.: the artist [through Picture Loan Society, Toronto].

EXHIBITIONS: A.G.T., *Canadian drawings*, 1960.

REFERENCES: *Canadian Art*, vol. XII (Winter, 1955), p. 56 (reprod.).

Gift from the Fund of the T. Eaton Co. Ltd. for Canadian Works of Art, 1954.

54/6

MAY DAY PROCESSION, MOSCOW   **1954**

Crayon, pastel and wash on paper, 9$\frac{1}{2}$" x 13$\frac{11}{16}$".

PROV.: the artist.

NOTES: Executed in Moscow, on a trip to Russia, April - May, 1954, with a group of artists and writers, as part of a cultural exchange between Canada and Russia, arranged by Canadian-Soviet Friendship Society, agents for VOKS, the Soviet Society of Cultural Relations with Foreign Countries.

EXHIBITIONS: A.G.T., and others, *Varley*, 1954-55 [not in catalogue; exhibited at A.G.T. only]; A.G.T., *Canadian drawings*, 1960; Windsor, *Varley retrospective*, 1964, no. 72.

REFERENCES: *Maclean's Magazine*, vol. 67 (Oct. 1, 1954), p. 10 (reprod. in colour).

Gift from the John Paris Bickell Bequest Fund, 1955.

60/30

SKIMMERHORN MOUNTAIN, B. C.   **1957**

Pencil on brown paper, 10$\frac{7}{8}$" x 13$\frac{7}{8}$" [sight].
Signed (lower right [vertically]): VARLEY.

PROV.: [Roberts Gallery, Toronto].

EXHIBITIONS: Roberts Gallery, *Varley*, 1961 (Jan. 5-18) [no catalogue].

Canada Council Joint Drawings Purchase Fund, 1961.

60/30   **Skimmerhorn Mountain, B.C.**

60/31

STEEPLE MOUNTAIN, B. C.   **1957**

Brown and blue wash on brown paper, $10^7/_8$" x $13^7/_8$" [sight].
Signed (lower right, in pencil): VARLEY.

PROV.: [Roberts Gallery, Toronto].

EXHIBITIONS: Roberts Gallery, *Varley*, 1961 (Jan. 5-18) [no cata-
logue].

Canada Council Joint Drawings Purchase Fund, 1961.

Robert VARVARANDE (1922-   )

BORN: Lyons, France, 1922.

LIVES: Toronto. Came to Canada in the winter
of 1953.

STUDY: Lyons, until 1940; Birmingham, England, 1947-53.

Served in the French army, with internship in
Germany, 1940-45.

TEACHING: Toronto, Ontario College of Art,
1959-61 and 1962-63.

TRAVEL: France, Italy, Switzerland, Germany
and England, 1945-47.

56/36

NATURE MORTE   **1956**

Oil on masonite, 24" x 48".
Signed and dated (lower left): R. Varvarande/1956.

EXHIBITIONS: *O.S.A.*, 1957, no. 83.

Gift of Emilio del Junco, Havana, Cuba, 1957.

56/36   **Nature morte**

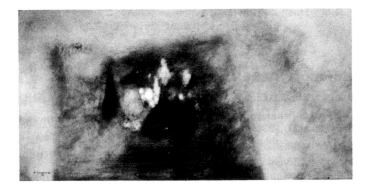

STUDY: Toronto, Ontario College of Art; Detroit Institute of Arts, but mainly self-taught.

Began his career as a commercial artist and illustrator; turned to painting in 1939.

SOCIETIES: A.R.C.A., 1945, R.C.A., 1948; O.S.A., 1942, Pres. 1946-48; C.G.P.; Arts and Letters Club, Toronto.

TRAVEL: Throughout Canada; Mexico, 1950-51; North Africa, Majorca, and the Canary Islands, 1952; Italy, Greece, Turkey.

Lived in Paris, 1960-64.

Commissioned to execute several murals, most notably, Imperial Oil Building, Toronto, 1957, and O'Keefe Centre, Toronto, 1959.

Painter, muralist.

PROV.: the artist [AGT, 1943].

EXHIBITIONS: A.G.T., *Non-jury show*, 1943, p. 17.

REFERENCES: *Saturday Night*, vol. 58 (Apr. 17, 1943), p. 2 (reprod.); *Canadian Review of Music and Art*, vol. 5 (Oct., 1946), p. 15 (reprod.).

Purchase, 1943.

2735   **Local Dance**

49/63

PEONS   **1950**

Duco on masonite, 20" x 15⅞".
Signed (lower right): R. York Wilson.

PROV.: the artist.

Gift from the Fund of the T. Eaton Co. Ltd. for Canadian Works of Art, 1950.

51/63

WHITE FIGURES OF ACAMBAY   **1951**

Duco on masonite, 24" x 32".
Signed (lower left): R. York Wilson.

PROV.: [Laing Galleries, Toronto].

EXHIBITIONS: *R.C.A.*, 1951-52, no. 104; Sarnia, and others, *Wilson retrospective*, 1965, no. 12.

REFERENCES: *R.A.I.C. Journal*, vol. 28 (Dec., 1951), p. 373, fig. 7 (reprod.); *Canadian Art*, vol. IX (Spring, 1952), p. 112 (reprod.).

Gift from the Fund of the T. Eaton Co. Ltd. for Canadian Works of Art, 1952.

51/63   **White Figures of Acambay**

54/16
JANITZIO ISLAND   **1954**

Duco on masonite, 24″ x 31 $^7/_8$ ″.
Signed (lower right): R. York Wilson.

PROV.: the artist [AGT, 1954].

EXHIBITIONS: A.G.T., *Three Canadians*, 1954, no. 6.

Purchase, 1955.

59/7   Venetian Vista

60/24
NYMPH   **1955**

Charcoal on paper, 29 $^1/_2$ ″ x 9 $^3/_4$ ″ [sight].
Signed (lower left): R. York Wilson.

PROV.: [Roberts Gallery, Toronto].

EXHIBITIONS: Roberts Gallery, *Wilson*, 1960 (Oct. 20 - Nov. 2) [no catalogue].

Canada Council Joint Drawings Purchase Fund, 1961.

59/7
VENETIAN VISTA   **1958**

Oil on canvas, 39 $^1/_4$ ″ x 29 $^3/_8$ ″.
Signed (lower left): R. York Wilson.

PROV.: [Roberts Gallery, Toronto].

Gift from the McLean Foundation, 1960.

60/25
ORPHEUS   **1960**

Tempera on paper, 27″ x 16 $^1/_4$ ″ [sight].
Signed (lower centre): R. York Wilson.

PROV.: [Roberts Gallery, Toronto].

EXHIBITIONS: Roberts Gallery, *Winter*, 1959 (Apr. 1-14) [no catalogue].

Gift from the McLean Foundation, 1959

58/67

DANDELIONS   **1958**

Oil on cardboard, 11$\frac{7}{8}$" x 16$\frac{1}{8}$".
Signed (lower right): WINTER.

PROV.: [Roberts Gallery, Toronto].

EXHIBITIONS: Roberts Gallery, *Winter*, 1959 (Apr. 1-14) [no catalogue].

Gift from the McLean Foundation, 1959.

Elizabeth Wyn WOOD (1903-1966)

BORN: Orillia, Ontario, October 8, 1903.

DIED: Toronto, January 27, 1966.

Married sculptor Emanuel Hahn [q.v.] in 1926.

STUDY: Toronto, Ontario College of Art, 1921-26, under Emanuel Hahn, Lismer, MacDonald, and others; New York, Art Students' League, 1926-27, with Robert Laurent.

SOCIETIES: A.R.C.A., 1930, R.C.A., 1948; O.S.A., 1929, resigned, 1933; S.S.C., founding member, 1928, Pres. 1933-35.

TEACHING: Toronto, Central Technical School, for some years.

Executed many fountains, wall reliefs and monuments, especially in the Niagara Peninsula.

Sculptor, monumentalist, muralist, medalist.

49/54

REEF AND RAINBOW   **1927-c.1935**

Cast tin, on black marble base, 9$\frac{3}{4}$" high (incl. base), 37$\frac{3}{4}$" long (incl. base).

PROV.: the artist.

EXHIBITIONS: *S.S.C.*, 1935, no. 249 (reprod.); *C.N.E.*, 1935, no. 285; *R.C.A.*, 1935, no. 298; *S.S.C. travelling exhibition*, 1936-37, no. 34; London, Tate, 1938, no. 251 (reprod.); New York, *World's Fair*, 1939, section SSC, p. 21, no. 25; *C.N.E.*, 1949, no. 143; *C.N.E.*, 1961; N.G.C., *300 years of Canadian art*, 1967, no. 246 (dated c. 1935), p. 151 (reprod.).

REFERENCES: A.G.T., *Bulletin* (Feb., 1935), reprod.; *Apollo*, vol. 28 (Nov., 1938), p. 247 (reprod.); *Maritime Art*, vol. 2 (June, 1942), p. 145 (says begun in 1927, but not finished for several years), p. 148; Colgate (1943), p. 202; *Studio*, vol. CXXIX (Apr., 1945), p. 132 (reprod.); *Saturday Night*, vol. 61 (Apr. 27, 1946), p. 5 (reprod.); *Canadian Art*, vol. III (Summer, 1946), p. 172 (reprod.); Ross, *The arts in Canada* (1958), p. 38; A.G.T., *Painting and sculpture* (1959), p. 67 (reprod.); Hubbard (1963), pl. 173 (reprod.).

Gift from the Albert H. Robson Memorial Subscription Fund, 1950.

49/54   **Reef and Rainbow**

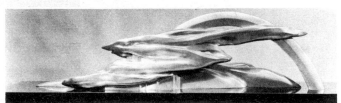

Tom WOOD (1913-   )

BORN: Thomas Charles Wood, Westboro, Ontario, May 2, 1913.

LIVES: Ottawa.

STUDY: Largely self-taught, but for short periods under Brownell, and Varley.

SOCIETIES: C.S.P.W.C.

Was chief of the Design Section of the Canadian Government Exhibition Commission at time of Brussels World's Fair, 1958.

Official war artist with the Royal Canadian Navy during World War II.

2575
DIRTY SNOW   1941

Oil on canvas, 21" x 26".
Signed and dated (lower right): T. WOOD '41.

PROV.: the artist [AGT, 1941].

EXHIBITIONS: A.G.T., *Goldhamer, Haworth, Lemieux, and Wood*, 1941: *D.P.C.*, 1945, no. 194.

Gift from the Albert H. Robson Memorial Subscription Fund, 1941.

W. J. WOOD (1877-1954)

BORN: William John Wood, Ottawa, Ontario, May 26, 1877.

DIED: Midland, Ontario, January 4, 1954.

Grew up at Port Colborne, Ontario; lived at Midland from about 1913, and there worked in the shipyards.

STUDY: Toronto, Central Ontario School of Art, 1904-05, under G. A. Reid, and William Cruikshank, and others; Boston, for a short time under Eric Pape.

SOCIETIES: C.G.P., founding member, 1933; C.P.E., 1920; C.S.G.A., 1913; Arts and Letters Club, Toronto, about 1912.

Met Frank Carmichael at Orillia in 1909, and formed a close friendship which lasted until Carmichael's death in 1946.

Painter, etcher.

70
HIS LETTER HOME   1915

Etching, Imp.: $10^5/_{16}$" x $10^1/_8$". Paper: $13^3/_4$" x $11^{15}/_{16}$".
Signed and dated (lower right, in pencil): Wm. J. Wood 1915.
Inscribed (on reverse, in pencil): His letter home.
Inscribed (upper left): W. J. Wood/1915.

NOTES: Permanent loan from C.N.E. Association, 1915-66.

Gift of the Canadian National Exhibition Association, 1966.

47/57
BEACH SCENE   1938

Oil on canvas, $21^7/_8$" x 36".
Signed and dated (lower right): W. J. Wood 1938.

EXHIBITIONS: *C.G.P.*, 1947-48, no. 108.

Gift of Miss M. Edna Breithaupt, 1948.

2526
MARCH   1939

Etching.: $6^7/_8$" x $8^3/_4$". Paper: $10^1/_8$" x $12^5/_8$".
Signed (lower right, in pencil): W. J. Wood.
Inscribed and dated (lower centre): W. J. Wood/1939.

PROV.: the artist [CPE, 1939].

EXHIBITIONS: *C.P.E.*, 1939, p. 4.

Purchase, 1939.

Mary E. WRINCH (1877-1969)

BORN: Mary Evelyn Wrinch, Kirby-le-Soken, Essex, England, 1877.

DIED: Toronto, Sept. 19, 1969. Came to Canada in 1885; married G. A. Reid in 1922.

STUDY: Toronto, Central Ontario School of Art, and under G. A. Reid; London, Grosvenor School of Art, under Walter J. Donne, and Alyn Williams (miniature painting); New York, Art Students' League, miniature painting under Alice Beckington.

SOCIETIES: O.S.A., 1901; A.R.C.A., 1918; C.P.E.

Miniaturist, landscape and figure painter, colour block printer.

637

PORTRAIT OF MARY H. REID   1906

Water colour on ivory, 2⁹/₁₆" x 1¹⁵/₁₆".
Signed (upper right): MARY·E·WRINCH.

NOTES: For biography of sitter see Mary Hiester Reid, p. 389.

REFERENCES: Miner, *G. A. Reid* (1946), p. 119 (reprod.).

Gift of George A. Reid, 1922.

637   Portrait of Mary H. Reid

842

AFTER A SNOWFALL   1920

Oil on canvas, 35" x 34".
Signed and dated (lower right): M. E. WRINCH — 1920 —.

PROV.: the artist.

EXHIBITIONS: *O.S.A.*, 1920, no. 130; *C.N.E.*, 1920, no. 139; London, *British Empire Exhibition*, 1924, Catalogue of the Palace of Arts, p. 95, no. EE. 36, and Canadian section of fine arts, no. 267 (lent by the artist); A.G.T., *Canadian paintings*, 1926, no. 95; A.G.T., *Loan exhibition*, 1935, no. 161.

REFERENCES: *A portfolio of pictures from the Canadian section... British Empire Exhibition* (1924), reprod.; MacTavish (1925), between p. 144 and 145 (reprod.).

Gift from the Reuben and Kate Leonard Canadian Fund, 1926.

53/47

RAPIDS, MONTREAL RIVER   1925

Oil on board, 10" x 12".
Signed (lower left): M E WRINCH.

PROV.: the artist.

Gift from J. S. McLean, Canadian Fund, 1954.

842   After a Snowfall

522

53/46

LIMESTONE SHORE, BRUCE PENINSULA   1926

Oil on card, 10" x 12".
Inscribed (on reverse): Limestone rocks/Bruce Peninsula.

PROV.: the artist.

Gift from J. S. McLean, Canadian Fund, 1954.

53/45

JUMPING CARIBOO CREEK, TEMAGAMI   1929

Oil on board, 10" x 12".
Signed (lower right): M E WRINCH.

PROV.: the artist.

NOTES: Possibly sketch for *The Old Flume, Jumping Cariboo Creek, Temagami*, exhibited at C.N.E., 1939; present whereabouts unknown.

Gift from J. S. McLean, Canadian Fund, 1954.

53/48

TURBULENT STREAM   c. 1930

Oil on board, 10" x 12".
Signed (lower right): M. E. WRINCH.

PROV.: the artist.

EXHIBITIONS: *C.N.E.*, 1935, no. 598, p. 81 (reprod.); *O.S.A. little pictures*, 1935, no. 147.

Gift from J. S. McLean, Canadian Fund, 1954.

Florence WYLE (1881-1968)

BORN: Trenton, Illinois, November 2, 1881.

DIED: Toronto, January 14, 1968. Came to Canada (Toronto) in 1913.

STUDY: University of Illinois, 1900-03, under Newton A. Wells; Art Institute of Chicago, 1903-08, under Charles J. Mulligan, and Vanderpoel.

SOCIETIES: A.R.C.A., 1920, R.C.A., 1938; O.S.A., 1920, resigned 1934, reinstated 1948; S.S.C., 1928, Pres. 1944; Canadian Guild of Potters.

Sculpted for the Canadian War Memorials, 1918.

Sculptor.

48/1

BLACK CAT   1947

Glazed terra cotta, 9$\frac{1}{2}$" high.

PROV.: Canadian Guild of Potters, Toronto.

EXHIBITIONS: *Canadian Guild of Potters*, 1948 (Apr.) [no catalogue]; *C.N.E.*, 1949, no. 49.

Gift from the Fund of the T. Eaton Co. Ltd. for Canadian Works of Art, 1948.

47/54

TORSO   1948

Carved walnut, 16$\frac{1}{2}$" high [without base].

PROV.: the artist [OSA, 1948].

EXHIBITIONS: *O.S.A.*, 1948, no. 122.

64/13
Nelson Cook, **Portrait of Tirzah Hopkins,** p. 80

55/37
Unknown,
Portrait of Mrs. D'Arcy Boulton, Jr., p. 476-77

Loan
George Theodore Berthon,
The Three Robinson Sisters, p. 27-8

2121   Paul Kane, **Indian Encampment on Lake Huron,** p. 226

529

2601
Antoine Plamondon,
La chasse aux tourtes, p. 379-80

2531   Cornelius Krieghoff, **Habitants Sleighing,** p. 233-4

884   Otto R. Jacobi,
Falls of Ste. Anne, Quebec, p. 214

2868
Robert Harris, **The News-boy,** p. 162-3

65/42
G. A. Reid, **Self Portrait,** p. 385

48/10   Homer Watson, **The Old Mill,** p. 502

52/45   F. M. Bell-Smith, **The Beach,** p. 18

58/15   L. R. O'Brien, **The O'Brien Home, College Avenue,** p. 342

56/29   Maurice Cullen, **Moret, Winter,** p. 93

47/1   James Wilson Morrice, **Return from School,** p. 316-7

2016   Robert Holmes, **Trilliums,** p. 180

784   Tom Thomson, **The West Wind,** p. 447-8

2544
A. Y. Jackson,
Springtime in Picardy,
p. 206-7

2467
Lawren Harris,
Red House and Yellow Sleigh,
p. 157

840
J. E. H. MacDonald,
The Beaver Dam, p. 274-5

2542
David Milne,
Boston Corner,
Berkshire Hills, p. 305

2417
James Wilson Morrice,
Landscape, Trinidad, p. 323-4

49/58   Arthur Lismer, **Sombre Hill, Algoma,** p. 249-50

896
Clarence A. Gagnon,
Horse Racing in Winter, Quebec, p. 128

273   Kenneth Forbes, **The Yellow Scarf,** p. 114

2419   M. Emily Carr, **Western Forest,** p. 62-3

2593   F. H. Varley, **Dhârâna,** p. 489-90

2549   Jack Humphrey, **Charlotte,** p. 200

2574   Jean-Paul Lemieux, **Lazare,** p. 241

56/7   Alfred Pellan,
Femme d'une pomme, p. 361-2

51/1   Jacques de Tonnancour,
The Pink Necklace, p. 451-2

546

47/56   Bertram Brooker, **Progression,** p. 47

51/66   Léon Bellefleur,
Clameur des signes en feu, p. 20

52/15   Goodridge Roberts, **Pleasant Island, Georgian Bay,** p. 396-97

59/22   Paul-Emile Borduas, **Les boucliers,** p. 38

53/23   Jean-Paul Riopelle, **Coups sur coups,** p. 393-94

55/39   Carl Schaefer, **Still Life Yellow,** p. 413

549

57/42   Alex Colville,
Elm Tree at Horton Landing, p. 75-6

58/70   Oscar Cahén, **Water Colour 120,** p. 56

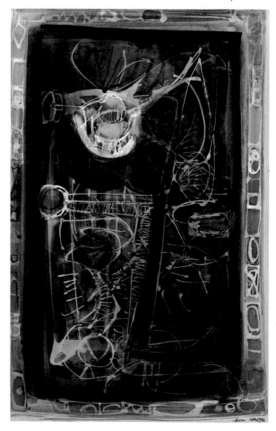

550

58/65
Jock (J.W.G.) Macdonald,
Fleeting Breath, p. 283

62/57   William Ronald, **Ginza,** p. 404

551

62/8
Kazuo Nakamura,
Blue Reflections, p. 331

61/64
Jean McEwen,
Meurtrière traversant le jaune, p. 288

63/43   Graham Coughtry, **Two Figures XII,** p. 87

64/20   Kenneth Lochhead, **Dark Green Centre,** p. 258-9

553

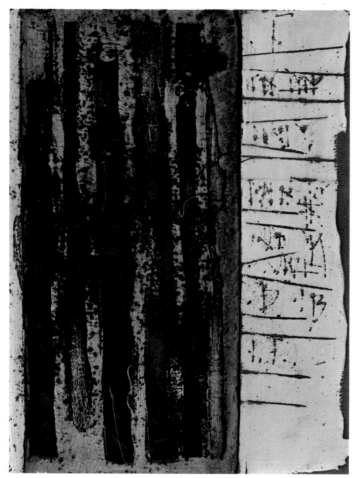

63/69   Jack Reppen, **Long Before Then,** p. 392

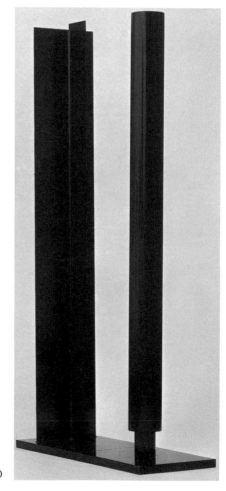

65/60   Robert Murray, **To,** p. 329-30

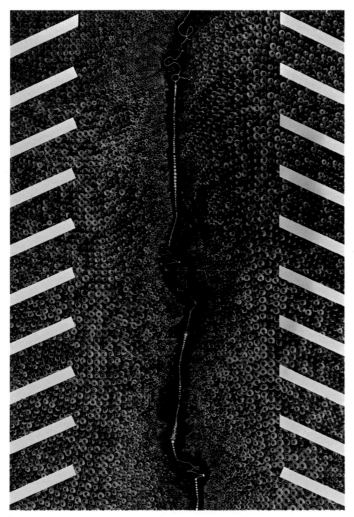

65/41   Harold Town, **Great Divide**, p. 467

64/23
Joyce Wieland,
Boat Tragedy, p. 511-12

65/73   Gershon Iskowitz, **Summer Sound,** p. 204

65/22
John Chambers,
Antonio and Miguel in the U.S.A., p. 71-2

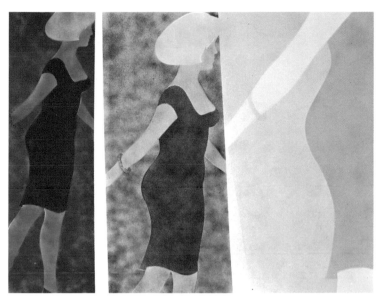

66/10   Michael Snow, **Test Focus Field Figure,** p. 426

65/38   Jack Bush, **Dazzle Red,** p. 54

BOOKS

NOTE: All books are available in the Art Reference library of The Art Gallery of Ontario, unless otherwise indicated.

n.d.

Exhibition of paintings by F. McGillivray Knowles, R.C.A., and Elizabeth A. McGillivray Knowles, A.R.C.A., with text on The art of F. McGillivray Knowles, and The art of Elizabeth A. McGillivray Knowles, by Katherine Hale.

Morisset, Gérard. "La Chasse aux Tourtres", in *Almanach de l'action sociale catholique.*

Morris, Edmund. *Art in Canada: the early painters,* Toronto, n.d. [?1911].

1859

Kane, Paul. *Wanderings of an artist among the Indians of North America.* From Canada to Vancouver's Island and Oregon through the Hudson's Bay Company's territory and back again, London, Longman, Brown, Green, Longmans, and Roberts.

1882

Grant, George Munro, ed. *Picturesque Canada; the country as it was and is,* Toronto, Belden Bros., 2 vols., illustrated under the supervision of L. R. O'Brien.

Sheldon, G. W. *Hours with art and artists,* New York, D. Appleton and Co. (pp. 163-168, Wyatt Eaton).
[not in A.G.O., 1968; see Frick Art Reference Library, New York].

1896-1898

Robertson, J. Ross. *Robertson's landmarks of Toronto,* a collection of historical sketches of the old Town of York from 1792 until 1883, and of Toronto from 1834 to 1898, republished from the Toronto *Evening Telegram,* Toronto, vol. II (1896); vol. III (1898).

1898

Mavor, James. *Notes on appreciation of art and on art in Ontario with remarks on the exhibition of the Ontario Society of Artists 1898,* Toronto.

1910

Cust, Lionel. *Eton College portraits,* London, Spottiswoode and Co. Ltd.
[not in A.G.O., 1968; see University of Toronto library].

1911

Smith, Goldwin. *Reminiscences by Goldwin Smith,* ed. by Arnold Haultain, New York, Macmillan.

1912

Morgan, Henry James, ed. *The Canadian men and women of the time: a handbook of Canadian biography of living characters,* 2nd edition, Toronto, W. Briggs.
[not in A.G.O., 1968; see Toronto Public Library].

1913

Arts and Letters Club of Toronto, *The year book of Canadian art 1913;* literature, architecture, music, painting, sculpture, London and Toronto, J. M. Dent and sons.

1914

Shortt, Adam, and Doughty, Arthur G., eds. *Canada and its provinces;* a history of the Canadian people and their institutions by one hundred associates, vol. 12, section VI, The Dominion Missions; Arts and Letters part II, Toronto, Glasgow, Brook and Company.

1916

Wood, S. T. *Rambles of a Canadian naturalist;* colour illustrations by Robert Holmes, decorative headings by students of the Ontario College of Art, London, J. M. Dent and Sons.

1917-21

Toronto Public Library. *Landmarks of Canada*... a guide to the J. Ross Robertson historical collection in the Public reference library, Toronto, 2 vols.

1918

Descriptive catalogue of the paintings, drawings, engravings, etc., belonging to Mrs. H. D. Warren, "Red Gables", Toronto.

1919

Canadian War Records Office. *Art and war; Canadian war memorials...,* with an article, "On war memorials", by P. G. Konody, London, for the Canadian war records office.

1919

Sherman, Frederic Fairchild. *American painters of yesterday and today*, New York, privately printed. (pp. 39-44, "Figure pictures by Wyatt Eaton").
[not in A.G.O., 1968; see Frick Art Reference Library, New York].

1921

Rous and Mann. *Toronto, the capital of Ontario*, eleven reproductions of etchings, made in the art department of Rous and Mann, Toronto.

1924

London, British Empire Exhibition. *A portfolio of pictures from the Canadian section of fine arts*, Toronto, Rous and Mann.

1925

Kane, Paul. *Wanderings of an artist among the Indians of North America from Canada to Vancouver's island and Oregon, through the Hudson's Bay company's territory and back again*, Toronto, The Radisson Society of Canada, limited.

MacTavish, Newton. *The fine arts in Canada*, Toronto, Macmillan company of Canada.

Rous and Mann. *Canadian drawings by members of the Group of Seven*, Toronto.

Smith, Ralph Clifton, *The wood engraved work of Timothy Cole*, Washington, private publisher.

1925-26

Bellerive, Georges. *Artistes-peintres canadiens-français: les anciens*, Québec, Garneau, 2 vols.

1926

Brown, Eric, ed. *A portfolio of Canadian art*, reproducing important Canadian paintings by Cornelius Krieghoff, Otto R. Jacobi, Paul Kane, and others, with introductory text by Eric Browne [sic] and biographical sketches by Fred R. Jacob, vol. I. Toronto, Rous and Mann.

Housser, F. B. *A Canadian art movement, the story of the Group of Seven*, Toronto, Macmillan.

Phillips, Walter Joseph. *The technique of the colour wood-cut*, New York, Brown-Robertson.

1927

Jackson, A. Y. *The far north, a book of drawings*, with introduction by Frederick Banting, Toronto, Rous and Mann.

Jefferys, C. W. *Collection of pictures illustrating the history of Canada*.

1928

Chauvin, Jean. *Ateliers*, études sur vingt-deux peintres et sculpteurs canadiens, Montreal and New York, Les éditions du Mercure.

Forster, John Wycliffe Lowes. *Under the studio light; leaves from a portrait painter's sketch book*, Toronto, The Macmillan company of Canada Ltd.

Price, Frederic Newlin. *Horato Walker*, New York and Montreal, L. Carrier and Co.

1929

Brooker, Bertram, ed. *Yearbook of the arts in Canada 1928-29*, Toronto, Macmillan.

Hussey, Christopher. *Tait McKenzie, a sculptor of youth*, London, Country Life.

Maurault, Olivier, *Marges d'histoire*, vol. I, "L'art au Canada". Montreal, Librairie d'action canadienne-française.

1930

Davies, Blodwen. *Paddle and palette; the story of Tom Thomson*, Toronto, Ryerson Press.

Hammond, M. O. *Painting and sculpture in Canada*, Toronto, Ryerson Press.

Jefferys, Charles William. *Dramatic episodes in Canada's story*, Toronto, Hunter Rose Co.

Phillips, W. J. *Essays in wood*, Toronto, Thomas Nelson and Sons.

Price, F. Newlin. *Ernest Lawson, Canadian-American*, New York, Ferargil, Inc.

Society of Canadian Painter-Etchers. *William J. Thomson, engraver 1857-1927*, Toronto, printed for private circulation to active and associate members of the Society of Canadian Painter-Etchers.

1931

Watson, William R. *Maurice Cullen, R.C.A.; a record of struggle and achievement*, Toronto, Ryerson Press.

1932

Robson, Albert H. *Canadian landscape painters*, Toronto, Ryerson Press.

1933

MacCallum, H. R. "The Group of Seven: a retrospect", in *Queen's Quarterly*, May.

MacDonald, J. E. H. *West by east and other poems;* with drawings by Thoreau MacDonald, Toronto, Ryerson Press.

1934

Barbeau, Marius. *Cornelius Krieghoff, pioneer painter of North America*, Toronto, The Macmillan company of Canada, Ltd.

Godenrath, Percy F. *Lest we forget*, a record in art of the Dominion's part in the war (1914-1918) and a memorial to those Canadians who made the great sacrifice, being the gift of the over-seas military forces to the nation, Ottawa.

Jefferys, C. W. *Canada's past in pictures*, Toronto, Ryerson Press.
[not in A.G.O., 1968; see Toronto Public Library].

Lismer, Arthur. "The West Wind", in *McMaster Monthly*, vol. XLIII, January.

Middleton, Jesse Edgar. *Toronto's 100 years*, Toronto, The Centennial committee.

1935

Davies, Blodwen. *A study of Tom Thomson, the story of a man who looked for beauty and for truth in the wilderness*, Toronto, The Discus Press.

1936

Barbeau, Marius. *Quebec, where ancient France lingers*, Toronto, Macmillan company of Canada.

Brooker, Bertram, ed. *Yearbook of the arts in Canada 1936*, Toronto, Macmillan.

Buchanan, Donald W. *James Wilson Morrice, a biography*, Toronto, Ryerson Press.

Phillips, Walter J., R.C.A. *Winter wood-cuts*, Toronto, Nelson and Sons.

1936-37

Morisset, Gérard. *Peintres et tableaux*, Québec, Les Editions du Chevalet, 2 vols.

1937

Barbeau, Charles Marius. *Québec, où survit l'ancienne France*, illus. de Marjorie Borden, Québec, Garneau.

Brookgreen Gardens, Sculpture by R. Tait McKenzie, Brookgreen Gardens, S. C.

Robson, Albert H. *Cornelius Krieghoff*, Toronto, Ryerson Press (Canadian artists series).

Robson, Albert H. *J. E. H. MacDonald, R.C.A.*, Toronto, Ryerson Press (Canadian artists series).

Robson, Albert H. *Tom Thomson*, Toronto, Ryerson Press (Canadian artists series).

1938

McEwen, Jessie, and Moore, Kathleen. *A picture history of Canada*, Toronto, Thomas Nelson and Sons, Ltd.

Miner, Muriel Miller. *Homer Watson, the man of Doon*... foreword by Sir Wyly Grier, Toronto, Ryerson Press.

Robson, Albert Henry. *Clarence A. Gagnon, R.C.A., LL.D.*, Toronto, Ryerson Press (Canadian art series).

Robson, Albert H. *A. Y. Jackson*, Toronto, Ryerson Press (Canadian artists series).

Robson, Albert H. *Paul Kane*, Toronto, Ryerson Press (Canadian artists series).

1939

Cox, Leo. "Fifty years of brush and pen", a historical sketch of the Pen and Pencil Club of Montreal, in *Queen's Quarterly*, Autumn (pp. 341-347).

Page, Frank E. *Homer Watson, artist and man*, foreword by Ross Hamilton, Kitchener, Commercial Printing Co.

194-

Goldhamer, Charles. *How to get started drawing for pleasure*, Canadian Y. M. C. A. War Service in cooperation with Canadian Legion Educational Services, Toronto.

1940

Falardeau, Emile. *Artistes et artisans du Canada*, Montreal, G. Ducharme.

Hunter, E. R. *J. E. H. MacDonald; a biography and catalogue of his work*, Toronto, Ryerson Press.

Lismer, Arthur. *Canadian picture study*, Toronto, Art Gallery of Toronto.

Maurault, Olivier. *Charles De Belle et Georges Delfosse...*, Montreal, Les Editions Archonte.

1941

Carr, Emily. *Klee Wyck*, with a foreword by Ira Dilworth, Toronto, New York, etc., Oxford University Press.

Morisset, Gérard. *Coup d'œil sur les arts en Nouvelle-France*, Québec, Charrier et Dugal, limitée.

1942

Colgate, William. "George Theodore Berthon", *Ontario Historical Society's 'Papers and Records'*, vol. XXXIV.

Hunter, E. R. *Thoreau MacDonald*, Toronto, Ryerson Press (Canadian art series).

Shoolman, Regina, and Slatkin, Charles E. *The enjoyment of art in America*, Philadelphia and New York, Lippincott.

1942-50

The picture gallery of Canadian history, illustrations drawn and collected by C. W. Jefferys, R.C.A., LL.D., assisted by T. W. McLean, Toronto, Ryerson Press, vol. I, 1942; vol. II, 1945; vol. III, 1950.

1943

Colgate, William. *Canadian art, its origin and development*, Toronto, Ryerson Press.

Elie, Robert. *Borduas*, Montreal, L'Arbre.

Gagnon, Maurice. *Pellan*, Montreal, L'Arbre (Collection Art Vivant).

Jackson, A. Y. *Banting as an artist*, Toronto, Ryerson Press (Canadian art series).

Laing Fine Art Galleries. *Pictures for lasting pleasure* [exhibition and sale], December.

1944

Colgate, William G. *C. W. Jefferys*, Toronto, Ryerson Press (Canadian art series).

Lasnier, Rina, and Barbeau, Marius. *Madones canadiennes*, Montreal, Beauchemin

MacDonald, Thoreau. *The Group of Seven*, Toronto, Ryerson Press (Canadian art series).

McRae, D. G. W. *The arts and crafts of Canada*, Toronto, Macmillan.
[not in A.G.O., 1968; see Toronto Public Library].

Middleton, Jesse Edgar. *Canadian landscape, as pictured by F. H. Brigden*, Toronto, Ryerson Press.

Tonnancour, Jacques G. de. *Roberts*, Montreal, L'Arbre (Collection Art Vivant).

1945

Bridle, Augustus. *The story of the club*, Toronto, The Arts and Letters Club.

Buchanan, Donald W. *Canadian painters from Paul Kane to the Group of Seven*, Oxford and London, Phaidon Press.

Lyman, John. *Morrice*, Montreal, L'Arbre (Collection Art Vivant, 5).

1946

Barbeau, Marius. *Painters of Quebec*, Toronto, Ryerson Press (Canadian art series).

Miner, Muriel Miller. *G. A. Reid, Canadian artist*, Toronto, Ryerson Press.

Woodley, E. C. *Old Quebec; trails and homes*, Toronto, Ryerson Press.
[not in A.G.O., 1968; see Toronto Public Library].

1947

Buchanan, Donald William. *James Wilson Morrice*, Toronto, Ryerson Press (Canadian art series).

Canadian Information Service. *Canada from sea to sea*, Ottawa, Edmond Cloutier, King's Printer.

Lambert, Richard S. *The adventure of Canadian painting*, Toronto, McClelland and Stewart.

Sclater, William. *Haida*, with an introduction by Rt. Hon. A. V. Alexander...and twenty-four drawings in colour by Grant Macdonald..., Toronto, Oxford University Press.
[not in A.G.O., 1968; see Toronto Public Library].

Scott, Duncan Campbell. *Walter J. Phillips*, Toronto, Ryerson Press (Canadian art series).

1948

Barbeau, Charles Marius. *Cornelius Krieghoff*, Toronto, Ryerson Press (Canadian art series).

Hoover, Dorothy. *J. W. Beatty*, Toronto, Ryerson Press (Canadian art series).

1949

Weelen, Guy. *Marthe Rakine*, Paris, Presses Littéraires de France (in French and English).

1950

A.G.T. *50th anniversary*, Toronto.

Buchanan, Donald W. *The growth of Canadian painting*, London and Toronto, Collins.

Canadian Museums Association. *Canadian painting*, a proposed travelling exhibition for UNESCO.

Gour, Romain. *Suzor-Coté; artiste multiforme*, Montreal, Editions éoliennes.

McInnes, Graham. *Canadian art*, Toronto, Macmillan company of Canada.

N.G.C. *A portfolio of Canadian paintings*, Ottawa.

1951

Duval, Paul. *Alfred Joseph Casson*, Toronto, Ryerson Press (Canadian art series).

1952

Duval, Paul. *Canadian drawings and prints*, Toronto, Burns and MacEachern.

Gour, Romain. *Maurice Cullen, un maître de l'art au Canada*, Montreal, Les éditions éoliennes.

N.G.C. *Paintings and drawings from the collection of J. S. McLean*, Ottawa.

Soby, James Thrall. "The fine arts: upsurge in painting", *Saturday review*, June 7.

Thompson, Oscar, ed. *International cyclopedia of music and musicians*, New York, Dodd Mead and Co.

1954

Canadian Pulp and Paper Association. *With palette and brush, Canada's great forest industry*, Montreal.

Duval, Paul. *Canadian water colour painting*, Toronto, Burns and MacEachern.

1955

Leys, Major James Farquharson. *Robert Tait McKenzie and the Mill of Kintail*, the life of a remarkable man, reprinted from the *Canadian Army Journal*, January.

Little, Dr. R. P. "Some recollections of Tom Thomson and Canoe Lake", *Culture*, vol. XVI, June ((pp. 200ff).

McLeish, John A. B. *September gale, a study of Arthur Lismer of the Group of Seven*, Toronto and Vancouver, J. M. Dent and Sons.

MacNutt, W. S. *The making of the Maritime provinces 1713-1784*, The Canadian Historical Association, Historical Booklets, no. 4, Ottawa.

Wade, Mason. *The French Canadians 1760-1945*, Toronto, Macmillan.
[not in A.G.O., 1968; see Toronto Public Library].

1956

Lee, Thomas Roche. *Albert H. Robinson, the painter's painter*, pen drawings by J. Patrick O. Lee, Montreal, privately printed.

1957

Barbeau, Charles Marius. *J'ai vu Québec*, dessiné par Arthur Price, Quebec, Garneau. Eng. ed. has title: *I have seen Quebec*.
[not in A.G.O., 1968; see Toronto Public Library].

Canada at Brussels, 1958, Ottawa, Queen's Printer.

Canada, Department of Citizenship and Immigration. *The arts in Canada*, Ottawa (Canadian Citizenship series pamphlet no. 6).

Hubbard, R. H. "*Growth in Canadian art*", in *The culture of contemporary Canada*, ed. by Julian Park, Toronto,

Ryerson Press, and Ithaca, N. Y., Cornell University Press (pp. 95-142).

Ostiquy, Jean-René. "L'art contemporain au Canada", in *Prisme des arts*, revue internationale d'art contemporain, no. 14, Fall.

Wallace, Elizabeth. *Goldwin Smith, Victorian liberal*, Toronto, University of Toronto Press.

1957-58

Los Angeles County Museum. *Canada visits California*, October, 1957 - June 1958 [see Los Angeles County Museum, *Quarterly*, vol. 14, no. 2 (Spring, 1958), pp. 14-16].

1958

Gardner, Helen. *Art through the ages*, Harcourt Brace.

Jackson, A. Y. *A painter's country*, Toronto and Vancouver, Clarke, Irwin and Company.

Ross. Malcolm, ed. *The arts in Canada, stock-taking at mid-century*, Toronto, Macmillan.

Stevens, Gerald F. *Frederick Simpson Coburn, R.C.A.*, Toronto, Ryerson Press.

1959

A.G.T. *Painting and sculpture*, illustrations of selected paintings and sculpture from the collection, Toronto.

Beaverbrook Art Gallery. *Paintings*, "a preliminary catalogue listing all paintings acquired prior to July 1st, 1959", Fredericton, N. B.

Carpenter, Edmund Snow. *Eskimo*, text by Edmund Carpenter, sketches and paintings by Frederick Varley, and sketches and photos of Robert Flaherty's collection of Eskimo carvings, Toronto, University of Toronto Press.

The Pen and Pencil Club, 1890-1959, Montreal.

1960

Canada, Department of Northern Affairs and Natural Resources. *Eskimo graphic art*, catalogue of prints produced in 1959, Ottawa, Queen's Printer.

Hubbard, R. H., ed. *An anthology of Canadian art*, Toronto, Oxford University Press.

Morisset, Gérard. "La peinture traditionnelle au Canada Français, II", *l'Encyclopédie du Canada Français*, Ottawa.

N.G.C. *Catalogue of paintings and sculpture*, vol. 3, Canadian School, ed. by R. H. Hubbard, Ottawa, University of Toronto Press.

1961

"Canadian painting in the twentieth century: an introduction", extract from Grade X history text, *Winds of Change*, Toronto, Ryerson Press.

Dale, William S. A. *Charles Stegeman, Françoise André*, Vancouver, Keystone Press.

1962

Barbeau, Charles Marius. *Cornelius Krieghoff*, Toronto, Society for Art Publications, McClelland and Stewart (The Gallery of Canadian Art, 1).

Buchanan, Donald William. *Alfred Pellan*, Toronto, Society for Art Publications, McClelland and Stewart (The Gallery of Canadian Art, 4).

Duval, Paul. "Canadian painting", *Encyclopedia Canadiana*, Ottawa, vol. 8,

Hubbard, R. H. "Recent discoveries in early Canadian art", *Journal of the Royal Society of Arts*, London, November.

Hubbard, Robert Hamilton. *Tom Thomson*, Toronto, Society for Art Publications, McClelland and Stewart (The Gallery of Canadian art, 2).

Jarvis, Alan Hepburn. *David Milne*, Toronto, Society for Art Publications, McClelland and Stewart (The Gallery of Canadian Art, 3).

Read, S. E. "Flight to the primitive", in *Canadian literature*, no. 13, Summer (re: Ernest Thompson Seton).

1963

City of Toronto. *St. Lawrence Hall 1850: 1967*, a proposal for the rehabilitation of St. Lawrence Hall as a major project for Toronto...Eric Arthur, Adviser to the Corporation.

Harper, J. Russell. "Ontario painters 1846-1867: a study of art at the Upper Canada Provincial exhibitions", in *National Gallery of Canada Bulletin*, vol. I, no. 1, May, pp. 16-31.

Hubbard, R. H. *The development of Canadian art*, Ottawa, Queen's Printer.

Robert, Guy. *Pellan: sa vie et son œuvre, his life and his art* [traduction anglaise: George Lach], Montréal, Editions du Centre de Psychologie et de Pédagogie.

Wallace, W. Stewart, ed. *The Macmillan dictionary of Canadian biography*, London, Toronto and New York, Macmillan.

1964

Art Gallery of Hamilton. *Handbook; a selection from the permanent collection*, Hamilton.

Arthur, Eric Ross. *Toronto, no mean city*, Toronto, University of Toronto Press.

Brieger, Peter H., Vickers, G. Stephen, and Winter, Frederick E. *Art and Man*, Toronto, Holt, Rinehart and Winston, Book Three, The modern world.

Robert, Guy. *Ecole de Montréal*, situation et tendences, situation and trends, Montréal, Editions du Centre de Psychologie et de Pédagogie (Collection artistes canadiens) [in English and French].

Town, Harold Barling. *Enigmas*, Toronto, McClelland and Stewart, limited edition of 175 copies [in Spanish, English and French].

1965

Betcherman, Lita-Rose. "Genesis of an early Canadian painter: William von Moll Berczy", *Ontario history*, Ontario Historical Society, Toronto, vol. LVII, no. 2, June, pp. 57-68.

Carr, Emily. *Hundreds and thousands; the journals of Emily Carr*, Toronto, Clarke, Irwin, edition limited to 1000 copies.

Dickinson, C. H. *Lorne Pierce; a profile*, Toronto, Ryerson Press.

Duval, Paul. *Group of Seven drawings*, Toronto, Burns and MacEachern.

Morris, Jerrold A. *On the enjoyment of modern art; an explanatory text*, illustrated by Canadian paintings, Toronto, Society for Art Publications, McClelland and Stewart (The Gallery of Canadian art, 5).

Swinton, George. *Eskimo sculpture*, Toronto and Montreal, McClelland and Stewart.

1966

Harper, J. Russell. *Painting in Canada, a history*, Toronto, University of Toronto Press.

Kilbourn, Elizabeth. *Great Canadian painting, a century of art*, Toronto, McClelland and Stewart, The Canadian Centennial Library, ed. by Pierre Berton.

Pepper, Kathleen Frances Daly. *James Wilson Morrice*, with a preface by A. Y. Jackson, Toronto, Clarke, Irwin.

1967

André, John. *William Berczy, co-founder of Toronto*, Toronto, the Borough of York.

Ballantyne, Michael. *Expo 67 art*, Montreal, Les editions Toundra-Tundra Books.

Griffith, Julius. *Watercolours*, Ontario Department of Education, Community Programs Divisions, Toronto, n.d. [1967].

and engravings on wood, copper and steel contributed by various collectors, April 11 - May 11.

Toronto, Metropole Galleries, *Exhibition of original etchings and water colors by John W. Cotton*, November 23 - December 6.

1913

A.A.M., *The work of ten years in sculpture...by R. Tait McKenzie*, December 17-31.
[not in A.G.O., 1968; see Montreal Museum of Fine Arts library].

Paris, Galerie A.-M. Reitlinger, *Clarence A. Gagnon*, November 27 - December 16.

1915

New York, Montross Gallery, and A.G.T., *Pictures, studies and sketches by Horatio Walker*, April 17 - May 8.

1917

Ottawa, *Central Canada exhibition, Fine Arts [catalogue]*.

Toronto, *Exhibition of sketches, and small pictures, by Owen 'Staples O.S.A.* at his studio 69 Hogarth Avenue from Saturday, November 10th to 17th.

1918-19

A.G.T., *Catalogue of three exhibitions, the Society of Canadian Painter-Etchers; J. E. H. MacDonald, A.R.C.A., Lawren Harris and Frank H. Johnston; and William Cruikshank, R.C.A.*

1919

London, Burlington House, Royal Academy of Arts, *Canadian War Memorials exhibition*, January - February.

N.G.C., *Canadian War Memorials exhibition*.

1920

N.G.C., *Canadian War Memorials paintings exhibition*, new series [2nd portion].

A.G.T., *Sixth loan exhibition, Catalogue of a loan collection of paintings contributed by private collectors and public institutions in the city of Toronto*, January 6 - February 8.

A.G.T., *Catalogue of a memorial exhibition of paintings by Tom Thomson and a collection of Japanese colour prints loaned by Sir Edmund Walker*, February 13 - 29.

A.G.T., *Seventh loan exhibition, catalogue of a loan collection of pen and ink, pencil and brush drawings and of etchings and engravings on wood and copper contributed by various collectors*, April 9 - May 2.

A.G.T., *Group of Seven, Catalogue exhibition of paintings*, May 7 - 27.

Toronto, Arts and Letters Club, *Arts and Letters Club auction sale of paintings...for the benefit of the club building fund*, Saturday, December 11.

Toronto, Heliconian Club, *Exhibition of paintings by Mr. and Mrs. G. A. Reid*, November.
[catalogue in G. A. Reid scrapbook, in Study Collection, Art Gallery of Ontario, p. 354].

1921

A.G.T., *Exhibition of paintings by the Group of Seven*, May 7-29.

Buffalo, N. Y., The Buffalo Fine Arts Academy, Albright Art Gallery, *Catalogue of three special exhibitions... paintings by the "Group of Seven" Canadian artists*, September 10 - October 3.

Winnipeg Gallery of Art, *Catalogue of an exhibition of paintings "Canadian art of today"*, October 15 - December 10.

Vancouver, Vancouver Art Gallery, *B. C. Art League souvenir catalogue, loan exhibition of paintings, and the Canadian Society Painter-Etchers travelling show for the B. C. Art League*, November 28.

1922

A.G.T., *Group of Seven, exhibition of paintings*, May 5-29.

A.G.T., *Memorial exhibition of paintings by Mary Hiester Reid, A.R.C.A., O.S.A. Catalogue*, October 6-30.

1923

Toronto, Eaton's Fine Art Galleries, *Exhibition of portraits by Archibald Barnes and paintings by Arthur Heming*, April 10-22.

A.A.M., *Paintings by Charles De Belle*, November.

1924

A.G.T., *Exhibition of Canadian graphic art*, held under the auspices of the Canadian Society of Graphic Art and the Society of Canadian Painter-Etchers, January.

Toronto, Jenkins' Art Galleries, *Catalogue sale of valuable paintings by J. W. Beatty, R.C.A.*, February 27.

Worcester, Mass., Worcester Art Museum, *Exhibition of paintings by Canadian artists*, April 6-27.

London (Wembley), *British Empire exhibition*, Catalogue of the Palace of Arts, London, Fleetway Press Ltd., April - October.

London (Wembley), *British Empire Exhibition*. Illustrated souvenir of the Palace of Arts, London, Fleetway Press Ltd.

1924-25

London (Wembley), *British Empire exhibition*, Canadian section of fine arts, April - October. Also exhibited, Leicester Museum and Art Gallery, November - December, and Glasgow Art Gallery and Museum, December 24 - January 17,

1925

London, *British Empire exhibition*, Canadian section of fine arts.

A.A.M., *Memorial exhibition of paintings by the late James W. Morrice, R.C.A.*, January 16 - February 15.

London, Whitechapel Art Gallery, *Exhibition of Canadian art*, November 26 - December 23.

1925-26

Boston, Mass., Doll and Richards, *Sculpture by R. Tait McKenzie*, December 30, 1925 - January 12, 1926.
[not in A.G.O., 1968; see Frick Art Reference Library, New York].

1926

Philadelphia, Pa., *Sesqui-Centennial international exposition, paintings, sculpture and prints in the department of fine arts*, Canadian section, p. 85.

N.G.C., *Special exhibition of Canadian art*, January 21 - February 28 [this was the first N.G.C. *Annual;* see *Annual and Biennial Exhibitions*, p. 548].

A.G.T., *Catalogue of inaugural exhibition*, January 29 - February 28.

A.G.T., *Robert Ford Gagen, R.C.A., O.S.A., memorial exhibition*, April 16 - May 2.

A.G.T., *Catalogue of the exhibitions of the Group of Seven, and painting, sculpture and wood carving of French Canada*, May 8-31.

A.G.T., *Catalogue of an exhibition of Canadian paintings by Clarence A. Gagnon, R.C.A., Lawren Harris, A. Y. Jackson, R.C.A., Laura Muntz Lyall, A.R.C.A., J. E. H. MacDonald, A.R.C.A., Tom Thomson, Mary E. Wrinch, A.R.C.A., Albert H. Robinson, R.C.A., and Curtis Williamson, R.C.A.*, August 9 - September 30.

Ottawa, *Central Canada exhibition*, Department of fine arts, an exhibition of paintings loaned by The Art Gallery of Toronto, August 21-28.

Manchester, Eng., Queen's Park Gallery, *Exhibition of Canadian pictures* [selected from the Canadian Section of Fine Arts at Wembley], August 28 - October 9.

1927

A.G.T., *An exhibition of oils, water colours and pastels by Mrs. C. H. Eastlake (M. A. Bell)*, January 15 - February 6.

A.G.T., *Catalogue of the exhibition of the international exhibition of modern art assembled by the Société Anonyme; the Canadian Society of Graphic Art; and historical paintings and drawings by C. W. Jefferys, R.C.A., O.S.A.* April 1-24.

Paris, Musée du Jeu de Paume, *Exposition d'art canadien*, April 11 - May 11.

London, Imperial Institute, Imperial Gallery of Art, *Exhibition of paintings, drawings, engravings and small sculpture by artists resident in Great Britain and the Dominions*, April 12 - June 30.
[not in A.G.O., 1968; see National Gallery of Canada library].

A.G.T., *Catalogue of a loan exhibition of portraits*, October 7 - November 6.

1928

A.G.T., *Catalogue of an exhibition of Canadian West Coast art native and modern, and of a group of water colour paintings by Robert D. Norton*, January.

A.A.M., *Catalogue of an exhibition of painting of At Home and Abroad by F. H. McGillivray, R.C.A., O.S.A.*, January 7-??

A.G.T., *Catalogue of an exhibition of Canadian paintings by the Group of Seven and etchings by Robert F. Logan*, February.

A.G.T., *Catalogue of the Ontario Society of Artists fifty-sixth annual exhibition, and Edmund Morris Memorial exhibition*, March 3 - April 8.

A.G.T., *Catalogue of six exhibitions; The Canadian Society of Graphic Art; The Toronto Camera Club; Paul Manship; R. Tait McKenzie; Robert Holmes; and Albrecht Dürer*, April 13 - May 6.

Toronto, Eaton's Fine Art Galleries, *Exhibition of sculpture by Dr. R. Tait McKenzie, thirty-two pieces including relief, statuettes and plaster models*, June 11-23.

Buffalo, Buffalo Fine Arts Academy, Albright Art Gallery, *Exhibition of paintings by Canadian artists*, September 14 - October 14.
[not in A.G.O., 1968; see National Gallery of Canada library].

A.G.T., *Exhibition of Canadian sculpture, Spanish paintings, water colours by Robert Riggs, wood-blocks by Elizabeth Keith, etchings by Emil Fuchs, batiks by Arthur and Lawrence Smith, recent accessions*, October 5 - November 1.

A.G.T., Print Room, *Rody Kenny Courtice, B. Cogill Haworth, Yvonne McKague Housser, Isabel McLaughlin*, November 15 - December 15 [typed list only].

1941

N.G.C., *Horatio Walker, R.C.A., N.A., 1858-1938 memorial exhibition*.

A.G.T., Print Room, *Mabel Lockerby, Pegi Nicol MacLeod, Kathleen Morris, Marion Scott*, January [typed list only].

A.G.T., *[Tom] Thomson — [Horatio] Walker exhibition*, January [typed list only].

Brooklyn, N. Y., Brooklyn Museum, *International water color exhibition, 11th biennial*, March 28 - May 11.
[not in A.G.O., 1968; see National Gallery of Canada library].

A.G.T., Print Room, *Charles Goldhamer, Jean-Paul Lemieux, Peter Haworth, Tom Wood*, October - November [typed list only].

1942

N.G.C., *Clarence A. Gagnon, R.C.A., LL.D., 1881-1942; memorial exhibition*.

London, Ont., Elsie Perrin Williams Memorial Public Library and Art Museum, *Milestones of Canadian art*, a retrospective exhibition of Canadian art from Paul Kane and Kreighoff [sic] to the contemporary painters, January.

A.G.T., Print Room, *Alexander Bercovitch, Kathleen Daly, George Pepper, William A. Winter*, January [typed list only],

New York, Grand Central Art Galleries, *Canadiana*, an exhibition of historical prints, water-colour drawings, oil paintings and maps, April 6-18.

Quebec, Musée de la province de Québec, *Catalogue; exposition rétrospective de Clarence A. Gagnon, R.C.A., 1881-1942;* juin - juillet.

A.A.M., *Catalogue of a memorial exhibition of paintings, sketches, etchings...by Clarence Gagnon, R.C.A.*, August 7 - September 30.

Andover, Mass., Phillips Academy, Addison Gallery of American Art, *Contemporary painting in Canada*, September 18 - November 8; at the close of the exhibition a travelling exhibition of the same works was organized, called "Aspects of contemporary painting in Canada", and circulated in several American centres throughout 1942-43, being exhibited last at the N.G.C., January 20 - February 7, 1944.

A.G.T., *C. W. Jefferys, R.C.A., LL.D., exhibition of drawings and water colours, the originals of the illustrations in the first volume of the series "The picture gallery of Canadian history" by C. W. Jefferys*, September 25 - October 11 [typed list only].

A.G.T., *Catalogue of memorial exhibitions of the work of Clarence Gagnon, R.C.A., J. W. Beatty, R.C.A., O.S.A.*, October - November.

A.G.T., Print Room, *Campbell Tinning, Ursula Rainnie, H. Mabel May, Ruth M. Eliot*, October - November [typed list only].

Toronto, University of Toronto, Hart House, *Canadian Armed Forces art exhibition*, November 14-29.

1943

A.G.T., *War record drawings*, January 9-31 [typed list only: attached to C.S.P.W.C. catalogue].

A.G.T., Print Room, *Marguerite Fainmel*, February [typed list only].

A.G.T., *Paintings by Emily Carr*, February [typed list only].

A.G.T., Print Room, *Painters under twenty*, March [typed list only].

A.G.T., *Non-jury exhibition of paintings by Canadians*, April 2-18 [typed list only].

A.G.T., Print Room, *R. S. Hewton, John M. Alfsen*, April 3 - May 5 [typed list only].

A.G.T., Print Room, *Edna Tacon, Jessie Faunt, Michael Forster, Gordon Webber*, May [typed list only].

1944

A.G.T., *Loan exhibition of great paintings in aid of Allied Merchant Seamen*, February 4 - March 5.

New Haven, Yale University Art Gallery, *Canadian art, 1760-1943*, March 11 - April 16 [catalogue in *Bulletin of the Associates in Fine Arts at Yale University*, vol. XII, no. 3, 1944].

Quebec, Musée de la province de Québec, *Catalogue: exposition de Marc-Aurèle Fortin, A.R.C.A., Adrien Hébert, R.C.A., Henri Hébert, R.C.A., Edwin Headley Holgate, R.C.A.*, Mai 3-31.

A.A.M., *Paintings and drawings by Stanley Cosgrove*, October 7-30.

Rio de Janeiro, Museu Nacional de Belas Artes; *Pintura canadense contemporanea*, November - December; also exhibited São Paulo, Municipal Library, January, 1945.

1944-45

Chicago, Art Institute of Chicago, *Art of the United Nations*, November 16, 1944 - January 1, 1945.

1945

A.G.T., *The development of painting in Canada 1665-1945*,

January; exhibited at A.A.M., February; N.G.C., March; Le Musée de la Province de Québec, April.

Montreal, Galerie Parizeau, *de Tonnancour*, March 17-31.

A.A.M., *Paintings and drawings by John S. Walsh*, June 7-30.

A.G.T., *Members' loan exhibition*, September [typed list only].

N.G.C., and A.G.T., *Emily Carr; her paintings and sketches*, Toronto, Oxford University Press; exhibited at A.G.T., October 19 - November 18.

1946

Paris, Musée d'art moderne, *UNESCO, Exposition internationale d'art moderne* [type-written copy of Canadian section only in A.G.O., 1968; for full catalogue see National Gallery of Canada library].

Albany, N.Y., Albany Institute of History and Art, *Painting in Canada, a selective historical survey*, January 10 - March 10.

Elmira, N. Y., Arnot Art Gallery, *Canadian water colour*, March (exhibition assembled by the C.S.P.W.C. in cooperation with the A.G.T.).

A.G.T., *Captain John A. E. Bennett water colours*, May 10 - June 9 [typed list only].

A.G.T., *Drawings and water colours by B. C. Binning*, May 11 - June 9 [typed list only].

Rio de Janeiro, Museu Nacional de Belas Artes, *Artes Gráficas do Canadá*, June.

London, Ont., London Public Library and Art Museum, *The Group of Seven 1919-1933*, September 20 - October 29.

New York, Chinese Gallery, *Edna Tacon, contextualist*, October 28 - November 16.

1946-47

Detroit, Detroit Institute of Arts, *The arts of French Canada, 1613-1870;* also exhibited at The Cleveland Museum of Art, Albany Institute of History and Art, A.A.M., N.G.C., and Le Musée de la Province de Québec.

1947

A.G.T., *Franklin Carmichael memorial exhibition*, March.

New York, Riverside Museum, *Canadian women artists* (sponsored by the National Council of Women of Canada and the National Council of Women of the United States), April 27 - May 18.

Columbus, Ohio, Columbus Gallery of Fine Arts, *The Colonial Americas*, October 9 - November 15 [catalogue issued in Columbus Gallery of Fine Arts, *Monthly Bulletin*, vol. 18, no. 1, October, 1947].

1948

N.G.C., *Prudence Heward, 1896-1947; memorial exhibition*.

A.G.T., and Toledo, Ohio, *Two cities collect*, catalogue of an exhibition held in Toronto in January and Toledo in April.

O.S.A., 76th annual spring exhibition; *The George A. Reid, memorial exhibition*, held at A.G.T., March 6-28.

A.G.T., *Lawren Harris, paintings, 1910-1948*, October - November.

Windsor, Willistead Art Gallery, *The Group of Seven*, November [mimeographed catalogue only].

1949

Richmond, Va., Virginia Museum of Fine Arts, *Exhibition of Canadian painting 1668-1948*, arranged in cooperation with the N.G.C.

Florence, Palazzo Strozzi, *Graphica — America, 1947, collages e gouaches — Grecia, 1948, Roloff Beny*, May.

A.G.T., *Canadian prints from the collections of the Art Gallery of Toronto, and of the National Gallery of Canada*, May 5 - June 5 [typed list only].

Boston, Boston Museum of Fine Arts, *Forty years of Canadian painting, from Tom Thomson and the Group of Seven to the present day*, July 14 - September 25.

Halifax, N. S., Queen Elizabeth High School, *200 years of art in Halifax, an exhibition prepared in honour of the bicentenary of the Founding of the City of Halifax, N. S., 1749-1949*, July 18 - August 20.

A.G.T., *Fifty years of painting in Canada*, October - November.

1950

N.G.C., *Contemporary Canadian sculpture;* an exhibition arranged in cooperation with the Sculptors' Society of Canada.

A.G.T., and N.G.C., *Arthur Lismer, paintings, 1913-1949*, A.G.T., January - February; N.G.C., March.

Toronto, Eaton's Fine Art Galleries, *An exhibition of paintings and drawings by Frederick Varley*, February 27 - March 16 [typed list only].

A.G.T., *Exhibition of contemporary Canadian arts*, being a joint exhibition of the following societies: R.C.A., O.S.A., C.G.P., C.S.P.W.C., S.S.C., C.S.G.A., R.A.I.C., and craft section, March 3 - April 16.

Vancouver, University of British Columbia, Art Centre Gallery, *Drawings, paintings by B. C. Binning*, n.d., March 14 - April 1.

ANNUAL AND BIENNIAL
EXHIBITIONS

NOTE: Most catalogues for the following exhibitions are available in
the Art Reference Library of the Art Gallery of Ontario.

CANADIAN

A.A.M./M.M.F.A., *Annual spring exhibition*, since 1860.

Burnaby, B. C., *Burnaby National Print Show*, organized
by the Burnaby Art Society, exhibitions held biennially
since 1961.

Canadian Art Club, exhibitions held annually in Toronto
from 1908 to 1915. In 1910, a special exhibition was
held in Montreal.

[C.G.P.], *Canadian Group of Painters*, exhibitions held
annually since 1933, and most frequently at the Art
Gallery of Toronto.

[C.N.E.], *Canadian National Exhibition*, Toronto, fine art
exhibitions held annually from 1879 to 1961, to the
exception of the war years, 1942-46, when no exhibitions took place.
[Named the *Toronto Industrial Exhibition* for some
years, the title was changed to *Dominion of Canada
Industrial Exhibition* in 1903, and in the following year
the name *Canadian National Exhibition of Toronto* was
adopted.].

[C.P.E.], *Society of Canadian Painter-Etchers and En-
gravers*, first annual exhibition held in A.G.T., 1919;
since then held fairly regularly in various centres, and
most frequently [until 1961] at the Royal Ontario
Museum, Toronto.

[C.S.G.A.], *Canadian Society of Graphic Art*, exhibitions
held annually since 1924, and most frequently at the
Art Gallery of Toronto.
[For history of the society, see *Graphic 58*, catalogue
for 25th anniversary exhibition, 1958].

[C.S.P.W.C.], *Canadian Society of Painters in Water
Colour*, exhibitions held annually since 1926, and most
frequently at the Art Gallery of Toronto.

N.G.C., *Annual exhibition of Canadian art*, held annually
from 1926 to 1933, when it was discontinued; revived
in 1953, then superseded by *Biennial*, held six times
from 1955 to 1965.

[O.S.A.], *Ontario Society of Artists*, exhibitions held annually in the spring, since 1873, and most frequently at
the Art Gallery of Toronto.

O.S.A., little pictures, exhibitions of small paintings held
under the auspices of the Ontario Society of Artists,
and usually in November.

[R.C.A.], *Royal Canadian Academy of Arts*, exhibitions
held annually since 1880 in various centres, and most
frequently at the Montreal Museum of Fine Arts, and
the Art Gallery of Toronto.

[S.S.C.], *Sculptors' Society of Canada*, exhibitions held
periodically since 1928.

Winnipeg Art Gallery, *Winnipeg Show*, exhibitions held
annually from 1955 to 1961, then biennially from 1962.

INTERNATIONAL EXHIBITIONS ABROAD

Guggenheim International Award Exhibition, held biennially in New York, since 1956. Canadians have always
participated.

Ljubljana, Yugoslavia, Moderna Galerija, *Mednarodna
grafična razstava; exposition internationale de gravure*,
exhibitions held biennially since 1955.

Lugano, Switzerland, *Mostra internazionale di bianco e
nero*, exhibitions held biennially since 1950. Canadians
have participated since 1952.

Paris, *Salon*, annual exhibitions of the *Société des Artistes
Français*, founded in 1872.

São Paulo, Brazil, *Bienal de São Paulo*, exhibitions held
biennially since 1951 in the Museu de Arte Moderna.
Canadians have always participated.
Special illustrated edition of the Canadian section, 1965,
issued by the National Gallery of Canada, in Portuguese,
English and French, with a preface by Willem A. Blom:
Canada at São Paulo 1965, Ottawa, Queen's Printer,
1965.

Venice, Italy, *Esposizione biennale internazionale d'arte,
Venezia*, exhibitions held biennially, in which Canadians
have participated regularly since the 26th exhibition
in 1952.

PERIODICALS

NOTE: Most of the following periodicals are available in Toronto;
consult the *Union list of serials in libraries of the United States and
Canada*, 3rd edition, 1965.

American Artist, Stamford, Conn.; New York.

American Magazine of Art; see *Magazine of Art*.

Anglo-American Magazine, Toronto.

Antiques, Boston; New York.

Apollo, London.

artscanada (formerly *Canadian Art*), Toronto.

Art Digest (later title changes to *Arts Digest* [1955]; *Arts* [1962]; *Arts Magazine* [1963]), New York.

A.G.T. *Accessions*, published from 1942 to 1959, and covering accessions 1939-58, in 11 volumes.

A.G.T. *Bulletin*, published in 14 numbers (vol. I, nos. 1-14) from November, 1926 to April, 1936, appearing at irregular intervals [semi-annually to December, 1929 and thereafter annually]. In addition, unnumbered Bulletins were issued from 1930 to 1936 irregularly, five to eight issues a year.

A.G.T./A.G.O. *Annual report*, published with the *Bulletin*, 1930-1937; separately 1940-44; with *Programme*, 1945-48; and in 1954. Only financial statements issued since, until *Annual report* for the year 1966-67 was published in 1967 under new name, Art Gallery of Ontario.

A.G.T. *Programme* (Education), published from 1945/46-1948/49.

A.G.T. *News and Notes*, published three times a year from January, 1957 to September, 1966, when publication ceased; 10 volumes, 3 issues a year.

Art in America, New York.

L'Art et les Artistes, Paris.

Art News, New York.

Art and Architecture, Los Angeles.

Arts et Pensée, Montreal.

Art Quarterly, Detroit Institute of Arts, Detroit, Michigan.

Arts
Arts Digest   } — see *Art Digest*
Arts Magazine

Canadian Art (changed in 1967 to *artscanada*), Ottawa, Toronto.

Canadian Collector, a journal of antiques and fine arts, Toronto.

Canadian forum; a monthly journal of literature and public affairs, Toronto.

Canadian Geographical Journal, Canadian Geographical Society, Montreal, Ottawa.

Canadian Magazine, Toronto.

Canadian Review of Music and other Arts, Toronto.

Connoisseur, an illustrated magazine for collectors, London.

Culture, revue trimestrielle, sciences religieuses et sciences profanes au Canada (Association de recherches sur les sciences religieuses et profanes au Canada), Montreal, Quebec.

Farmer's Magazine, Toronto.

Gazette des Beaux-Arts, Paris; American edition, New York.

International Studio, London.

Listener, British Broadcasting Corporation, London.

Maclean's Magazine, Toronto.

Magazine of Art, American Federation of Arts, Washington, D.C., vol. 1-7, no. 2, published under title *Art and Progress;* changed to *American Magazine of Art* for vol. 7, no. 3 through vol. 29; then changed to *Magazine of Art*.

Maritime Art, Maritime Art Association, Wolfville, N.S.

Mayfair, Toronto.

N.G.C. Bulletin, Ottawa, no. 1 (May, 1963); issued twice yearly.

New Frontier, Toronto.

New Liberty, see *New World Illustrated*.

INDEX TO ACCESSION NUMBERS OF CANADIAN WORKS

584

INDEX TO ARTISTS

INDEX TO ARTISTS REPRESENTED BY SCULPTURE

603